The Wetland Bird Survey
Wildfowl and Wader Counts

**Mark Pollitt, Colette Hall, Steve Holloway, Richard Hearn,
Paul Marshall, Andy Musgrove, James Robinson and Peter Cranswick**

Published by

British Trust for Ornithology, The Wildfowl & Wetlands Trust,
Royal Society for the Protection of Birds and Joint Nature Conservation Committee

June 2003

ISBN 0 900806 36 2
ISSN 1353–7792

This publication should be cited as:
Pollitt, M.S., Hall, C., Holloway, S.J., Hearn, R.D., Marshall, P.E., Musgrove, A.J., Robinson, J.A. & Cranswick, P.A. 2003. *The Wetland Bird Survey 2000–01: Wildfowl and Wader Counts.* BTO/WWT/RSPB/JNCC, Slimbridge.

Published by: BTO/WWT/RSPB/JNCC

Cover: Dark-bellied Brent Geese by Bruce Pearson

Line Drawings: Mark Hulme, Dan Powell and Joe Blossom

Designed and produced by The Wildfowl & Wetlands Trust, Slimbridge.

Printed by Severnprint Ltd, Unit 8-10, Ashville Industrial Estate, Bristol Road, Gloucester Gl2 5EU

Typeset in Cheltenham ITC and Gill Sans fonts.

Available from: WeBS Secretariat, WWT Slimbridge, Gloucestershire GL2 7BT, and Natural History Book Service, 2–3 Wills Road, Totnes, Devon TQ9 5XN, UK.

This report is provided free to all WeBS counters and those who participate in the other national waterbird surveys, none of whom receive financial reward for their invaluable work. Further feedback is provided to counters through the twice-yearly WeBS Newsletter. For further information please contact the WeBS Secretariat or relevant National Organiser.

ACKNOWLEDGEMENTS

This book represents the twenty-first report of the Wetland Bird Survey and comprises information from WeBS and complementary national and local surveys, e.g. goose censuses. It is entirely dependent on the many thousands of dedicated volunteer ornithologists who supply the data and to whom we are extremely grateful. The Local Organisers who co-ordinate these counts deserve special thanks for their contribution.

The WeBS Steering Group members are Peter Cranswick, James Robinson, Rowena Langston, Andy Musgrove, Mark Rehfisch, Helen Baker and David Stroud.

We are also grateful to the following people for providing technical assistance, supplementary information and additional data, and comments on draft texts:

Helen Baker, Dave Butterfield, Sue Carman, Kendrew Colhoun, Simon Delany, Tony Fox, Ian Francis, Larry Griffin, Martin Heubeck, Baz Hughes, Rowena Langston, Roderick MacDonald, Margaret McKay, Malcolm Ogilvie, David Paynter, Steve Percival, Eileen Rees, Mark Rehfisch, Maggie Sage, Arnor Sigfusson, John Simpson, Mark Smart, Lucy Smith, David Stroud, Paul Walkden and Chris Waltho. Many amateur observers also provide reports of their studies; these are acknowledged within the text.

Grateful thanks to all and apologies to anyone who has inadvertently been missed.

Dedicated to the memory of

GEORGE ATKINSON-WILLES, 1922-2002

who pioneered waterbird monitoring in this country and internationally.
Many conservation achievements and success have arisen from these data over
the last 50 years, yet the schemes and their application, even today, remain
based on the same foundations that George established at Slimbridge.

WETLAND BIRD SURVEY

Organised and funded by

British Trust for Ornithology
The Nunnery, Thetford, Norfolk IP24 2PU

The Wildfowl & Wetlands Trust
Slimbridge, Gloucestershire GL2 7BT

Royal Society for the Protection of Birds
The Lodge, Sandy, Bedfordshire SG19 2DL

Joint Nature Conservation Committee
Monkstone House, City Road, Peterborough
PE1 1JY

CONTACTS

WeBS Secretariat and Core Counts
  Head of Secretariat: **Peter Cranswick**
  National Organiser (Core Counts): **Mark Pollitt**
  Assistant National Organiser: **Colette Hall**

The Wildfowl & Wetlands Trust, Slimbridge,
Gloucestershire GL2 7BT
Tel: 01453 891926
 (or 01453 891900 x 255/261/265)
Fax: 01453 891901
e-mail: firstname.surname@wwt.org.uk

Low Tide Counts
  National Organiser: **Andy Musgrove**
  Assistant Organiser: **Steve Holloway**

British Trust for Ornithology, The Nunnery,
Thetford, Norfolk IP24 2PU
Tel: 01842 750050
Fax: 01842 750030
e-mail: firstname.surname@bto.org

For general enquiries, please contact the WeBS
Secretariat. More detailed data than published in
this report can be obtained from Colette Hall
(Core Counts) or Steve Holloway (Low Tide
Counts).

NATIONAL GOOSE CENSUSES

Data collated under a WWT/JNCC partnership
programme

Contact: Richard Hearn
The Wildfowl & Wetlands Trust
Tel: 01453 891900 x 185
(other contact details as for WeBS Secretariat)

ERRATA TO 1999-2000 REPORT

Please note the following corrections to data
presented in the 1999-2000 WeBS annual
report:
p16 dots on the distribution map have been
     slightly displaced.
p128 the count of 337 Greenshank at Chichester
     Harbour in September should have read
     188
p142 headings for Table 4 should begin 95-96
     through to 99-00 rather than as printed.
p175 The UK annual indices values presented in
     table A8 in Appendix 3 were transposed
     for Knot, Sanderling and Dunlin. The
     column headed Knot refers to Sanderling,
     those for Sanderling refer to Dunlin and
     those for Dunlin refer to Knot.

During summation of counts for wildfowl
species at complex sites an error occurred
when species were present but not counted on
one or other sector. This resulted in the counts
for these sites being summed incorrectly
(typically between one and five less than the
correct figure). This error is not believed to have
caused the omission of any sites from the tables
of important sites for each species or affected
the qualification of sites as nationally or
internationally important.

Please note also that tabulations for herons,
gulls and terns in the 1999-2000 report used
different months to define a year to those
presented in the current report. As a result,
peak counts at some sites will differ and some
counts may appear in a different reporting year
where the peak count fell in April, May or June.

CONTENTS

Summary

The Wetland Bird Survey and Wildfowl and Wader Counts

The Wetland Bird Survey (WeBS) is a joint scheme of the British Trust for Ornithology (BTO), The Wildfowl & Wetlands Trust (WWT), Royal Society for the Protection of Birds (RSPB) and Joint Nature Conservation Committee (JNCC) to monitor non-breeding waterbirds in the UK. The principal aims of the scheme are to identify population sizes, determine trends in numbers and distribution, and to identify important sites for waterbirds. WeBS Core Counts are made annually at around 2,000 wetland sites of all habitats; estuaries and large still waters predominate. Monthly co-ordinated counts are made mostly by volunteers, principally from September to March, with fewer observations during summer months. Data from other sources, e.g. roost counts of grey geese, are included in this report where relevant.

This report presents total numbers counted for all species in the most recent year in Great Britain and Northern Ireland. Annual indices, calculated using the 'Underhill' method, are provided for the more numerous species. For certain wildfowl species, monthly indices, showing relative abundance during the winter, are also provided.

Species accounts provide yearly maxima for all sites supporting internationally and nationally important numbers. Sites with changed status are highlighted and significant counts at a national or site level are discussed. Counts are placed in an international context where possible, and relevant research is summarised. Waterbird totals are provided for all sites meeting criteria for international importance and species occurring in internationally important numbers on each are identified. Brief overviews of research initiated by WeBS or using WeBS data, and of conservation issues pertaining to UK waterbirds, are provided.

WeBS Low Tide Counts are made on selected estuaries to determine the distribution of birds during low tide and to identify important feeding areas that may not be recognised during Core Counts which are made mostly at high tide. A summary of results for these estuaries, and distribution maps for selected species, are provided.

Waterbird totals recorded by the Irish Wetland Bird Survey, a similar scheme operating in the Republic of Ireland, are also included.

Appendices list statistics on sites designated under the Ramsar Convention and Special Protection Areas classified under the EC Directive on the Conservation of Wild Birds. Also, waterbird count totals for the most recent year are provided separately for England, Scotland, Wales, the Isle of Man and the Channel Islands.

The 2000–01 year

This report summarises counts during 2000–01 and previous years (since 1960 for wildfowl, 1969 for waders and the early 1980s or 1990s for other species groups). More than 1,550 sites were visited each month during the September to February period although the outbreak of Foot and Mouth Disease severely affected coverage in March.

Counts of all diver species were above average, largely a result of improved coverage of key areas. Both Little and Great Crested Grebes were recorded in record numbers in Britain. Cormorants peaked at a similar level to the previous year, British totals surpassing 16,000 for only the second time. Numbers of Little Egret continued to rise, the typical September peak up 37% on that of the previous year. The high counts of Grey Heron in 1999–2000 were sustained.

Mute Swan counts in Great Britain reached record levels for the fifth consecutive year, exceeding 20,000 for the first time. It was a mixed year for migratory swans; counts of Bewick's were low and the index for Great Britain fell sharply, whilst Whooper numbers remained close to the high levels recorded in the previous winter.

Counts of Pink-footed and Greylag Geese recorded by the Icelandic-breeding Goose Census increased slightly, counts of the former being the second highest since the census began in 1960. The decline in numbers of European White-fronted Geese continued, the peak being the second lowest since counts began. In contrast, Greenland Whitefronts continued to fare well, numbers remaining relatively stable over the past six years following a prolonged and steady increase. Counts and annual indices of re-established Greylag and Canada Geese reached record levels. Numbers of Barnacle Geese and Dark-bellied Brent Geese were unremarkable. Exceptional counts of Light-bellied Brent Geese at Strangford Lough contributed to high totals in Northern Ireland;

the all-Ireland census total of 20,223 was the highest since the census began in 1994–95.

Despite a slight increase on the previous year, Shelduck numbers in Great Britain remained relatively low. Peak numbers of Wigeon, Gadwall, Shoveler and Teal in Britain were all high, the last reaching record levels and consolidating a steadily increasing long-term trend. In contrast, annual indices for Mallard continued to decline, falling for the eleventh time in 13 years, whilst the peak Pintail count in Great Britain of just over 20,000 was the lowest for 25 years. Pochard numbers in Britain dipped below 35,000 for the only the second time in 20 years, whilst those of Tufted Duck reached record levels. Numbers of Long-tailed Duck were unusually high, a result of large counts on the Moray Firth. Whilst counts of Common Scoter were unremarkable, numbers of Velvet Scoter increased sharply as a result of high counts at St Andrews Bay. Both Red-breasted Merganser and Goosander counts fell markedly. The influence of the control trials was evident in the counts of Ruddy Ducks, the peak being some 17% below that of the previous year. Coot numbers in Britain were amongst the highest recorded by WeBS.

Record numbers of Avocets were counted in January 2001, with almost 1,500 present in Poole Harbour alone. Ringed Plover counts remained low in both Britain and Northern Ireland, whilst the relatively mild winter was no doubt partly responsible for low numbers on Lapwing and Golden Plover. Grey Plover and Knot numbers were above the average for recent winters. The Great Britain maximum for Dunlin was the lowest for more than a decade and annual indices remained correspondingly low. Whilst Black-tailed Godwit numbers reached their highest level to data, numbers of Bar-tailed Godwit remained at the relatively low levels of recent winters and annual indices fell to their lowest ever level. Redshank and Curlew numbers were around average, and though the peak count of Turnstone was the highest for several years indices remained at to their recent low levels.

Counts of gulls and terns, for which recording by counters is optional, are strongly influenced by coverage of a small number of key sites. Peak numbers of Black-headed and Common Gulls were down on the previous year whilst those of Herring Gull rose slightly. Both Common and Sandwich Terns were recorded in their highest numbers to date.

Introduction

The UK is of outstanding international importance for waterbirds. Lying on some of the major flyways for arctic-nesting species, large numbers of waterbirds are attracted, especially during winter, by the relatively mild climate and extensive areas of wetland, notably estuaries. The UK thus has both moral and legal obligations to conserve both these waterbirds and the wetlands upon which they depend.

The UK is bound by international law by being a signatory to a number of international conservation conventions, as well as being a member of the EU. In particular, the 'Ramsar' Convention on Wetlands of International Importance especially as Waterfowl Habitat, the EC Birds Directive and the EU Habitats and Species Directive, between them, require the UK to identify important examples of wetland and other habitats and sites important for birds and designate them for protection. Implicit in these obligations is the need for regular monitoring to identify and monitor such sites. These instruments also lay particular significance on the need to conserve migratory populations, and consequently most of the waterbird populations in the UK.

The UK has ratified the Agreement on the Conservation of African-Eurasian Migratory Waterbirds (AEWA) of the 'Bonn' Convention on the Conservation of Migratory Species of Wild Animals. AEWA entered into force in 1999. It is a specific Agreement requiring nations to take co-ordinated measures to conserve migratory waterbirds given their particular vulnerability due to their migration over long distances and their dependence on networks that are decreasing in extent and becoming degraded through non-sustainable human activities. Article three of the Agreement requires, among other things, that sites and habitats for migratory waterbirds are identified, protected and managed appropriately, that parties initiate or support research into the ecology of these species, and exchange information and results. Explicit in this Agreement is that adequate monitoring programmes are set in place to fulfil these objectives and the Action Plan to the Agreement specifically requires that nations endeavour to monitor waterbird populations.

AIMS AND OBJECTIVES OF WEBS

The Wetland Bird Survey (WeBS) aims to monitor all non-breeding waterbirds in the UK to provide the principal data on which the conservation of their populations and wetland habitats is based. To this end, WeBS has three main objectives:

- to assess the size of non-breeding waterbird populations in the UK;
- to assess trends in their numbers and distribution; and
- to assess the importance of individual sites for waterbirds.

A programme of research, to understand the ecology of waterbirds and investigate the effects of habitat change and anthropogenic impact, underpins and enhances these objectives.

These results also form the basis for informed decision-making by conservation bodies, planners and developers and contribute to the sustainable and wise use and management of wetlands and their dependent waterbirds. The data and the WeBS report also fulfil some of the objectives of the Conventions and Directives listed above. WeBS also provides UK data to Wetlands International to assist their function to co-ordinate and report upon waterbird monitoring at an international scale.

Structure and organization of WeBS

WeBS is partnership scheme of the British Trust for Ornithology (BTO), The Wildfowl & Wetlands Trust (WWT), Royal Society for the Protection of Birds (RSPB) and the Joint Nature Conservation Committee (JNCC), the last on behalf of English Nature (EN), Scottish Natural Heritage (SNH) and the Countryside Council for Wales (CCW), and the Environment and Heritage Service in Northern Ireland (EHS).

WeBS continues the traditions of two, long-running count schemes which formed the mainstay of UK waterbird monitoring since 1947 (Cranswick *et al.* 1997). WeBS Core Counts are made at a wide variety of wetlands throughout the UK. Synchronised counts are conducted once per month, primarily from September to March, to fulfil all three main objectives. In addition, WeBS Low Tide Counts are undertaken on selected estuaries with the aim of identifying key areas used during the low tide period, principally by feeding birds; areas not otherwise noted for their importance by Core Counts which are normally conducted at high tide.

The day-to-day running of the Core and Low Tide Count schemes is the responsibility of the National Organisers, with assistance from a number of other staff.

The success and growth of these count schemes reflects accurately the enthusiasm and dedication of the several thousands of volunteer ornithologists who participate. It is largely due to their efforts that waterbird monitoring in the UK is held in such international high regard.

Aim of this report

This report presents syntheses of data collected in 2000–01 and previous years in line with the WeBS objectives. Data from other national and local waterbird monitoring schemes are included where WeBS data alone are insufficient to fulfil this aim, so that the report provides a single, comprehensive source of information on waterbird status and distribution in the UK. All nationally and internationally important sites for which data exist are listed, as are all sites designated under international law or Conventions (see Appendices 1 & 2).

We recommend that the National Organisers (see Contacts) are contacted in the first instance by anyone with queries regarding this report or requiring further information.

WEATHER IN 2000–01

This summary of UK weather is drawn from the journal *Weather* and from the Meteorological Office web site at www.metoffice.gov.uk. Figures in brackets following the month refer to the Core Count priority date for the month in question. European weather is summarised from information provided by the NOAA-CIRES Climate Diagnostics Centre, Boulder, Colorado, USA, from their Web site at www.cdc.noaa.gov. Arctic breeding conditions for birds that winter in the UK are summarised from information collated by Soloviev & Tomkovic at the web site www.arcticbirds.ru.

United Kingdom

April (9) opened with heavy rain and wintry weather for most of the UK. High pressure dominated during the second week bringing sunshine to most areas. A cold front on the 11th brought further rain and snow which persisted for the rest of the month. It was the wettest April on record since the late 18th century, rainfall totalling 143mm in England and Wales. Temperatures for the month were about 1°C below the long-term average.

The first days of **May** (7) were predominately warm and sunny. England had a brief period of damp and cooler weather but by the second week temperatures had risen to a maximum of 24°C. The warm and humid weather that

followed brought low cloud and fog to the Midlands and eastern England and thunderstorms to the Southeast while much of Scotland, Northern Ireland and northwest England stayed dry. The second half of May was cooler and much more unsettled, with deep depressions bringing heavy rain to the south by the end of the month.

Whilst northern and western Scotland stayed dry and sunny, low pressure in early **June** (25) brought outbreaks of rain to many areas, with prolonged downpours leading to flooding in northeast England. During the second week, north and west Scotland suffered a brief period of high winds averaging 40–50kn, gusting to 70kn. By mid month a high over the UK saw hot and sunny weather over England and Wales, though Scotland and Northern Ireland stayed mainly cloudy and damp. The month ended with a mixture of sun and showers.

Temperatures in the first half of **July** (23) were low for the time of year. Rain spread through most of the UK with southern England experiencing thunderstorms that brought some very heavy showers (falls of 50–80mm were reported in places). Western areas saw the driest and brightest of the weather. Towards the end of the month the anticyclone retreated northwards and most parts had a brief spell of warmer, dryer weather before depressions moving in from the west brought more rain.

Much of **August** (20) was warm and showery with thunderstorms in places and heavy rain at times. Unsettled weather on the 21st brought widespread hail. Whilst eastern and central districts had the warmest of the weather during the first few weeks, high pressure towards the end of the month brought hot and sunny weather to much of the UK, temperatures reaching 30°C in Southampton.

For most of **September** (17) the weather was unsettled with a mix of sun, showers and heavy rain, causing localised flooding in parts of Scotland. Whilst temperatures in the first few days dropped low enough at night for ground frost, in the second week parts of England and Wales had hot and sunny weather; 29°C was recorded near Chester on the 10th. Northwest Scotland experienced the driest of the weather in comparison to the rest of the UK; over England and Wales the rainfall averaged 127mm, the wettest September since 1981.

For much of the UK, **October** (22) was wet and windy with only a few sunny spells. Rainfall in the UK was 174% of the long term average with torrential downpours causing floods in many parts. Plumton in East Sussex recorded 174mm in just 48 hours. At the end of the month severe gales caused extensive damage in places with gusts of between 70–80kn around the cost; a gust of 84kn was recorded at Mumbles, Swansea and a tornado was recorded on 28th at Bognor Regis, West Sussex.

Throughout **November** (19) low pressure brought unsettled weather to much of the UK. Scotland experienced the sunniest of the weather particularly in Shetland and Orkney whilst in Northern Ireland it was dull and very wet; sunshine was 110% and 65% of the long-term average for Scotland and Northern Ireland, respectively. Whilst temperatures were slightly above average in most parts of Britain, in Northern Ireland it was the coldest November since 1996 (0.3°C below average).

December (17) began very mild with frequent rain and temperatures reaching 11–14°C. Mid month the wind turned westerly and then northerly bringing a colder, dryer spell with fog and night-time frosts. As the cold weather moved gradually southwards wintry showers fell in may parts of the UK. In Glasgow snow fell to a depth of 20cm on 28th and in England and Wales depths of between 5 and 15 cm were recorded on 29th and 30th.

Though **January** (14) opened wet and mild, for most of the month it was dry and sunny; sunshine for the UK was 154% of the long term average. High pressure moving across Scotland brought a drop in temperature with patches of freezing fog and frost in places, falling to -13°C in Aviemore and -8°C at Redesdale, Northumberland and Redhill, Surrey. Unsettled weather at the end of the month led to occasional outbreaks of rain, sleet and snow.

February (11) started cold with snowfalls in eastern Scotland and northeast England. During the second week the weather turned mild especially in southern areas (14°C at Poole,

Dorset) bringing outbreaks of rain and thunder. High pressure mid month led to several days of sunny and dry weather. The end of the month saw more snow for northern areas particularly over high ground.

During the first week of **March** (11) light winds and clear skies caused low temperatures and snow fell over many parts, particularly in northern areas. Boltshope Park, Durham recorded 30cm of snow on 1st and temperature of -17.1°C overnight on 2nd and 3rd. Milder weather then followed with a mix of sun and rain, south and southwest regions experiencing the worst of the downpours. There were a few scattered snow showers towards the end of the month but by 31st it was much warmer.

Northwest Europe

For most of autumn and winter 2000–01 temperatures across northwest Europe were above average. Only one significant cold snap occurred during the course of the winter, as cold air pushed westwards from northeast Russia across Scandinavia and Denmark during late January and early February, immediately prior to the Core Count priority date that month. Following a brief warmer spell March was unusually cold across most of northern Europe.

Figure 1. Surface temperature anomalies in early February 2001 (source: NOAA-CIRES Climate Diagnostics Centre).

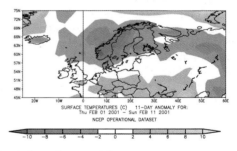

Arctic breeding conditions

Productivity in arctic-breeding birds was mixed in 2000. Rodent abundance was low in Greenland and to the west of the Taimyr Peninsula though generally higher than average further east. Temperatures in northwest Russia and western Greenland were above average, and spring phenology was correspondingly early in these areas. Early summer temperatures around the arctic islands of Svalbard and Franz Josef Land were near or slightly below normal. As summer progressed, temperatures in Greenland and northwest Russia remained above average though cooler conditions prevailed east of the Urals.

Table i. The proportion of stillwater count units (lakes, reservoirs and gravel pits) in the UK with any ice and with 75% or more of their surface covered by ice during WeBS counts in 2000–01 (England divided by a line drawn roughly between the Humber and the Mersey Estuaries).

Region	Ice	S	O	N	D	J	F	M
Northern	>0%	0	0	0	4	4	0	n/a
Ireland	>74%	0	0	0	0	0	0	n/a
Scotland	>0%	0	0	1	24	64	38	n/a
	>74%	0	0	0	10	47	21	n/a
N England	>0%	0	0	0	12	53	6	n/a
	>74%	0	0	0	6	27	1	n/a
S England	>0%	0	0	<1	4	33	14	n/a
	>74%	0	0	<1	1	15	0	n/a
Wales	>0%	0	0	0	0	41	0	n/a
	>74%	0	0	0	0	26	0	n/a

WeBS Core Counts

SURVEY METHODS

The main source of data for this report is the WeBS scheme, providing regular monthly counts for most waterbird species at the majority of the UK's important wetlands. In order to fulfil the WeBS objectives, however, data from a number of additional schemes are included in this report. In particular, a number of species groups necessitate different counting methodologies in order to monitor numbers adequately, notably grey geese and seaducks, and the results of other national and local schemes for these species are routinely included. Additional, *ad hoc*, data are also sought for important sites not otherwise covered by regular monitoring, particularly open coast sections in Scotland, whilst the results of periodic, co-ordinated surveys, such as the non-estuarine coastal waterfowl survey, are included where the data collected are compatible with the presentation formats used in this report. The methods for these survey types are outlined below and more detail can be found in Gilbert *et al.* (1998). Although the precise methods for some of the additional count data presented within this report are unknown, it is safe to assume that they will follow closely the general methods presented here.

WeBS Core Counts

WeBS Core Counts are made using so-called 'look-see' methodology (Bibby *et al.* 2000), whereby the observer, familiar with the species involved, surveys the whole of a predefined area.

Counts are made at all wetland habitats, including lakes, lochs/loughs, ponds, reservoirs, gravel pits, rivers, freshwater marshes, canals, sections of open coast and estuaries.

Numbers of all waterbird species, as defined by Wetlands International (Rose & Scott 1997), are recorded. In the UK, this includes divers, grebes, Cormorant, herons, Spoonbill, swans, geese, ducks, rail, cranes, waders and Kingfisher. Counts of gulls and terns are optional. Vagrants, introductions and escapes are included.

Most waterbirds are readily visible. Secretive species, such as snipes, are generally under-recorded. No allowance is made for these habits by the observer and only birds seen or heard are recorded. The species affected by such biases are well known and the problems of interpretation are highlighted individually in the Species Accounts.

Most species and many sub-species are readily identifiable during the counts. Categories may be used, e.g. unidentified scoter species, where it is not possible to be confident of identification, e.g. under poor light conditions.

Species present in relatively small numbers or dispersed widely may be counted singly. The number of birds in large flocks is generally estimated by mentally dividing the birds into groups, which may vary from five to 1,000 depending on the size of the flock, and counting the number of groups. Notebooks and tally counters may be used to aid counts.

Counts are made once per month, ideally on predetermined 'priority dates'. This enables counts across the whole country to be synchronised, thus reducing the likelihood of birds being double-counted or missed. Such synchronisation is imperative at large sites which are divided into sectors, each of which can be practicably counted by a single person in a reasonable amount of time. Local Organisers ensure co-ordination in these cases due to the high possibility of local movements affecting count totals.

The priority dates are pre-selected with a view to optimising tidal conditions for counters covering coastal sites at high tide on a Sunday (see Coverage). The dates used for individual sites may vary due to differences in the tidal regime around the country. Co-ordination within a site takes priority over national synchronisation.

The accuracy of each count is recorded. Counts suspected to be gross underestimates of the true number of non-secretive species present are specifically noted, e.g. a large flock of roosting waders only partially counted before being flushed by a predator, or a distant flock of sea-duck in heavy swell. These counts may then be treated differently when calculating site totals (see Analysis).

Data are input by a professional data input company. Data are keyed twice by different people and discrepancies identified by computer for correction. Any particularly unusual counts are checked by the National Organisers and are confirmed with the counters if necessary.

Goose roost censuses

Since many 'grey geese' spend daylight hours in agricultural landscapes, most are missed during counts at wetlands by WeBS. These species are usually best counted as they fly to or from their roost sites at dawn or dusk since these are generally discrete wetlands and birds often follow traditional flight lines approaching or leaving the site. Even in half-light, birds can generally be counted with relative ease against the sky, although they may not be specifically identifiable at mixed species roosts.

In order to produce population estimates, counts are synchronised nationally for particular species (see Appendix 3), though normally only one or two such counts are made each year. The priority count dates are determined according to the state of the moon, since large numbers of geese may remain on fields during moonlit nights. Additional counts are made by some observers, particularly during times of high turnover when large numbers may occur for just a few days.

In some areas, where roost sites are poorly known or difficult to access, counts of birds in fields are made during the daytime.

As with WeBS Core Counts, the accuracy of the count is noted.

Sea-ducks

The accuracy of counts of waterbirds on the sea is particularly dependent on prevailing weather conditions at the time of or directly preceding the count. Birds are often distant from land, and wind or rain can cause considerable difficulty with identifying and counting birds. Wind not only causes telescope shake, but even a moderate swell at sites without high vantage points can hamper counts considerably. Many sites may be best covered using aerial surveys, though these are usually expensive and require experienced, professional counters. In many cases, birds can only be identified to genus, e.g. grebe species or scoter species.

Consequently, the best counts of most divers, grebes and sea-duck at open coast and many estuarine sites are made simply when conditions allow; only rarely will such conditions occur by chance during WeBS counts. Synchronisation between different sites may be difficult or impossible to achieve, and thus co-ordination of most counts to date has occurred at a regional or site level, e.g. within the Moray Firth and within North Cardigan Bay.

Irish Wetland Bird Survey

The Irish Wetland Bird Survey (I-WeBS) monitors non-breeding waterbirds in the Republic of Ireland (Colhoun 2001). I-WeBS was launched in 1994 as a joint partnership between BirdWatch Ireland, National Parks and Wildlife Service of Dúchas — The Heritage Service of the Department of Environment and Local Government (Ireland) — and WWT, with additional funding and support from the Heritage Council and WWF UK (World Wide Fund for Nature). I-WeBS is complementary to and compatible with the UK scheme. The main methodological difference from UK-WeBS is that counts are made only between September and March, inclusive.

Productivity monitoring

Changes in numbers of waterbirds counted in the UK between years are likely to result from a number of factors, including coverage and weather, particularly for European and Russian-breeding species which may winter further east or west within Europe according to the severity of the winter. However, genuine changes in population size will result from differences in recruitment and mortality between years.

For several species of swans and geese, young of the year can be readily identified in the field and a measure of productivity can be obtained by recording the number of young birds in sampled flocks, expressed as a percentage of the total number of birds aged. Experienced fieldworkers, by observing the behaviour of and relationship between individuals in a flock, can record brood sizes as the number of young birds associating with two adults.

ANALYSIS

In fulfilment of the WeBS objectives, results are presented in a number of different sections. An outline of the analyses undertaken for each is given here; further detail is provided in Appendix 3. A number of limitations of the data or these analytical techniques necessitate caution when interpreting the results presented in this report (see Interpretation of Waterbird Counts).

National totals

Population estimates are revised once every three years, in keeping with internationally agreed timetables (Rose & Stroud 1994). The Great Britain population estimates have been revised during the production of this report (Kershaw & Cranswick in press; Rehfisch *et al.* in press). The revised figures from these publications have not been used in analyses of data presented in this report but will be used in subsequent WeBS reports.

Total numbers of waterbirds recorded by WeBS and other schemes are presented separately for Great Britain (including the Isle of Man but excluding the Channel Islands) and Northern Ireland in recognition of the different legislation that applies to each. Separate totals for England, Scotland, Wales, and the Channel Islands are provided in Appendices 4–7. Numbers of waterbirds found on coastal (including estuarine) and inland habitats are provided separately in Appendices 8 & 9, particularly for comparison of numbers of waders with those in reports prior to 1994 when waders were not counted at inland sites.

Numbers presented in this report are not rounded. National and site totals calculated as the sum of counts from several sectors or sites may imply a false sense of accuracy if different methods for recording numbers have been used, e.g. 1,000 birds estimated on one sector and a count of seven individuals on another is presented as 1,007. It is safe to assume that any large count includes a proportion of estimated birds. However, reproducing the submitted counts in this way is deemed the most appropriate means of presentation and avoids the summation of 'rounding error'.

The count nearest the monthly priority date or, alternatively, the count co-ordinated with nearby sites if there is considered to be significant interchange, is chosen for use in this report if several accurate counts are available for the same month. A count from any date is used if it is the only one available.

Data from other national surveys are used instead of WeBS Core Counts where the census total provides a better estimate of the total numbers, e.g. the national census of Pink-footed and Greylag Geese in October and November. Totals from different censuses are not combined to produce national totals due to lack of synchronisation (birds counted at roost by one method may be effectively double-counted during the WeBS count at a different site in that month), with the exception of a few goose populations where the risk of double-counting is minimal (see Appendix 3). Consequently, counts from site or regional-based surveys of sea-ducks, for example, are not included in

national totals. Data from WeBS special surveys are not included in national totals.

For some scarcer species, including many escaped or introduced species, an estimate of the total number recorded by WeBS throughout the country has been provided using summed site maxima, calculated by summing the highest count at each site, irrespective of the month in which it occurred. For some species, this is likely to result in double-counting where birds move between sites.

Annual indices

Because the same WeBS sites are not necessarily covered each year, changes in waterbird population sizes cannot be determined simply by comparing the total number of birds counted in each year. Consequently, indexing techniques have been developed which allow between-year comparisons of numbers, even if the true population size is unknown.

The 'Underhill index' (Underhill 1989) was specifically developed for waterbird populations and is used in this report for most species. A full explanation of this indexing process is given in Prŷs-Jones *et al.* (1994), Underhill & Prŷs-Jones (1994) and Kirby *et al.* (1995), with additional information on its use in this report presented in Appendix 3.

In summary, where sites have not been visited, a count for each species is calculated based on counts in other months and years and at other sites. This effectively means that data are available for the same set of sites in each year and counts are thus directly comparable from one year to the next. Changes in the population can be calculated and the relative difference expressed as an index.

Not all species are included in the indexing process. Notably, many of the goose populations are excluded, partly because their reliance on non-wetland sites requires different count methodologies, but also because regular censusing of substantially the whole of the British populations negates the need for an index to be calculated using the Underhill technique. Thus, change indices for Pink-footed, Icelandic Greylag, Greenland White-fronted and Svalbard Barnacle Geese have been derived from the highest total count obtained during censuses of the population in each year (see Appendix 3). Many sea-duck are also excluded from the indexing process because of the extreme counting difficulties involved. Waders excluded from the index include those for which large numbers occur away from wetlands, e.g. Lapwing and Golden Plover, and those that are difficult to count accurately using WeBS methods, e.g. Snipe and Jack Snipe. Waterbird species which only occur in small numbers in Britain and Ireland have also been excluded.

Index values for wildfowl species have been provided separately for Britain and Northern Ireland. However, values calculated for waders in Northern Ireland were found to be statistically unreliable due to the small number of estuaries contributing to each index value, and consequently indices have been calculated for the UK as a whole for these species.

For all species, the index value has been constrained to equal 100 in the most recent year. In particular, this enables direct comparison of values for wildfowl in Great Britain with Northern Ireland despite the different availability of data as a consequence of the later start of the scheme in the province (see Appendix 3 for availability of data for different species groups and countries).

Monthly indices

The abundance of different wildfowl species varies during the winter due to a number of factors, most notably the timing of their movements along the flyway, whilst severe weather, particularly on the continent, may also affect numbers in the UK. However, due to differences in site coverage between months, such patterns cannot be reliably detected using count totals. Consequently, an index is calculated for each month to reflect changes in relative abundance during the season.

The index uses only counts from sites covered in all seven months (September to March). Totals calculated for each month from these sites only can then be compared directly (expressed as a percentage of the maximum numbers), thus revealing patterns of seasonality for the species considered. These are presented as graphs in the species accounts, giving both the value for the 2000–01 winter, and the average value from the five preceding winters, 1995–96 to 1999–00. Non-migratory, scarce and irregularly counted species are omitted and only WeBS Core Counts have been used in the index.

Broad differences in the monthly values between species reflect their status in the UK. Resident species, or those with large UK breeding populations, e.g. some grebes and Mallard, are present in large numbers early in the winter. Declines through the winter result in part from mortality of first year birds, but also birds returning to remote or small breeding sites

that are not covered by WeBS. The majority of UK wildfowl either occur solely as winter visitors, or have small breeding populations that are swelled by winter immigrants, with peak abundance generally occurring in mid winter.

The vast majority of the wintering populations of many wader species are found on estuaries, and, since coverage of this habitat is relatively complete and more or less constant throughout winter, meaningful comparisons of total monthly counts can be made for many species. Consequently, monthly indices are not calculated for waders. As counting of gulls and terns is optional, indices are not calculated for these species either.

Site importance

Tables in the Species Accounts rank the principal sites for each species according to average seasonal maxima for the last five seasons in line with recommendations of the Ramsar Convention (see Appendix 2 and Presentation and notation).

The count nearest the priority date or, alternatively, the count co-ordinated with nearby sites if there is considered to be significant interchange, is chosen for use in this report if several accurate counts are available for the same month. A count from any date is used if it is the only one available.

In accounts for most divers, grebes, Cormorant, herons, wildfowl, gulls, terns and Kingfisher, annual maxima are derived from any month, with the season running from July to June inclusive. Average maxima for sites listed in the wader accounts are calculated using data from only the winter period, November to March. For species which occur primarily as summer visitors, e.g. Garganey, Little Ringed Plover, annual statistics are calculated using the calendar year.

Data from other sources, often involving different methods, e.g. goose roost censuses, are used where these provide better, i.e. larger, counts for individual sites. Non-estuarine Coastal Waterfowl Survey (NEWS) data have only been presented for selected species (Ringed Plover, Sanderling, Purple Sandpiper, Bar-tailed Godwit and Turnstone) and only for sites previously noted as being of national importance.

In the first instance, average maxima were calculated using only complete counts but, if any incomplete counts exceeded this initial average, they were also incorporated and the averages recalculated. Averages enclosed by brackets are based solely on incomplete counts.

Counts at any site are considered to be incomplete whenever significant under-recording is thought to have occurred, due to part of the site not being counted or adverse counting conditions. This information is provided by the observer on the accuracy of the overall count (either 'OK' or 'Low', the latter indicating that a significant proportion of birds present were thought to have been missed, e.g. due to poor visibility) or for individual species.

For sites comprising just one count unit, completeness is assessed on a species-by-species basis using the accuracy information provided by the observer.

For complex sites (i.e. those comprising more than one count unit), counts from individual count sectors might have been made under very different conditions, particularly at very large sites, and consequently may have quite different qualities assigned to accuracy of the count. Additionally a variable amount of the overall site may have been uncounted.

For wildfowl and their allies, completeness assessments for the major complex sites (most estuaries, gravel pit complexes etc.) have been made according to the number of sectors covered. If a significant proportion of the total number of sectors were not counted, and the total number of wildfowl was correspondingly lower than normal, all counts of those species at that site in that month are deemed incomplete.

For waders, gulls, terns and herons, more sophisticated species-by-species completeness qualities are assigned. In this case, the importance of the contribution of each count sector to the site total is based on its average contribution to the total at the time of year in question and on recent years (to allow for seasonal and long-term trends). Further, consideration is given to the fact that a count sector which normally holds a significant proportion of a site total for species A may hold only a small proportion of the site total for species B. Consequently, if such a count sector is not completely counted, the site total will now be treated as complete for species B but incomplete for species A.

In addition to the assessment of sites in Species Accounts, sites are identified for their importance in terms of overall waterbird numbers in Principal Sites. The peak count at each site is calculated by summing the individual species maxima during the season, irrespective of the month in which they occurred. Only WeBS Core Counts and national goose censuses (see Appendix 3) are included in totals. Note that non-native introduced or escaped species (i.e. those not in BOURC

category A; see Introduced and Escaped Waterbirds under Total Numbers) are not included in these totals. Additional counts made using different methodologies, such as those of sea-ducks on the Moray Firth, are not incorporated.

The locations of all sites named in this report are given in Appendix 10.

PRESENTATION AND NOTATION

Detail is provided here on the format of presentation and the notation used in Species Accounts in particular. The information provided in Analysis and Interpretation of Waterbird Counts should mean that results presented in other sections are self-explanatory.

The main purpose of the Species Accounts is to list important sites for each species, sub-species or population, as relevant. This is done using certain numerical criteria adopted widely for use in conservation legislation and guidelines for site designation (see Appendix 2), although a number of exceptions have been made in some cases. Where available, the international and national importance thresholds are listed at the start of each account, although, for some numerous species, no population estimates, and therefore no thresholds, are available. Less numerous species, for which thresholds are not likely to be produced, are classified as 'scarce' whilst species are classified as a 'vagrant' where the UK does not fall within its normal range of distribution. In line with the recommendations of Vinicombe *et al.* (1993), records of all species recorded by WeBS, including escapes, have been published to contribute to the proper assessment of naturalised populations and escaped birds. Following Holmes & Stroud (1995), non-native species which have become established are termed 'naturalised'. These species are categorised according to the process by which they became established: naturalised feral (domesticated species gone wild); naturalised introduction (introduced by man); naturalised re-establishment (species re-established in an area of former occurrence); or naturalised establishment (a species which occurs, but does not breed naturally, e.g. potentially Barnacle Goose in southern England). With the exception of vagrants, all other non-native species have been classed as 'escapes'. The native range is given in the species account for naturalised species, escapes and vagrants.

The maximum count in any month of 2000–01, and the month of occurrence, is given for

Great Britain and Northern Ireland in each account except for species occurring in very small numbers. Where productivity data have been collected, the proportion of young and mean brood size, where available, are also listed at the start of the account for ease of reference.

Index values, where calculated, are graphed within each account. Where separate British and Northern Ireland values have been calculated (for certain wildfowl species), these are presented on the same graph to allow direct comparison but with different y-axes (vertical axes) for clarity. British indices are denoted using circles and the left-hand axis, and Northern Ireland values using squares and the right hand axis. Where only one index series is presented, circles and the left-hand axis have been used regardless of country.

Monthly indices, where calculated, are graphed within each account. Mean values for the previous five years (1995–96 to 1999–2000) are shown using black columns and values for the most recent year using white columns.

Text in each account highlights significant points, e.g. coverage, changes in numbers or indices and at individual sites, and provides an overview of any recently published relevant research or surveys. The terms 'recent average' and 'previous average' refer to averages based on the winters 1995–96 to 1999–2000, i.e. those presented in the previous WeBS report.

Tables provide data for all internationally important sites and all nationally important sites (either in a Great Britain context or, for sites in Northern Ireland, in an all-Ireland context) monitored by WeBS or other appropriate surveys. For each site, the maximum count in each of the five most recent years, the month of occurrence of the 2000–01 peak and the mean of the maxima is given. Incomplete counts are bracketed and missing counts are denoted using a dash '-'.

Sites are selected for presentation using a strict interpretation of the 1% threshold (for convenience, sites in the Channel Islands and Isle of Man are identified using 1% thresholds for Great Britain and included under the Great Britain section of the tables). For some species with very small national populations, and consequently very low 1% thresholds, an arbitrary, higher level has been chosen for the inclusion of sites and is highlighted in the text. Where no thresholds are given, e.g. for introduced species, and where no or very few sites in the UK reach the relevant national qualifying levels, an arbitrary threshold has been chosen to select a list of sites for this report.

These thresholds are highlighted in the text. A blank line has been inserted in the table to separate sites that qualify as nationally important from those with five-year peak mean counts of less than 50 birds.

Where the importance of a site has changed as a result of the 2000–01 count, i.e. it has become nationally or internationally important but was not following the previous year, or it has changed from international to national importance or vice versa, this is indicated in the table. Sites with elevated status have a black triangle pointing up (▲) to the right of the average, whilst those with lowered status are indicated using a triangle pointing down (▼). Sites for which the average fell below the threshold for national importance following 2000–01 are listed under the heading 'Sites no longer meeting table qualifying levels'.

A few sites that have not been counted in recent years, in most cases due to their isolated location, but were of national or international importance for one or more species when last counted (and thus retain that status in the absence of data to the contrary), are listed in the accounts under the section 'Internationally or nationally important sites not counted in last five years'. This also serves to highlight the need for counting to be resumed.

All sites which, in 2000–01, held numbers exceeding the relevant national threshold (or adopted qualifying level), but with five year means below this value are listed under 'Other sites surpassing table qualifying levels in 2000–01'. This serves to highlight important sites worthy of continued close attention.

It should be noted that a site may appear to have been flagged erroneously as having elevated status if the most recent count was below the relevant threshold. However, a particularly low count six years previously will have depressed the mean in the previous report. The converse may be true for sites with lowered status and thus, in exceptional circumstances, a site may be listed in the relevant sections of the table as both no longer being of national importance and with a peak count in the most recent year exceeding the national threshold.

For a number of wader species, different thresholds exist for passage periods. The list of 'sites surpassing passage thresholds in 2000–01' includes all those with counts above the relevant number, even if already listed in the main part of the table by virtue of the winter mean surpassing the national threshold.

See page 32 for symbols and notation used.

INTERPRETATION OF WATERBIRD COUNTS

Caution is always necessary in the interpretation and application of waterbird counts given the limitations of these data. This is especially true of the summary form which, by necessity, is used in this report. A primary aim here remains the rapid feedback of key results to the many participants in the WeBS scheme. More detailed information on how to make use of the data for research or site assessment purposes can be obtained from the appropriate National Organisers.

Information collated by WeBS and other surveys can be held or used in a variety of ways. Data may also be summarised and analysed differently depending on the requirements of the user. Consequently, calculations used to interpret data and their presentation may vary between this and other publications, and indeed between organisations or individual users. The terminology used by different organisations may not always highlight these differences. This particularly applies to summary data. Such variations do not detract from the value of each different method, but offer greater choice to users according to the different questions being addressed. This should always be borne in mind when using data presented here.

For ease of reference, the caveats provided below are broadly categorised according to the presentation of results for each of the key objectives of WeBS. Several points, however, are general in nature and apply to a broad range of uses of the data.

National totals

The majority of count data are collected between September and March, when most species of waterbird are present in the UK in highest numbers. Data are collected during other months and have been presented where relevant. However, caution is urged regarding their interpretation both due to the relative sparsity of counts from this period and the different count effort for different sites.

A number of systematic biases of WeBS or other count methodology must be borne in mind when considering the data. Coverage of estuarine habitats and large, standing waters by WeBS is good or excellent. Consequently, counted totals of those species which occur wholly or primarily on this habitat during winter will approximate the true number. However, those species dispersed widely over rivers, non-estuarine coast or small inland waters are likely to be considerably under-represented, as will secretive or cryptic species, such as snipes, or those which occur on non-wetlands, e.g. grassland plovers. Species which occur in large numbers during passage are also likely to be under-represented, not only because of poorer coverage at this time, but due to the high turnover of birds in a short period. Further, since counts of gulls and terns are optional, national totals are likely to be considerable underestimates of the number using the WeBS network of sites. Only for a handful of species, primarily geese, do count totals approach the true number in the UK.

One instance of possible over-estimation is the use of summed site maxima to determine the total number of scarcer species. For species with mobile flocks in an area well covered by WeBS, e.g. Snow Goose in south-east England, it is likely that a degree of double-counting will occur, particularly if birds move between sites at different times of the year. These cases are highlighted in the Species Accounts.

The publication of records of vagrants in this report does not imply acceptance by the British Birds Rarities Committee (e.g. Rogers and the Rarities Committee 1998).

Annual indices

For all species, the long-term trends in index values can be used with confidence to assess changes in overall wintering populations. Because short-term fluctuations provide a less rigorous indication of population changes, care should be taken in their interpretation.

Caution should be used in interpreting figures for species which only occur in small numbers. Thus, numbers tend to fluctuate more widely for many species in Northern Ireland, largely as a result of the smaller numbers of birds involved but also, being at the westernmost limit of their range, due to variable use being made of Ireland by wintering wildfowl.

It should be borne in mind that the missing values used in the Underhill index are calculated anew each year. Because the index formula uses data from all years, each new year's counts will slightly alter the site, month and year factors. In turn, the missing counts may differ slightly and, as a result, the index values produced each year are likely to differ from those published in the previous Wildfowl and Wader Counts. The indices published here represent an improvement on previous figures as the additional year's data allow calculation of the site, month and year factors with greater confidence. Index values are given in Appendix 3

Monthly indices

As for annual indices, the reduced numbers of both sites and birds in Northern Ireland result in a greater degree of fluctuation in numbers used in the analyses of data from the province.

Site importance

Criteria for assessing the international importance of wetlands have been agreed by the Contracting Parties to the Ramsar Convention on Wetlands of International Importance (Ramsar Convention Bureau 1998). Under criterion 6, a wetland is considered internationally important if it regularly supports 1% of the individuals in a population of one species or subspecies of waterbird, whilst any site regularly supporting 20,000 or more waterbirds qualifies under criterion 5. Similar criteria have been adopted for identification of SPAs under the EC Birds Directive in the UK legislation. A wetland in Britain is considered nationally important if it regularly holds 1% or more of the estimated British population of one species or subspecies of waterbird, and in Northern Ireland, important in an all-Ireland context if it holds 1% or more of the estimated all-Ireland population. The relevant 1% thresholds are given in Appendix 2.

Sites are selected for presentation in this report using a strict interpretation of the 1% threshold. However, it should be noted that, where 1% of the national population is less than 50 birds, 50 is normally used as a minimum qualifying threshold for the designation of sites of national importance. It should also be noted that the 'qualifying levels' used for introduced species are used purely as a guide for presentation of sites in this report and do not infer any conservation importance for the species or the sites concerned since protected sites would not be identified for these non-native birds.

It is necessary to bear in mind the distinction between sites that regularly hold wintering populations of national or international importance and those which may happen to exceed the appropriate qualifying levels only in occasional winters. This follows the Ramsar Convention, which states that key sites must be identified on the basis of demonstrated regular use (calculated as the mean winter maxima from the last five seasons for most species in this report), otherwise a large number of sites might qualify as a consequence of irregular visitation by one-off large numbers of waterbirds. However, the Convention also indicates that provisional assessments may be made on the basis of a minimum of three years' data. These rules of thumb are applied to SPAs and national assessments also. Sites with just one or two years' data are also included in the tables if the mean exceeds the relevant threshold for completeness but this does not, as such, imply qualification.

Nevertheless, sites which irregularly support nationally or internationally important numbers may be extremely important at certain times, e.g. when the UK population is high, during the main migratory periods, or during cold weather, when they may act as refuges for birds away from traditionally used sites. For this reason also, the ranking of sites according to the total numbers of birds they support (particularly in Principal Sites) should not be taken as a rank order of the conservation importance of these sites, since certain sites, perhaps low down in terms of their total 'average' numbers, may nevertheless be of critical importance to certain species or populations at particular times.

Peak counts derived from a number of visits to a particular site in a given season will reflect more accurately the relative importance of the site for the species than do single visits. It is important to bear this in mind since, despite considerable improvements in coverage, data for a few sites presented in this report derive from single counts in some years. Similarly, in assessing the importance of a site, peak counts from several winters should ideally be used, as the peak count made in any one year may be unreliable due to gaps in coverage and disturbance- or weather-induced effects. The short-term movement of birds between closely adjacent sites may lead to altered assessments of a site's apparent importance for a particular species. More frequent counts than the once-monthly WeBS visits are necessary to assess more accurately the rapid turnover of waterbird populations that occurs during migration or cold weather movements.

This list of potential sources of error in counting wetland birds, though not exhaustive, suggests that the net effect tends towards under- rather than over-estimation of numbers and provides justification for the use of maximum counts for the assessment of site importance or the size of a populations. Factors causing under-estimation are normally constant at a given site in a given month, so that while under-estimates may occur, comparisons between sites and years remain valid.

It should be recognised that, in presenting only sites of national importance, this report provides just one means of identifying important sites and does not provide a definitive statement on the conservation value of individual sites for waterbirds, let alone other conservation interests. The national thresholds have been chosen to provide a reasonable amount of information in the context of this report only. Thus, for example, many sites of regional importance or those of importance because of the assemblage of species present are not included here. European Directives and conservation Conventions stress the need for a holistic approach to effect successful conservation, and lay great importance on maintaining the distribution and range of species, in addition to the conservation of networks of individual key sites.

For the above reasons of poor coverage, geographically or temporally, outlined above, it should be recognised that lists of internationally and nationally important sites are limited by the availability of WeBS and other survey data. Whilst the counter network is likely to cover the vast majority of important sites, others may be missed and therefore will not be listed in the tables due to lack of appropriate data.

Some counts in this report differ from those presented previously. This results from the submission of late data and corrections, and in some cases, the use of different count seasons or changes to site structures. Additionally, some sites may have been omitted from tables previously due to oversight. It is likely that small changes will continue as part of the current site mapping project and as the database, developed initially for waders, is brought on line for wildfowl. Most changes are minor, but comment is made in the text where they are significant. Where a site has apparently changed status as a result of recalculations or omissions, comment is made in the text but it is not flagged in the tables in the Species Accounts.

Note that sites listed under 'Sites no longer meeting table qualifying levels' represent those that were listed in the 1999–2000 report as of national importance but which, following the 2000–01 counts, no longer meet the relevant threshold. It is not an exhaustive list of sites which, at any time in the past, have been of national or all-Ireland importance.

Counts made using non-WeBS methodologies, such as those of sea-ducks on the Moray Firth, are not incorporated into the site totals presented in Principal Sites, with the exception of goose roost counts. Thus, it should be borne in mind that other sites that are important for certain waterbird species are not included in the table, whilst the sites listed may be of 'greater importance' for the species listed if additional data were included.

Lastly, owing to possible boundary differences, totals given for WeBS sites in this report are not necessarily the same as totals for designated statutory sites (ASSIs/SSSIs, SPAs or Ramsar Sites) having the same or similar names.

COVERAGE

WeBS Core Counts

Co-ordinated, synchronous counts are advocated to prevent double-counting or birds being missed. Consequently, priority dates are recommended nationally. Due to differences in tidal regimes around the country, counts at a few estuaries were made on other dates to match the most suitable conditions. Weather and counter availability also result in some counts being made on alternative dates.

Table ii. WeBS Core Count priority count dates in 2000–01

9 April	22 October
7 May	19 November
25 June	17 December
23 July	14 January
20 August	11 February
17 September	11 March

Counts were received from 2,053 sites of all habitats for the period April 2000 to March 2001, comprising 3,465 count units (the sub-divisions of large sites for which separate counts are provided). The number of sites and count units remains at the high level of recent years. Counts of the NW Scottish mainland by the Royal Air Force Ornithological Society provided valuable information on a remote and sparsely populated area which has traditionally received little coverage. Of the key waterbird sites, 2000-01 counts for the Lower Derwent Valley, Ythan Estuary and Upper Lough Erne were not received in time for publication of this report.

During the reporting period of this publication, a major Foot and Mouth Disease (FMD) epidemic spread across many parts of the UK. The first case was confirmed on February 20th and by March 32 separate outbreaks had been confirmed. As a result of subsequent restrictions on access in the countryside , the WeBS partners suspended the counts until further notice. Consequently, only 5% of count units were visited in March.

Figure 2. Coverage by 10-km grid squares for WeBS Core Counts in the UK, Isle of Man and the Channel Islands and for I-WeBS in the Republic of Ireland in 2000–01. Small dots represent 1–2 count units per 10-km square, medium dots represent 3–4 units and large dots represent five or more units.

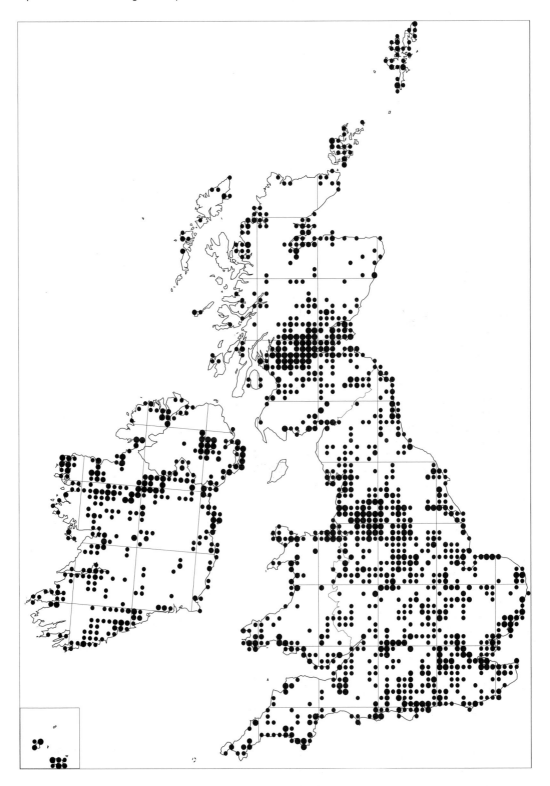

WeBS and I-WeBS coverage in 2000–01 is shown by 10-km squares in Figure 2. The location of each count unit is shown using only its central grid reference. Thus, for example, the 19 count sectors of the North Norfolk Coast fall in four 10-km squares, broadly indicating the extent of the whole site. In all, WeBS count units were visited in 1,133 different 10-km squares during 2000–01, typical of coverage in recent years. As ever, areas with few wetlands or small human populations are apparent on the map as areas with little coverage. The location of many of the key sites mentioned in the report and all estuaries is shown in Figure A1 in Appendix 10. The county and grid reference of all sites mentioned by name in this report are given in Appendix 10.

Goose censuses

In 2000–01, as in previous years, Bean Geese were censused regularly on the Slamannan Plateau (Simpson & MacIver 2001). National surveys of Pink-footed and Icelandic Greylag Geese were undertaken in October and November (Hearn 2002), involving counts of birds arriving at or leaving roosts. Censuses of the native Scottish Greylag population on the Uists were made in August and February (R. MacDonald in litt.). Censuses of Greenland White-fronted Geese, including birds in Ireland, were undertaken in autumn 2000 by the Greenland White-fronted Goose Study and Irish National Parks and Wildlife Service (Fox & Francis 2002) though the spring 2001 census failed to take place due to the outbreak of Foot and Mouth Disease. Greenland Barnacle Geese were counted regularly by SNH and others on Islay and main islands in Argyll (M. McKay in litt.). The Svalbard Barnacle Goose population was counted frequently on the Solway Firth by WWT staff and volunteers (Griffin & Coath 2001). Dark-bellied Brent Geese were censused in January and February by the WeBS network, with counters at key sites making special effort to locate birds using adjacent areas, particularly fields, which would ordinarily be missed during normal Core Counts.

Sea-duck surveys

Data were received from the following regional or site-based surveys for counts of sea-duck, divers and grebes at coastal sites, many continuing studies from previous years: counts in the Moray Firth between November and January (D. Butterfield in litt.); at least once monthly aerial and/or land-based counts of Common Scoter in Carmarthen Bay between

April and March (L. Smith in litt.); and counts of key sites around the Isles of Shetland by SOTEAG (Heubeck in litt.). However, no data were received for Cardigan Bay, Scapa Flow or parts of SE Scotland where dedicated counts have been made in recent years.

TOTAL NUMBERS

The total numbers of waterbirds recorded by WeBS in 2000–01 are given in Tables 1 and 2 for Great Britain (including the Isle of Man, but excluding the Channel Islands) and Northern Ireland, respectively. Counts of waterbirds in the Republic of Ireland by I-WeBS are provided in Table 3.

Site coverage for gulls and terns is given separately since recording of these species was optional.

Winter 2000-01 was generally mild, with only a few relatively short cold snaps. The only significant cold period in Europe occurred in early February just prior to the Core Count priority date, and is reflected in increased numbers of Golden Plover and Lapwing recorded that month. Several species were recorded in record numbers in Great Britain though few in Northern Ireland. March totals for all species were severely affected by poor coverage as a result of access restrictions following the outbreak of Foot and Mouth Disease. More detailed discussion of the totals in relation to counts from previous years is given in the individual species accounts.

Introduced and escaped waterbirds

Many species of waterbird occur in the UK as a result of introductions, particularly through escapes from collections. Several have become established, such as Canada Goose and Ruddy Duck. The British Ornithologists' Union Records Committee recently established a category 'E' for 'species that have been recorded as introductions, transportees or escapes from captivity, and whose breeding populations (if any) are not thought to be self-sustaining' (BOURC 1999).

WeBS records of these species are included in this report both for the sake of completeness and in order to assess their status and monitor any changes in numbers, a key requirement given the need, under the African-Eurasian Waterbird Agreement of the Bonn convention '. . . to prevent the unintentional release of such species . . .' and once introduced, the need '. . . to prevent these species from becoming a threat to indigenous species' (Holmes *et al.* 1998).

Figure 3. Number of species (white bars), number of sites at which birds were recorded (grey bars) and summed sites maxima (black bars) for waterbirds in the BOURC's category E.

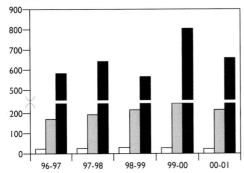

Numbers of established populations (e.g. Canada Goose and Ruddy Duck, which are placed in category 'C') are excluded from the statistics below since the large numbers involved would swamp numbers of other species.

Figure 3 shows data for species in category E, although these data exclude species which occur in both category A and E (e.g. Pink-footed Goose) since separation of escaped from wild birds is not readily possible using WeBS methods. A total of 23 species were recorded in 2000–01 at 217 sites, both slightly below the previous year. The summed site maxima of 659 birds, whilst also down on the previous year, was the second highest to date. Although this figure will undoubtedly include some duplication of individual birds recorded at more than one site and occasional records of pinioned birds, this figure probably provides a truer reflection of the numbers of introduced or escaped waterbirds frequenting WeBS sites than the peak monthly total of 249 birds in October.

Table 1. Total numbers of waterbirds recorded by WeBS Core Counts in Great Britain, 2000–01[†].

		Apr	May	Jun	Jul	Aug
	Number of sites visited	*963*	*890*	*858*	*884*	*921*
	Number of sectors visited	*1,538*	*1,373*	*1,309*	*1,323*	*1,445*
RH	Red-throated Diver	247	56	27	43	79
BV	Black-throated Diver	15	2	0	5	6
ND	Great Northern Diver	61	43	1	0	6
UL	Unidentified diver	0	0	0	3	0
LG	Little Grebe	1,718	1,090	1,078	1,527	2,665
GG	Great Crested Grebe	4,374	3,689	3,673	5,042	6,611
RX	Red-necked Grebe	10	4	2	11	26
SZ	Slavonian Grebe	79	9	5	3	6
BN	Black-necked Grebe	39	15	44	33	26
CA	Cormorant	6,401	4,650	4,262	6,402	9,777
BI	Bittern	0	2	1	0	1
QH	Squacco Heron	0	0	1	0	0
EC	Cattle Egret	0	0	0	0	1
ET	Little Egret	338	156	181	588	1,119
HW	Great White Egret	0	0	0	2	1
H.	Grey Heron	1,643	1,590	2,112	2,403	3,305
UR	Purple Heron	0	0	0	1	1
OR	White Stork	0	0	0	2	3
NB	Spoonbill	2	6	8	9	10
YV	Fulvous Whistling Duck	1	0	0	0	0
MS	Mute Swan	9,737	9,424	10,484	12,138	14,115
AS	Black Swan	21	22	25	31	44
BS	Bewick's Swan	6	3	0	0	0
WS	Whooper Swan	321	28	22	28	30
ZS	hybrid Cygnus	0	2	1	0	0
MJ	Magpie Goose	0	0	0	0	0
HN	Swan Goose	14	14	18	19	20
BE	Bean Goose	0	2	2	0	0
XF	Taiga Bean Goose	0	0	0	0	0
PG	Pink-footed Goose	9,220	631	13	17	12
WG	White-fronted Goose[1]	0	0	0	0	0
EW	European White-fronted Goose	1	4	17	0	4
NW	Greenland White-fronted Goose	99	0	0	0	1
LC	Lesser White-fronted Goose	0	0	1	1	0
JI	Greylag Goose (Iceland)	3,381	0	0	0	0
JH	Greylag Goose (NW Scotland)	123	27	13	5	8,366
JE	Greylag Goose (naturalised)	5,654	5,218	12,142	11,799	19,177
HD	Bar-headed Goose	6	9	17	15	10
SJ	Snow Goose	18	12	33	11	17
RJ	Ross's Goose	0	0	0	0	0
EM	Emperor Goose	2	1	1	1	4
CG	Canada Goose	14,752	11,686	29,875	30,997	35,550
YN	Barnacle Goose (Greenland)	90	16	0	0	0
YS	Barnacle Goose (Svalbard)	14,813	5,010	0	0	0
YE	Barnacle Goose (naturalised)	132	84	195	215	168
BG	Brent Goose[1]	0	0	0	0	0
DB	Dark-bellied Brent	14,695	10,234	86	72	63
BB	Black Brant	0	0	0	0	0
QS	Light-bellied Brent (Svalbard)	13	7	0	1	1
QN	Light-bellied Brent (Canada)	16	2	0	1	1
EB	Red-breasted Goose	0	0	0	1	0
EG	Egyptian Goose	112	114	259	182	316
ZL	hybrid goose	62	50	51	60	48
ZM	feral/domestic goose	142	132	149	154	153
UO	unidentified goose	0	0	0	0	0
UD	Ruddy Shelduck	6	4	3	7	10
UE	Cape Shelduck	0	0	0	0	0
UA	Australian Shelduck	0	0	0	0	0
SU	Shelduck	29,286	18,753	19,358	23,270	22,615
ZT	hybrid Shelduck	0	0	0	0	0

Table 1. continued

	Sep	Oct	Nov	Dec	Jan	Feb	[2]Mar
Sites	*1,430*	*1,661*	*1,656*	*1,669*	*1,619*	*1,556*	*157*
Count units	*2,226*	*2,648*	*2,633*	*2,682*	*2,661*	*2,609*	*175*
RH	190	247	307	491	1,023	448	53
BV	3	7	7	38	53	145	32
ND	12	29	48	103	146	99	18
UL	0	1	2	0	0	0	0
LG	4,618	4,531	3,843	3,459	3,577	2,619	224
GG	9,899	9,816	8,570	7,024	7,311	6,947	336
RX	32	20	23	19	37	20	4
SZ	60	81	163	130	307	140	9
BN	41	40	35	52	34	34	1
CA	15,761	16,315	13,982	12,145	12,750	10,748	791
BI	2	8	7	16	14	8	2
QH	0	0	0	0	0	0	0
EC	1	1	0	0	0	0	0
ET	1,373	1,209	751	663	631	667	42
HW	2	1	0	0	0	0	0
H.	4,269	4,176	3,082	2,961	3,246	2,836	228
UR	0	0	0	0	0	0	0
OR	2	2	2	2	0	2	0
NB	8	12	12	14	2	9	0
YV	0	0	0	0	0	0	0
MS	18,450	20,699	18,830	17,878	18,412	15,232	1,324
AS	53	56	45	40	29	35	1
BS	3	152	1,701	3,893	5,232	2,220	0
WS	40	3,414	4,823	5,177	5,429	4,868	1,071
ZS	1	0	0	0	0	1	0
MJ	0	0	0	6	0	0	0
HN	44	22	32	43	20	35	0
BE	1	187	30	193	276	51	0
XF	2	4	0	0	0	0	0
PG	3,139	242,419	177,479	84,140	81,968	53,599	46
WG	0	0	2	0	0	5	0
EW	7	10	162	542	2,291	1,120	1
NW	1	359	21,148	341	900	572	2,735
LC	0	0	0	0	0	2	0
JI	0	25,251	78,608	31,286	24,888	22,217	804
JH	1,309	913	880	794	631	3,375	0
JE	25,550	19,521	21,292	20,266	19,025	11,692	463
HD	11	26	13	18	9	6	0
SJ	45	29	41	57	20	14	2
RJ	0	1	1	1	1	0	0
EM	5	2	2	5	2	2	0
CG	54,557	44,061	46,179	45,975	45,956	34,001	2,096
YN	28	99	39,757	123	168	229	0
YS	111	21,217	18,598	24,047	17,988	22,314	1,805
YE	203	464	686	947	712	602	14
BG	0	1,175	400	0	1	0	0
DB	3,083	39,489	65,992	65,921	91,400	84,069	1,615
BB	0	1	0	0	3	4	0
QS	3,139	2,133	3,196	1,584	2,508	330	0
QN	126	10	74	164	178	164	14
EB	1	1	1	0	1	1	0
EG	329	233	183	161	129	160	2
ZL	113	86	114	128	133	126	10
ZM	346	395	391	433	326	329	19
UO	4	250	0	0	10	0	0
UD	7	5	4	2	3	6	2
UE	0	1	0	1	1	1	0
UA	1	0	0	0	0	0	0
SU	37,139	40,922	51,135	50,521	60,692	55,948	2,072
ZT	1	0	0	1	1	1	0

Table I. continued

		Apr	May	Jun	Jul	Aug
MY	Muscovy Duck	33	13	13	20	12
DC	Wood Duck	2	4	2	1	1
MN	Mandarin	111	96	123	118	106
WN	Wigeon	19,673	496	219	354	1,458
AW	American Wigeon	1	1	1	1	1
HL	Chiloe Wigeon	0	0	0	2	0
GA	Gadwall	2,741	1,763	2,187	3,105	4,149
T.	Teal	15,558	580	873	1,467	11,517
TA	Green-winged Teal	1	0	0	0	0
KQ	Speckled Teal	0	0	0	0	0
MA	Mallard	28,107	24,242	36,006	48,573	74,390
BD	Black Duck	0	0	0	0	1
QB	Chestnut Teal	0	0	0	0	0
PT	Pintail	579	44	11	19	47
YL	Yellow-billed Pintail	0	0	0	0	1
PN	Bahama Pintail	2	2	1	1	0
YR	Red-billed Teal	0	1	0	0	1
GY	Garganey	30	56	25	41	47
TB	Blue-winged Teal	1	1	0	0	2
SV	Shoveler	2,891	744	470	723	3,093
IE	Ringed Teal	0	0	0	1	0
RQ	Red-crested Pochard	15	7	6	8	9
QR	Rosybill	0	0	0	0	0
PO	Pochard	1,722	898	1,665	3,599	8,848
NG	Ring-necked Duck	2	0	2	0	0
FD	Ferruginous Duck	0	0	0	0	0
NZ	New Zealand Scaup	0	0	0	0	0
TU	Tufted Duck	24,215	12,278	11,343	25,820	38,144
SP	Scaup	563	19	2	4	8
AY	Lesser Scaup	1	2	0	0	0
E.	Eider	16,258	11,674	11,201	20,003	24,198
KE	King Eider	0	1	0	0	0
LN	Long-tailed Duck	476	104	0	4	3
CX	Common Scoter	5,286	943	3,253	507	348
FS	Surf Scoter	4	2	0	0	0
VS	Velvet Scoter	712	117	23	12	26
UX	Unidentified scoter sp.	0	0	0	0	0
GN	Goldeneye	4,361	202	49	179	120
SY	Smew	3	0	0	0	0
RM	Red-breasted Merganser	2,191	771	599	896	1,490
GD	Goosander	330	233	319	533	1,139
RY	Ruddy Duck	1,557	752	628	773	1,432
OI	Argentine Blue-bill	0	0	0	0	0
ZF	feral/hybrid Mallard type	267	261	321	361	250
ZR	hybrid Anas	13	8	5	5	8
ZD	hybrid Aythya	2	1	1	2	1
UM	unidentified duck	7	0	4	10	2
WA	Water Rail	126	85	67	60	83
AK	Spotted Crake	0	0	0	0	0
MH	Moorhen	6,058	4,126	3,933	5,470	7,622
CO	Coot	26,336	15,165	23,233	43,080	63,165
AN	Crane	3	0	0	0	1
	TOTAL WILDFOWL [3]	277,888	148,493	180,745	250,851	366,091

Table 1. continued

	Sep	Oct	Nov	Dec	Jan	Feb	[2]Mar
MY	27	91	87	79	74	79	46
DC	7	10	6	5	8	4	0
MN	357	400	332	491	479	428	7
WN	78,512	277,058	263,661	344,815	382,015	290,273	8,123
AW	2	3	3	4	7	7	4
HL	0	0	0	2	0	1	0
GA	9,844	12,791	11,374	11,180	13,562	10,669	656
T.	75,252	117,390	125,994	144,402	149,276	137,856	5,922
TA	0	2	1	5	7	4	1
KQ	4	2	1	2	0	2	0
MA	119,082	136,129	133,686	139,169	147,684	101,082	5,845
BD	1	1	0	1	0	1	0
QB	0	0	0	0	0	1	0
PT	6,466	10,599	18,846	20,052	18,427	17,416	266
YL	0	0	0	0	0	0	0
PN	3	2	0	1	0	0	0
YR	1	0	0	0	0	0	0
GY	35	5	4	1	1	0	0
TB	1	0	0	1	0	0	0
SV	8,432	10,472	11,501	11,430	10,658	9,419	803
IE	2	0	0	0	0	0	0
RQ	35	56	74	57	110	70	0
QR	0	1	1	0	0	1	0
PO	9,378	21,121	27,472	33,072	34,240	30,670	1,617
NG	0	0	1	3	3	3	0
FD	2	1	0	4	4	1	0
NZ	0	1	1	0	0	0	0
TU	44,216	50,773	54,294	53,264	57,207	45,517	2,717
SP	219	1,025	1,617	2,924	4,122	2,188	48
AY	0	0	1	0	0	0	0
E.	22,453	21,397	18,998	17,099	19,569	15,417	623
KE	0	0	0	0	0	0	0
LN	245	521	500	2,604	4,693	2,219	13
CX	1,626	3,689	3,620	5,224	7,416	5,569	902
FS	0	1	1	3	5	6	0
VS	121	258	760	2,464	1,999	912	6
UX	0	0	0	0	6	290	0
GN	265	1,149	6,467	10,655	14,826	14,767	557
SY	1	2	11	75	224	194	7
RM	1,799	1,863	2,887	3,148	3,425	3,438	201
GD	907	1,166	1,512	1,690	2,356	2,413	121
RY	2,504	3,558	2,977	2,495	3,760	3,255	83
OI	1	0	0	0	0	0	0
ZF	446	1,148	1,423	1,357	418	414	53
ZR	9	16	12	13	6	6	3
ZD	4	2	5	11	12	8	0
UM	14	45	11	1	1,814	10	0
WA	155	332	350	449	366	269	36
AK	4	2	0	0	0	0	0
MH	12,268	13,313	11,365	12,023	10,876	10,328	1,209
CO	103,969	109,688	105,926	95,396	94,860	70,075	3,033
AN	0	0	0	0	0	0	0
WILDFOWL [3]	682,791	1,296,186	1,388,415	1,297,476	1,392,989	1,113,335	48,738

Table 1. continued

		Apr	May	Jun	Jul	Aug
OC	Oystercatcher	72,914	50,515	38,880	77,769	173,969
IT	Black-winged Stilt	1	0	0	0	1
AV	Avocet	1,463	1,057	912	1,595	917
TN	Stone-curlew	0	0	0	0	1
LP	Little Ringed Plover	246	220	215	209	80
RP	Ringed Plover	4,330	11,109	1,510	2,167	17,840
KP	Kentish Plover	1	0	0	0	0
DO	Dotterel	0	0	0	0	1
IF	Pacific Golden Plover	0	0	0	1	0
GP	Golden Plover	12,769	750	85	4,802	33,960
GV	Grey Plover	28,647	39,231	3,523	2,629	26,078
IP	Sociable Plover	0	0	0	0	0
L.	Lapwing	6,647	5,253	10,860	28,339	68,166
KN	Knot	100,594	29,432	12,569	29,142	74,526
SS	Sanderling	8,166	13,924	1,781	1,075	9,615
PZ	Semipalmated Sandpiper	0	0	0	0	1
LX	Little Stint	5	20	2	9	31
TK	Temminck's Stint	0	6	0	0	0
WU	White-rumped Sandpiper	0	0	0	0	1
PP	Pectoral Sandpiper	0	0	0	1	0
CV	Curlew Sandpiper	1	17	1	30	112
PS	Purple Sandpiper	650	262	0	3	19
DN	Dunlin	93,534	150,895	1,861	44,117	102,611
OA	Broad-billed Sandpiper	0	1	0	0	0
BQ	Buff-breasted Sandpiper	0	0	0	0	0
RU	Ruff	272	65	9	191	947
JS	Jack Snipe	35	1	0	0	0
SN	Snipe	1,244	109	79	276	1,084
LD	Long-billed Dowitcher	1	0	0	0	0
WK	Woodcock	2	0	0	0	1
BW	Black-tailed Godwit	9,168	733	567	8,045	15,004
BA	Bar-tailed Godwit	9,876	7,845	3,670	6,439	23,522
WM	Whimbrel	82	2,343	117	1,033	741
CU	Curlew	31,183	6,021	9,504	52,063	81,209
DR	Spotted Redshank	53	41	21	124	163
RK	Redshank	40,522	4,236	3,745	26,803	63,518
MD	Marsh Sandpiper	1	0	0	0	0
GK	Greenshank	154	542	28	837	2,133
GE	Green Sandpiper	80	16	82	440	537
OD	Wood Sandpiper	0	30	2	32	36
CS	Common Sandpiper	80	837	361	1,116	852
TT	Turnstone	6,195	3,463	384	1,723	6,038
PL	Grey Phalarope	0	0	0	0	0
U.	Unidentified wader	10	2	0	3	2
	TOTAL WADERS	428,926	328,976	90,768	291,013	703,716
	TOTAL WATERBIRDS [4]	706,814	477,469	271,513	541,864	1,069,807

Table 1. continued

	Sep	Oct	Nov	Dec	Jan	Feb	[2]Mar
OC	241,357	236,502	227,791	221,132	222,685	223,469	7,075
IT	1	1	1	1	1	0	1
AV	1,931	1,423	3,185	3,060	4,564	3,978	437
TN	0	0	0	0	0	0	0
LP	20	0	0	0	2	0	4
RP	16,407	11,709	8,427	9,105	9,545	7,516	762
KP	0	0	0	0	0	0	0
DO	0	0	0	0	0	0	0
IF	0	0	0	0	0	0	0
GP	57,708	115,466	142,167	104,481	106,455	144,549	6,418
GV	31,051	32,814	36,864	28,517	43,984	51,943	851
IP	0	0	1	0	0	0	0
L.	123,724	174,325	259,293	272,141	258,064	349,548	4,580
KN	166,667	181,428	296,206	226,721	312,646	250,904	3,499
SS	8,165	7,642	6,714	5,267	7,767	8,414	980
PZ	1	0	0	0	0	0	0
LX	139	38	15	18	23	6	0
TK	0	0	0	0	0	0	0
WU	2	1	0	0	0	0	0
PP	3	0	0	0	0	0	0
CV	194	21	0	0	0	0	0
PS	139	382	1,102	1,057	1,247	1,325	89
DN	104,434	181,988	334,786	356,110	390,055	402,888	3,429
OA	0	0	0	0	0	0	0
BQ	2	0	0	0	0	0	0
RU	1,142	569	423	310	769	368	35
JS	8	68	95	95	128	125	4
SN	3,922	6,229	6,655	6,090	7,505	5,802	320
LD	0	1	1	1	1	1	0
WK	0	4	17	37	30	28	1
BW	21,183	14,057	17,845	10,830	11,555	19,543	1,034
BA	40,356	47,071	37,662	21,305	48,459	31,567	1,338
WM	218	17	25	2	8	3	1
CU	87,521	80,704	71,887	81,576	81,990	83,229	2,463
DR	268	163	72	53	76	70	4
RK	94,213	92,888	81,319	81,334	74,647	74,352	2,111
MD	1	0	0	0	0	0	0
GK	1,936	900	242	225	200	218	21
GE	337	161	131	127	129	101	19
OD	29	2	0	0	0	0	0
CS	403	75	34	38	27	22	2
TT	9,895	12,155	11,762	12,366	12,312	14,057	696
PL	1	1	1	2	0	0	0
U.	0	40	18	50	3	0	0
WADERS	1,013,378	1,198,845	1,544,741	1,442,051	1,594,877	1,674,026	36,174
WATERBIRDS[4]	1,696,169	2,495,031	2,933,156	2,739,527	2,987,866	2,787,361	84,912

Table 1. continued

	Apr	May	Jun	Jul	Aug
Number of sites where gulls were counted [5]	*818*	*756*	*742*	*773*	*797*
MU Mediterranean Gull	97	25	11	100	62
LU Little Gull	75	78	169	129	10
ON Bonaparte's Gull	0	0	0	0	0
BH Black-headed Gull	56,379	28,794	36,724	73,076	104,447
IN Ring-billed Gull	3	0	1	0	0
CM Common Gull	9,864	4,115	3,366	7,259	24,180
LB Lesser Black-backed Gull	34,228	39,325	41,220	45,768	28,241
HG Herring Gull	51,773	36,267	39,092	43,466	46,113
YG Yellow-legged Gull	1	0	1	12	111
YC Caspian Gull	0	0	0	0	0
YM Western Yellow-legged Gull	0	1	0	0	0
IG Iceland Gull	5	2	0	0	0
GZ Glaucous Gull	4	1	0	1	0
GB Great Black-backed Gull	2,526	1,517	1,998	3,207	5,185
KI Kittiwake	104	212	251	233	2,903
UU Unidentified gull	440	88	20,601	197	3,002
ZU hybrid gull	6	4	0	0	0
TOTAL GULLS	155,505	110,429	143,434	173,448	214,254
Number of sites where terns were counted [5]	*841*	*810*	*779*	*797*	*824*
TE Sandwich Tern	851	4,494	6,321	6,307	8,871
RS Roseate Tern	0	1	3	3	2
CN Common Tern	62	2,553	3,854	4,671	7,560
AE Arctic Tern	25	981	696	671	689
FO Forster's Tern	0	0	0	0	1
AF Little Tern	8	540	656	606	370
BJ Black Tern	0	389	2	9	16
WJ White-winged Black Tern	0	0	0	0	0
UT Unidentified tern	0	2	0	18	7
UI 'Commic' tern	0	2	7	6	62
TOTAL TERNS	946	8,962	11,539	12,291	17,578
KF Kingfisher	96	102	117	158	238

† See Appendix 3 for calculation of totals for goose populations
1 Indicates White-fronted and Brent Geese not identified to race
2 Note that coverage during March was severely affected by access restrictions resulting from the outbreak of Foot and Mouth Disease.
3 Total wildfowl and allies represents numbers of all divers, geese, Cormorant, swans, geese, ducks and rails
4 Total waterbirds represents numbers of all species except gulls, terns and Kingfisher
5 Counting gulls and terns was optional, thus totals are incomplete at a national level

Table I. continued

	Sep	Oct	Nov	Dec	Jan	Feb	[2]Mar
Sites	*1,183*	*1,388*	*1,395*	*1,403*	*1,319*	*1,241*	*119*
MU	62	55	39	36	53	55	4
LU	208	38	8	8	4	1	0
ON	0	0	0	0	0	0	0
BH	158,504	168,922	231,923	224,185	267,408	210,999	22,264
IN	0	2	2	2	6	6	0
CM	37,962	39,757	66,852	58,315	70,892	62,473	4,376
LB	11,294	15,243	15,465	11,346	6,768	11,622	962
HG	35,783	36,365	41,549	41,200	78,827	52,124	7,493
YG	104	78	24	47	25	13	0
YC	0	0	1	1	0	0	0
YM	0	14	4	1	1	0	0
IG	1	1	0	1	6	2	0
GZ	1	1	7	1	6	6	2
GB	7,738	7,773	10,500	9,377	8,163	4,939	794
KI	483	338	190	86	106	299	0
UU	5,841	2,185	1,841	1,441	8,416	8,267	0
ZU	0	130	0	0	0	0	0
GULLS	257,981	270,902	368,405	346,047	440,681	350,806	35,895
Sites	*1,188*	*1,369*	*1,367*	*1,365*	*1,285*	*1,197*	*106*
TE	2,869	37	2	2	1	1	1
RS	0	0	0	0	0	0	0
CN	986	9	0	1	0	0	0
AE	26	3	0	0	0	0	0
FO	0	0	0	0	0	0	0
AF	28	0	0	0	0	0	0
BJ	33	1	1	0	0	0	0
WJ	1	0	0	0	0	0	0
UT	0	0	0	0	0	0	0
UI	0	2	0	0	0	0	0
TERNS	3,943	52	3	3	1	1	1
KF	390	363	297	241	193	167	20

Table 2. Total numbers of waterbirds recorded by WeBS Core Counts in Northern Ireland, 2000–01[†].

		Apr	May	Jun	Jul	Aug
Number of sites visited		*4*	*2*	*2*	*2*	*2*
Number of sectors visited		*16*	*10*	*10*	*10*	*10*
RH	Red-throated Diver	1	0	0	0	0
BV	Black-throated Diver	0	0	0	0	0
ND	Great Northern Diver	0	0	0	0	0
LG	Little Grebe	3	1	0	4	0
GG	Great Crested Grebe	0	0	0	0	0
SZ	Slavonian Grebe	0	0	0	0	0
CA	Cormorant	43	12	25	15	56
H.	Grey Heron	7	8	5	8	11
MS	Mute Swan	126	85	33	11	7
AS	Black Swan	0	1	0	0	0
BS	Bewick's Swan	0	0	0	0	0
WS	Whooper Swan	34	0	0	0	0
HN	Swan Goose	0	0	0	0	0
PG	Pink-footed Goose	1	0	0	0	0
NW	Greenland White-fronted Goose	30	0	0	0	0
GJ	Greylag Goose	713	0	0	0	0
SJ	Snow Goose	0	0	0	0	0
CG	Canada Goose	0	0	0	0	0
YE	Barnacle Goose (naturalised)	0	0	0	0	0
DB	Dark-bellied Brent	0	0	0	0	0
QN	Light-bellied Brent (Canada)	505	0	0	0	0
ZL	hybrid goose	0	0	0	0	0
SU	Shelduck	323	53	64	17	3
MN	Mandarin	4	0	2	0	0
WN	Wigeon	53	2	0	0	5
GA	Gadwall	0	0	0	0	0
T.	Teal	70	0	0	0	5
TA	Green-winged Teal	0	0	0	0	0
MA	Mallard	118	49	40	62	193
PT	Pintail	2	0	0	0	0
SV	Shoveler	0	0	0	0	0
PO	Pochard	0	0	0	0	0
FD	Ferruginous Duck	0	0	0	0	0
TU	Tufted Duck	0	0	0	0	0
SP	Scaup	0	0	0	0	0
E.	Eider	0	6	0	0	0
LN	Long-tailed Duck	0	0	0	0	0
CX	Common Scoter	0	0	0	0	0
GN	Goldeneye	26	0	0	0	0
RM	Red-breasted Merganser	41	2	0	1	1
GD	Goosander	0	0	0	0	0
RY	Ruddy Duck	0	0	0	0	0
WA	Water Rail	0	0	0	0	0
MH	Moorhen	3	1	0	2	0
CO	Coot	2	0	0	0	0
	TOTAL WILDFOWL[1]	2,105	220	169	120	281
OC	Oystercatcher	1,202	433	269	494	789
RP	Ringed Plover	45	25	2	1	71
GP	Golden Plover	6,140	0	0	0	0
GV	Grey Plover	2	0	0	0	2
L.	Lapwing	56	1	46	98	210

Table 2. continued

	Sep	Oct	Nov	Dec	Jan	Feb	[2]Mar
Sites	*14*	*18*	*15*	*18*	*18*	*19*	*1*
Count units	*147*	*154*	*186*	*154*	*154*	*189*	*9*
RH	8	11	24	13	17	24	0
BV	0	0	3	1	0	3	0
ND	1	0	3	7	16	18	0
LG	550	458	549	534	414	346	3
GG	2,654	1,579	1,995	2,025	1,447	2,030	0
SZ	0	0	1	9	3	0	0
CA	2,490	1,678	1,294	1,061	732	1,088	7
H.	459	328	182	175	200	209	0
MS	2,316	2,177	1,693	1,569	1,544	1,443	31
AS	0	0	0	0	0	0	0
BS	0	102	0	3	2	25	0
WS	15	750	624	1,172	685	1,014	0
HN	0	0	0	0	0	2	0
PG	0	6	0	0	0	0	0
NW	0	0	2	0	0	60	0
GJ	201	373	347	629	629	1,168	0
SJ	1	0	1	1	1	1	0
CG	0	6	218	310	117	58	0
YE	138	158	156	153	153	132	0
DB	0	0	0	0	0	1	0
QN	5,996	17,077	18,591	9,565	3,775	2,849	135
ZL	0	0	0	1	0	0	0
SU	76	532	1,774	3,652	4,353	2,855	79
MN	0	0	0	0	0	0	0
WN	1,756	11,747	9,303	4,495	4,809	3,156	381
GA	194	217	156	115	132	129	0
T.	4,590	2,347	2,377	3,759	4,454	2,595	0
TA	0	1	1	1	1	0	0
MA	10,028	6,489	5,302	5,279	5,502	3,225	0
PT	13	13	91	97	257	326	0
SV	65	100	168	156	212	70	0
PO	1,241	2,835	13,382	24,430	16,178	10,262	0
FD	0	0	0	0	1	1	0
TU	4,374	17,679	22,863	26,598	18,679	17,495	0
SP	10	57	1,537	2,616	3,205	3,711	0
E.	1,491	1,833	2,141	927	1,461	1,629	0
LN	0	0	182	27	12	35	0
CX	1	4	0	3	0	0	0
GN	69	500	7,768	7,304	7,823	9,309	12
RM	447	423	372	365	332	358	3
GD	1	1	1	1	1	1	0
RY	6	27	22	40	1	53	0
WA	0	35	0	1	0	0	0
MH	307	258	244	211	180	213	5
CO	6,376	7,240	6,103	5,145	5,638	3,324	6
WILDFOWL [1]	45,874	78,363	99,470	102,450	82,966	69,218	662
OC	17,582	15,919	17,814	17,672	13,421	14,169	349
RP	579	750	728	400	345	560	16
GP	1,730	10,678	12,206	9,160	5,905	12,418	367
GV	6	82	204	118	111	328	10
L.	2,810	6,018	17,044	16,364	14,156	16,780	102

Table 2. continued

		Apr	May	Jun	Jul	Aug
KN	Knot	0	0	1	0	7
SS	Sanderling	4	0	0	0	0
LX	Little Stint	0	0	0	0	0
CV	Curlew Sandpiper	0	0	0	0	0
PS	Purple Sandpiper	0	0	0	0	0
DN	Dunlin	87	29	10	10	69
RU	Ruff	0	0	0	0	1
JS	Jack Snipe	0	0	0	0	0
SN	Snipe	2	0	0	0	0
LD	Long-billed Dowitcher	0	0	0	0	0
BW	Black-tailed Godwit	0	0	4	0	14
BA	Bar-tailed Godwit	24	0	0	0	5
WM	Whimbrel	0	18	0	1	0
CU	Curlew	1,053	32	209	152	582
DR	Spotted Redshank	0	0	0	0	0
RK	Redshank	1,703	42	54	361	949
GK	Greenshank	4	0	12	7	31
CS	Common Sandpiper	0	0	0	5	2
TT	Turnstone	46	0	0	1	32
	TOTAL WADERS	10,368	580	607	1,130	2,764
	TOTAL WATERBIRDS [3]	12,473	800	776	1,250	3,045

		Apr	May	Jun	Jul	Aug
Number of sites where gulls were counted [4]		4	2	2	2	2
MU	Mediterranean Gull	0	0	0	0	0
LU	Little Gull	0	1	0	0	0
BH	Black-headed Gull	254	65	81	515	564
CM	Common Gull	80	128	38	86	343
LB	Lesser Black-backed Gull	8	7	9	4	1
HG	Herring Gull	44	103	127	132	120
IG	Iceland Gull	0	0	0	0	0
GZ	Glaucous Gull	0	0	0	0	0
GB	Great Black-backed Gull	113	56	78	72	57
KI	Kittiwake	0	1	27	6	1
	TOTAL GULLS	499	361	360	815	1,086

		Apr	May	Jun	Jul	Aug
Number of sites where terns were counted [4]		4	2	2	2	2
TE	Sandwich Tern	196	81	180	201	169
CN	Common Tern	0	2	2	2	0
UI	'Commic' tern	0	18	0	0	0
	TOTAL TERNS	196	101	182	203	169
KF	Kingfisher	0	0	0	1	1

† See Appendix 3 for calculation of totals for goose populations
1 Total wildfowl and allies represents numbers of all divers, geese, Cormorant, swans, geese, ducks and rails
2 Note that coverage during March was severely affected by access restrictions resulting from the outbreak of Foot and Mouth Disease.
3 Total waterbirds represents numbers of all species except gulls, terns and Kingfisher
4 Counting gulls and terns was optional, thus totals are incomplete at a national level

Table 2. continued

	Sep	Oct	Nov	Dec	Jan	Feb	[2]Mar
KN	513	359	473	3,956	7,125	2,410	164
SS	127	109	90	93	105	110	132
LX	6	0	0	0	0	0	0
CV	17	0	0	0	0	0	0
PS	1	3	93	7	13	86	0
DN	1,366	1,688	4,707	7,348	12,749	10,966	840
RU	4	2	5	2	2	2	0
JS	1	0	2	2	2	0	0
SN	45	84	211	186	218	225	24
LD	0	0	0	1	1	1	0
BW	406	330	303	93	243	75	0
BA	206	524	447	906	1,719	1,318	0
WM	1	0	0	0	0	0	0
CU	4,394	5,674	6,776	6,058	4,605	6,893	243
DR	0	0	0	1	0	0	0
RK	7,048	8,827	8,778	7,571	6,196	8,394	753
GK	108	148	88	69	58	54	9
CS	1	0	0	0	0	0	0
TT	790	809	1,606	879	659	1,411	82
WADERS	37,741	52,004	71,575	70,886	67,633	76,200	3,091
WATERBIRDS[3]	83,615	130,367	171,045	173,336	150,599	145,418	3,753
Sites	*12*	*12*	*13*	*12*	*12*	*13*	*1*
MU	0	0	0	1	0	0	0
LU	1	1	0	0	0	0	0
BH	7,259	8,223	10,095	8,952	11,884	11,208	86
CM	1,668	7,250	3,313	4,423	2,572	3,993	34
LB	89	58	26	8	16	50	0
HG	2,038	2,692	3,084	4,953	4,869	8,055	26
IG	0	0	0	0	1	1	0
GZ	0	0	0	0	1	1	0
GB	436	392	526	467	372	472	7
KI	2	0	0	0	1	0	0
GULLS	11,493	18,616	17,044	18,804	19,716	23,780	153
Sites	*8*	*8*	*8*	*8*	*8*	*8*	*1*
TE	421	0	0	0	0	0	0
CN	13	0	0	0	0	0	0
UI	0	0	0	0	0	0	0
TERNS	434	0	0	0	0	0	0
KF	1	1	1	0	0	0	0

Table 3. Total numbers of waterbirds counted by I-WeBS in the Republic of Ireland, 2000–01[†].

	Sep	Oct	Nov	Dec	Jan	Feb	[1] Mar
Number of sites visited	*128*	*150*	*182*	*175*	*234*	*177*	*45*
Number of count units visited	*312*	*357*	*416*	*392*	*649*	*390*	*62*
Red-throated Diver	14	111	96	76	136	62	3
Black-throated Diver	0	0	52	3	31	0	0
Great Northern Diver	8	37	167	189	318	149	3
Pied-billed Grebe	0	1	0	0	0	0	0
Little Grebe	519	390	295	312	475	265	51
Great Crested Grebe	320	564	541	709	1,157	803	26
Slavonian Grebe	4	0	2	4	10	30	0
Black-necked Grebe	1	2	1	1	2	0	0
Cormorant	2,608	2,023	2,153	1,721	2,657	1,745	213
Little Egret	208	62	49	32	38	38	15
Grey Heron	560	559	458	396	675	304	82
Mute Swan	1,731	2,270	2,297	2,035	3,518	2,002	382
Bewick's Swan	0	2	100	171	180	18	0
Whooper Swan	27	2,609	2,614	1,906	5,069	1,845	239
Pink-footed Goose	0	12	6	9	29	20	0
Greenland White-fronted Goose	0	4,275	8,422	7,951	9,576	1,548	3
Greylag Goose	407	1,828	1,315	1,708	5,848	2,789	299
Canada Goose	187	68	91	4	220	40	1
Barnacle Goose	0	21	352	259	524	478	0
Dark-bellied Brent Goose	0	0	0	0	1	2	0
Light-bellied Brent Goose	64	1,947	5,328	10,612	12,888	10,943	766
feral/hybrid Goose.	1	181	59	37	98	84	21
Shelduck	147	338	1,570	3,351	5,408	5,007	340
Wigeon	3,434	12,833	29,986	24,294	42,898	22,198	839
American Wigeon	0	0	0	1	1	2	0
Gadwall	49	138	165	237	244	246	17
Teal	3,539	7,949	12,128	12,481	24,922	15,516	1,403
American Green-winged Teal	0	0	0	1	0	1	1
Mallard	10,563	9,611	11,791	8,934	15,829	5,963	593
Pintail	14	77	147	354	668	381	0
Garganey	0	0	0	0	1	0	0
Shoveler	137	638	903	751	2,512	1,650	95
Pochard	42	10,698	16,289	815	9,163	1,259	59
Ring-necked Duck	0	1	0	1	3	0	0
Tufted Duck	645	3,336	4,577	2,276	6,540	2,788	174
Scaup	7	10	191	311	319	128	0
Eider	3	1	2	7	1	6	0
Long-tailed Duck	0	0	47	6	34	0	0
Common Scoter	2,038	3,423	4,387	6,457	7,198	693	463
Surf Scoter	0	0	0	0	2	0	0
Velvet Scoter	0	0	0	14	2	1	0
Goldeneye	8	34	485	495	1,353	1,026	9
Smew	0	1	1	1	1	0	0
Red-breasted Merganser	310	380	603	515	852	606	20
Goosander	0	0	0	0	2	0	0
Ruddy Duck	0	3	1	1	0	0	0
Water Rail	8	13	19	9	19	9	2
Moorhen	410	300	250	260	339	298	85
Coot	1,646	4,871	8,899	1,249	18,250	1,163	136
TOTAL WILDFOWL [2]	28,891	70,996	116,332	90,528	179,298	81,764	6,243

†	*See Appendix 3 for calculation of totals for goose populations*
1	*Note that coverage during March was severely affected by access restrictions resulting from the outbreak of Foot and Mouth Disease.*
2	*Total wildfowl and allies represents numbers of all divers, geese, Cormorant, swans, geese, ducks and rails*
3	*Total waterbirds represents numbers of all species except gulls, terns and Kingfisher*

Table 3. continued

	Sep	**Oct**	**Nov**	**Dec**	**Jan**	**Feb**	**[1] Mar**
Oystercatcher	23,252	20,347	22,771	18,359	20,038	18,093	968
Ringed Plover	2,122	3,434	4,111	2,578	2,991	1,906	195
American Golden Plover	1	0	0	0	0	0	0
Golden Plover	3,096	38,269	63,424	37,337	48,360	57,319	4,166
Grey Plover	859	1,470	1,151	2,137	1,785	1,295	217
Lapwing	3,893	13,232	42,554	48,651	54,435	33,143	132
Knot	2,986	2,811	5,998	9,599	11,340	12,015	248
Sanderling	728	1,086	1,250	1,291	1,099	605	155
Little Stint	4	0	0	0	0	0	0
White-rumped Sandpiper	0	1	0	0	0	0	0
Baird's Sandpiper	1	0	0	0	0	0	0
Curlew Sandpiper	29	0	0	0	0	0	0
Purple Sandpiper	33	17	32	60	34	40	10
Dunlin	5,083	15,388	19,040	35,729	41,387	28,663	1,297
Buff-breasted Sandpiper	1	0	0	0	0	0	0
Ruff	60	14	3	1	4	5	0
Jack Snipe	1	2	13	23	22	19	17
Snipe	92	282	550	681	772	512	179
Woodcock	0	0	0	2	3	0	0
Black-tailed Godwit	5,412	3,799	8,523	6,846	9,935	5,691	237
Bar-tailed Godwit	3,285	3,133	6,126	6,245	6,174	5,776	347
Whimbrel	23	3	0	0	2	8	1
Curlew	13,133	12,561	15,384	17,315	17,337	18,375	626
Spotted Redshank	2	27	4	1	105	0	0
Redshank	10,641	11,644	8,968	7,343	9,459	9,585	565
Greenshank	382	367	341	256	279	274	33
Green Sandpiper	9	7	5	1	7	1	0
Wood Sandpiper	1	0	0	0	0	0	0
Common Sandpiper	9	15	6	11	8	3	0
Turnstone	858	1,144	1,927	1,349	1,579	1,356	225
Grey Phalarope	0	0	0	1	0	0	0
TOTAL WADERS	75,996	129,053	202,181	195,816	227,155	194,684	9,618
TOTAL WATERBIRDS [3]	105,655	200,670	319,020	286,772	407,166	276,790	15,958
Mediterranean Gull	7	1	1	1	2	4	1
Little Gull	0	0	0	0	1	0	0
Black-headed Gull	18,697	17,767	20,794	21,068	19,856	15,133	668
Ring-billed Gull	0	1	1	3	0	3	1
Common Gull	4,069	4,634	4,859	6,483	7,264	3,509	226
Lesser Black-backed Gull	10,443	5,387	3,552	1,665	2,051	1,212	369
Herring Gull	1,718	2,003	1,883	1,999	2,163	1,022	154
Iceland Gull	0	0	0	1	0	1	0
Glaucous Gull	1	0	0	0	5	1	0
Great Black-backed Gull	1,647	1,302	1,497	1,882	1,717	522	182
Kittiwake	6	0	0	787	227	32	2
TOTAL GULLS	36,588	31,095	32,587	33,889	33,286	21,439	1,603
Sandwich Tern	574	0	0	0	0	0	3
Common Tern	7	1	0	0	0	0	0
Arctic Tern	1	0	0	0	0	0	0
Black Tern	2	2	0	0	0	0	0
TOTAL TERNS	584	3	0	0	0	0	3
Kingfisher	12	11	10	7	11	6	0

SPECIES ACCOUNTS

Key to symbols commonly used in the species accounts (see Presentation and notation).

As footnotes to thresholds (see Appendix 2)

?   population size not accurately known

+   population too small for meaningful threshold

*   where 1% of the national population is less than 50 birds, 50 is normally used as a minimum threshold for national importance

**   a site regularly holding more than 20,000 waterbirds (excluding non-native species) qualifies as internationally important by virtue of absolute numbers

†   denotes that a qualifying level different to the national threshold has been used for the purposes of presenting sites in this report

In tables of important sites:

\-   no data available

( )   incomplete count

†   same meaning as when used for thresholds

▲   site was of a lower importance status in the previous year

▼   site was of a higher importance status in the previous year

[1,2]   count obtained using different survey methodology (see table below for sources and references)

A blank line within a section of a table is used to separate sites holding 50 or more birds where the relevant threshold is below this figure (e.g. Little Grebe, p37).

Sources of additional survey information used in compiling tables of important sites. Non-WeBS counts are identified in the table by the relevant number or letter below given in superscript preceding the count, e.g. [22] 231 represents a count from Greenland White-fronted Goose Study surveys.

1	Argyll Bird report & SNH	16	M. Tickner (in litt.)
2	Bean Goose Working Group, e.g. Smith et al. (1994), Simpson & Maciver (2001)	17	NEWS data
3	C Hartley (in litt.)	18	Orkney Bird Report & J. Plowman (in litt.)
4	Chown (1999), Avalon Marshes Wintering Bird Survey 1998/99	19	P Reay (in litt.)
5	Clyde Bird Report, e.g. Gibson (2001)	20	R. Godfrey (in litt.)
6	Cranswick et al. (1998)	21	R. MacDonald (in litt.)
7	D Carrington (in litt.)	22	Roost counts
8	D. Walker (in litt.)	23	RSPB pers comm.
9	Delany & Ogilvie (1994), SNH data and Mitchell et al. (1997)	24	RSPB/Talisman Energy studies, e.g. Stenning (1998)
10	Firth of Clyde Eider counts, e.g. Waltho, C.M. (2001)	25	SNH (in litt.)
		26	SNH 'adopted' counts
11	Friends of Cardigan Bay, e.g. Green & Elliott (1993) & R. Thorpe (in litt.)	27	SNH Greenland Goose Census
12	G. Rees in litt.	28	SOTEAG reports, e.g. Heubeck (1998)
13	Greenland White-fronted Goose Study, e.g. Fox & Francis (1998)	29	Supplementary daytime counts
		30	WeBS Low Tide Counts
14	Little Egret Roost counts	31	Williams (1999)
15	M. Howe (in litt.)	32	Woolmer et al. (2001)
		33	WWT data
		34	WWT studies, e.g. Rees et al. (2000)
		35	WWT/JNCC National Grey Goose Census

RED-THROATED DIVER
Gavia stellata

International threshold:	750
Great Britain threshold:	50
All-Ireland threshold:	10*

*50 is normally used as a minimum threshold

GB Max: 1,023 Jan
NI Max: 24 Nov/Feb

The total numbers recorded in Britain and Northern Ireland in 2000–01 by WeBS Core Counts were similar to those in previous winters, though surpassing 1000 in Great Britain (and exceeded only by the 1,361 in December 1995), aided by the relatively high count in Cardigan Bay.

Red-throated Divers may be dispersed over relatively large areas, and detecting birds distributed in this way may require concerted effort to ensure the importance of a site is recorded. At some favoured locations, however, they are present in relatively high densities, such as the Suffolk coastline, and dedicated counts are made at several vantage points – encouraged by the relative ease of counting these flocks – now that the regular occurrence of large numbers has been established.

Peak counts at most sites were similar to the averages for recent winters. The consistency of numbers both nationally and at individual sites is remarkable for a species that is relatively difficult to record accurately, primarily because counts of birds on the sea require good or ideal weather conditions. Aerial surveys for seaducks around Welsh coasts in February 2001 also recorded very large numbers of Red-throated

Divers, with many hundreds and perhaps as many as 1000, in each of Colwyn, Cardigan and Carmarthen Bays, often several kilometres offshore (WWT data). Regular surveys of the Arklow Bank, lying around 15 km off the east coast of Ireland, during winter 2000–01 also noted a considerable though short-lived influx in February (J. Coveney pers. comm.), suggesting that the Irish Sea and surrounding waters may be of particular importance during passage periods.

In the Government's recent review of the Special Protection Area (SPA) network in the United Kingdom, JNCC published guidelines for the selection of SPAs (Stroud *et al.* 2001). Guideline 1.1 states that any site holding nationally important numbers of species listed on Annex 1 of the EC Birds Directive may be considered for classification as an SPA. Currently, only one site, the Forth Estuary, is classified for non-breeding Red-throated Divers (Stroud *et al.* 2001) because significantly marine sites were not included within the scope of the review. The 11 sites listed in the table below will be assessed in the current marine SPA review given the regular presence of nationally important numbers.

	96–97	97–98	98–99	99–00	00–01	Mon	Mean	
Sites of international importance in the UK								
Minsmere	[29] 600	[29] 1,500	[29] 500	[29] 717	[29] 700	Dec	803	▲
Sites of national importance in Great Britain								
Cardigan Bay	528	[11] 536	270	229	460	Jan	405	
Moray Firth	(61)	[24] 284	[24] 179	[24] 103	[24] 119	Nov	171	
Clyde Estuary	195	[5] 178	138	123	145	Jan	156	
Forth Estuary	124	75	121	(75)	104	Nov	106	
Dengie Flats	96	100	45	92	145	Feb	96	
Don Mouth to Ythan Mouth	35	166	81	101	33	Aug	83	
The Wash	15	26	224	24	14	Jan	61	
Scapa Flow	-	-	[31] 59	-	-		59	
Sites of all-Ireland importance in Northern Ireland								
Belfast Lough	11	41	57	39	14	Nov	32	
Lough Foyle	18	4	[29] 50	15	5	Jan	18	

Sites no longer meeting table qualifying levels
Solway Estuary

Important sites not counted in last five years
Craigalea to Newcastle

Other sites surpassing table qualifying levels in 2000–01
Traeth Lafan	[29] (72)	Mar
Outer Ards	18	Feb

BLACK-THROATED DIVER
Gavia arctica

International threshold:	1,200
Great Britain threshold:	7[*]
All-Ireland threshold:	1[*]

[*] *50 is normally used as a minimum threshold*

GB Max:	145 Feb
NI Max:	3 Nov/Feb

The British peak of this species was by far the largest yet recorded by WeBS, easily surpassing the previous highest of 89 two winters before. That in Northern Ireland was, as normal, small by comparison.

WeBS counts at several sites were much larger than normal, and it is notable that at six, counts reached double figures. The high national total results from improved coverage of some of the known key sites for Black-throated Divers. Counts for Gerrans Bay, part of the South Cornwall Coast IBA identified specifically for its wintering divers (Geary & Lock 2001), were made for WeBS for the first time. There was also extensive coverage of the west coast of Highland by the RAF Ornithological Society in February. Waterbird count totals for the coast in Wester Ross included a remarkable 101 Black-throated Divers (as well as 14 Red-throated and 42 Great Northern Divers). Birds were distributed in reasonably equal numbers between the major sea lochs. Only dedicated co-ordinated coverage of large areas, as achieved by RAFOS, will enable us to deduce whether the occasional large counts, such as that of 68 in Gruinard Bay in January 1998, represent genuinely greater numbers, or simply an aggregation of the birds in the region into one site.

That the high national total of Black-throats fell in February is largely a consequence of visits to these favoured sites all fortuitously occurring in February – it is likely that these sites hold equally high numbers throughout the midwinter period.

	96–97	97–98	98–99	99–00	00–01	Mon	Mean	
Sites of national importance in Great Britain								
Scapa Flow	-	-	[31] 57	[29] (14)	-		57	
Gruinard Bay	-	[29] 68	[29] 34	14	(11)	Feb	39	
Gerrans Bay	-	-	-	-	35	Feb	35	▲
Applecross Bay - Sand	-	-	[29] 40	-	0		20	▲
Moray Firth	(6)	[24] 22	20	[24] 14	[24] 17	Nov	19	
Loch Ewe	[29] 8	[29] 7	26	29	15	Feb	17	
Red Point to Port Henderson	-	[29] 29	3	9	11	Feb	13	▲
Loch Caolisport	-	-	12	-	-		12	
Loch Gairloch	-	-	4	5	23	Feb	11	▲
Girvan to Turnberry	8	23	3	7	(7)	Dec	10	
Little Loch Broom	-	-	4	1	17	Feb	7	▲
Sites of all-Ireland importance in Northern Ireland								
Strangford Lough	[30] 2	[30] 7	0	0	0		2	
Belfast Lough	2	0	0	3	2	Feb	1	
Outer Ards	0	0	0	2	3	Nov	1	▲
Sites no longer meeting table qualifying levels								
Forth Estuary								
Other sites surpassing table qualifying levels in 2000–01								
Poole Harbour		7	Dec					

GREAT NORTHERN DIVER
Gavia immer

International threshold:	50
Great Britain threshold:	30[*][†]
All-Ireland threshold:	?[†]

[*] *50 is normally used as a minimum threshold*

GB Max:	146 Jan
NI Max:	18 Feb

Matching large counts of the other two species of divers, the British total of Great Northerns in 2000–01 was the highest yet recorded by WeBS, continuing the rise in recent winters, albeit still representing only a small proportion of the true number present in British waters. Numbers in

Northern Ireland were around normal, though the count at Carlingford Lough was noteworthy.

A greater proportion of counts in the table below derive from dedicated surveys or supplementary counts than for many other waterbirds, owing to this species' occurrence around the islands and relatively inaccessible coasts of northern and northwest Scotland. Nevertheless, interest in this species – and particularly in obtaining counts from these important areas – is clearly increasing. A team from the RAF Ornithological Society recorded a total of 42 birds in February, covering much of the coastline in Wester Ross, north to Cape Wrath. This increased observational interest is also evidenced by the growing number of very large counts in the table below. Continuation of such monitoring – indeed, counts from other areas and with increased frequency – is all the more vital to ensure that the true distribution of this species can be accurately mapped, particularly given the continued threat of oil spills and increasing aquaculture in region. It is notable that no especially large counts were made in 2000–01. Dedicated survey of the two sites of international importance, adjacent to one another in Orkney, is necessary to identify the true extent and size of this important concentration, and the degree of interchange between sites in the area.

	96–97	97–98	98–99	99–00	00–01	Mon	Mean	
Sites of international importance in the UK								
Scapa Flow	-	-	[31] 781	[29] (82)	-		781	
Deer/Shapinsay Sounds & T'ness	[28] 393	[28] 330	-	[29] 375	[29] 67	Feb	291	
Sites of national importance in Great Britain								
Whiteness to Scarvister	-	-	[28] 44	-	-		44	
Moray Firth	(8)	[24] 54	19	12	[24] 38	Nov	31	
Sites with mean peak counts of 5 or more birds in Great Britain [†]								
Loch Indaal	11	33	27	31	19	Nov	24	
Gruinard Bay	-	[29] 42	5	9	(7)	Feb	19	
Traigh Luskentyre	39	8	16	8	6	Jan	15	
Loch Eriboll	-	-	-	15	(1)	Feb	15	
Uyea Sound	-	-	-	26	1	Oct	14	▲
Gerrans Bay	-	-	-	-	13	Feb	13	▲
Loch Ewe	[29] 22	[29] 20	4	8	6	Feb	12	
Egilsay	-	4	1	6	28	Jan	10	▲
Camas Dubh-aird	-	[29] 10	[29] 9	-	-		10	▲
Little Loch Broom	-	-	(5)	2	16	Feb	9	▲
South Yell Sound	[28] 10	[28] 10	[28] 11	[28] 4	-		9	
Applecross Bay - Sand	-	[29] 14	[29] 6	-	0		7	▲
Lochs Beg & Scridain	(6)	6	6	(8)	4	Jan	6	
Sullom Voe	-	[28] 5	[28] 5	[28] 8	-		6	
Fleet/Wey	0	2	5	8	14	Dec	6	▲
Forth Estuary	3	2	2	17	2	Nov	5	
Aignish Bay	5	3	8	10	0		5	▲
Red Point to Port Henderson	-	[29] 7	9	4	0		5	
Easting/Sand Wick	-	-	-	5	-		5	
Hascosay, B'mull & C'grave Sounds	-	-	[28] 5	-	-		5	▲
Loch Caolisport	-	-	5	-	-		5	▲
Sites with mean peak counts of 5 or more birds in Northern Ireland [†]								
Lough Foyle	9	3	[29] 22	2	0		7	
Carlingford Lough	1	2	6	7	16	Jan	6	

Sites no longer meeting table qualifying levels
Kyle of Tongue

Other sites surpassing table qualifying levels in 2000–01

Cleddau Estuary	7	Jan	Poole Harbour	5	Jan
Traeth Lafan	[29] (7)	Mar	Kyle of Durness	5	Feb
The Ouse & Lairo Water	6	Jan			

†   *as few sites in Great Britain exceed the British threshold, and as no all-Ireland threshold has been set, a qualifying level of five has been chosen to select sites for presentation in this report*

LITTLE GREBE
Tachybaptus ruficollis

International threshold: **?**
Great Britain threshold: **30**[*]
All-Ireland threshold: **?**[†]

[*] *50 is normally used as a minimum threshold*

GB Max: 4,618 Sep
NI Max: 550 Sep

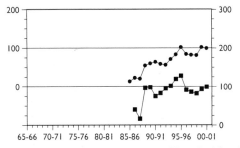

Figure 4. Annual indices for Little Grebe in GB (circles, left axis) and NI (squares, right axis)

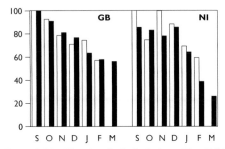

Figure 5. Monthly indices for Little Grebe in GB and NI (white bars 2000–01; black bars 1995–96 to 1999–2000)

The peak count for Britain was the largest yet recorded by WeBS, over 5% higher than the previous record count of 4,382 in 1999–2000. The annual indices have increased by 57% over the past ten years. The maximum count for Northern Ireland was 5% lower than the most recent five-year peak mean. In contrast, annual winter indices fell slightly in Britain but increased for the second year running in the province. Given that the maximum counts recorded by WeBS account for perhaps only a quarter of the British breeding population, it is clear that many birds may be wintering in habitats poorly covered by WeBS, e.g. small freshwaters and rivers.

Monthly indices show the gradual decline in numbers through the winter, following the peak in September. Two long-distance ring-recoveries indicate that an unknown number of immigrants from Northern Europe join the largely sedentary resident birds during the winter (Moss 2002). These patterns suggest that resident and immigrant birds may move away from counted sites as the winter progresses and are therefore missed later in the season.

Individual site maxima are generally similar between years. The number of sites which held 30 or more birds increased by 5 to 56 but the number holding 50 or more fell by 2 to 22. The most notably high count was at the Thames Estuary where the November count was 62% higher than the most recent five-year peak mean with other high counts on the River Avon, East Wretham Meres, Old Moor Wetlands and, continuing the recent increase, at Dungeness Gravel Pits. Numbers, however, fell further at Eyebrook Reservoir.

	96–97	97–98	98–99	99–00	00–01	Mon	Mean	
Sites of national importance in Great Britain								
Swale Estuary	213	244	201	238	195	Jan	218	
Thames Estuary	255	124	132	214	348	Nov	215	
Holme Pierrepont Gravel Pits	80	100	109	158	107	Sep	111	
Chew Valley Lake	152	105	80	65	95	Sep	99	
Somerset Levels	55	47	[4] 176	56	74	Oct	82	
North Norfolk Coast	51	87	105	74	77	Aug	79	
Rutland Water	35	62	78	120	87	Oct	76	
Cleddau Estuary	91	72	56	69	66	Nov	71	
Deben Estuary	63	78	[30] 84	72	59	Dec	71	
Otmoor	-	-	-	-	[29] 70	Oct	70	▲
Chichester Harbour	52	72	50	58	78	Oct	62	
Tees Estuary	47	52	67	56	82	Sep	61	
R. Test: Fullerton to Stockbridge	52	52	63	51	47	Dec	53	
Lee Valley Gravel Pits	39	56	77	37	55	Sep	53	
Eyebrook Reservoir	76	56	49	-	28	Oct	52	
Sutton & Lound Gravel Pits	39	72	-	45	-		52	
Alde Complex	38	44	47	72	58	Jan	52	

	96–97	97–98	98–99	99–00	00–01	Mon	Mean	
Middle Tame Valley Gravel Pits	(53)	(68)	36	40	58	Sep	51	
Blackwater Estuary	44	47	41	70	53	Oct	51	
Kirby-on-Bain Gravel Pits	(6)	40	43	68	45	Sep	49	▼
R. Avon: Fordingbridge to R'wood	39	49	34	52	70	Sep	49	▼
Hogganfield Loch	45	56	35	72	36	Aug	49	
King's Dyke Pits	18	31	52	92	-		48	
Dungeness Gravel Pits	16	19	39	73	86	Jun	47	
Langstone Harbour	24	37	60	55	57	Jan	47	
Rye Harbour & Pett Level	28	37	51	65	50	Sep	46	
Portsmouth Harbour	30	35	43	65	(27)	Jan/Feb	43	
Bewl Water	44	36	43	38	54	Sep	43	
Southampton Water	^{30}46	34	^{30}43	40	^{30}42	Jan	41	
Abberton Reservoir	21	24	(12)	96	24	Aug	41	
The Wash	53	29	32	56	36	Jan	41	▼
Kilconquhar Loch	42	49	25	44	(41)	Sep	40	
Hamford Water	18	26	61	41	52	Jan	40	
Barton Pits	43	44	47	24	29	Aug	37	
Cameron Reservoir	33	56	44	24	25	Aug	36	
Fleet/Wey	30	34	27	47	41	Dec	36	
R. Avon: R'wood to Christchurch	2	3	58	76	(40)	Nov	36	▲
Humber Estuary	(10)	(22)	30	40	33	Nov	34	
Blagdon Lake	23	31	29	46	42	Sep	34	
Purfleet Chalk Pit	-	-	-	24	44	Nov	34	▲
Pitsford Reservoir	32	10	(27)	50	42	Sep	34	
R. Avon: Salisbury to F'bridge	38	33	25	38	(18)	Oct/Jan	34	
Orwell Estuary	45	34	21	^{30}28	37	Sep	33	
Cardigan Bay	21	45	23	48	29	Jan	33	▲
East Wretham Meres	-	(1)	12	32	(53)	Aug	32	▲
Wraysbury Gravel Pits	32	27	47	38	16	Feb	32	
Old Moor Wetlands	12	13	26	56	52	Aug	32	▲
Medway Estuary	42	(18)	(13)	16	37	Nov	32	
Woolston Eyes	22	28	21	46	39	Sep	31	▲
Crouch-Roach Estuary	28	16	21	42	44	Nov	30	▲

Sites with mean peak counts of 30 or more birds in Northern Ireland [†]

	96–97	97–98	98–99	99–00	00–01	Mon	Mean	
Loughs Neagh & Beg	376	330	380	413	400	Nov	380	
Strangford Lough	140	101	99	87	72	Nov	100	
Upper Lough Erne	73	50	86	67	-		69	
Lough Money	35	51	46	55	48	Oct	47	
Larne Lough	24	28	48	35	36	Oct	34	

Important sites not counted in last five years
R. Soar: Leicester

Sites no longer meeting table qualifying levels
Lower Derwent Valley
Hampton & Kempton Reservoirs
Pirton Pool
Hilfield Park Reservoir

Other sites surpassing table qualifying levels in 2000–01

Stanford Training Area	48	Aug	Morecambe Bay	38	Feb
Draycote Water	44	Jan	Loch Etive	37	Nov/Dec
R. Irwell	44	Jan	Minsmere	31	Jul
R. Test: Broadlands Estate	41	Aug	Fairburn Ings	31	Sep
Belfast Lough	41	Oct	Chichester Gravel Pits	31	Oct
Hillsborough Lakes	40	Sep	Cotswold Water Park (West)	30	Sep
Dee Estuary (Eng/Wal)	39	Aug	Skelton Lake	30	Sep

†   *as no all-Ireland threshold has been set, a qualifying level of 30 has been chosen to select sites for presentation in this report*

GREAT CRESTED GREBE
Podiceps cristatus

International threshold: 1,500
Great Britain threshold: 100
All-Ireland threshold: 30*

* *50 is normally used as a minimum threshold*

GB Max: 9,899 Sep
NI Max: 2,654 Sep

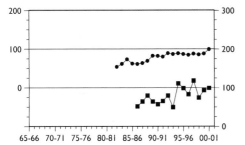

Figure 6. Annual indices for Great Crested Grebe in GB (circles, left axis) and NI (squares, right axis)

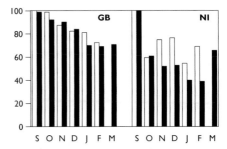

Figure 7. Monthly indices for Great Crested Grebe in GB and NI (white bars 2000–01; black bars 1995–96 to 1999–2000)

The peak British count was the highest yet recorded by WeBS, exceeding the previous highest of 9,571 in 1992–93. The Northern Ireland peak was around average for recent winters. Annual indices increased in both Britain and Northern Ireland, the former reaching the highest value since indexing for this species began in the early 1980s and having increased by 17% over the last ten years. Monthly indices for Northern Ireland were much higher than average for most of the winter, mirroring the pattern recorded in the previous year.

Belfast Lough continues to be the only site in Britain and Northern Ireland regularly supporting internationally important numbers of Great Crested Grebes during the winter. The peak count in 2000–01 was, however, 20% lower than the five-year peak mean. Elsewhere in the province, larger than average peak counts were recorded at all but one of the sites currently surpassing the threshold for all-Ireland importance; peak numbers at Lough Foyle were low for the second winter running. An extraordinary count of 199 birds from Outer Ards means that this site has been added to the table.

There were notably low counts at a number of key resorts in Britain, including Grafham Water (67% lower than the most recent five-year peak mean), Abberton Reservoir (62%) and Queen Elizabeth II Reservoir (71%). There were, however, higher than average numbers at many other sites including Thanet Coast, Bewl Water and Pegwell Bay, and a notably high count of 348 birds at King George VI Reservoir.

	96–97	97–98	98–99	99–00	00–01	Mon	Mean	
Sites of international importance in the UK								
Belfast Lough	1,200	2,403	1,935	1,508	1,338	Feb	1,677	
Sites of national importance in Great Britain								
Rutland Water	378	767	843	726	997	Oct	742	
Lade Sands	[8] 300	425	730	[29] 1,100	[29] 1,012	Jan	713	
Chew Valley Lake	645	460	585	550	690	Oct	586	
Forth Estuary	597	491	319	297	290	Feb	399	
Solway Firth	[29] 430	[29] 710	191	248	[30] 336	Jan	383	
Queen Mary Reservoir	593	271	185	312	246	Feb	321	
Traeth Lafan	[15] 244	[15] 360	[15] 389	[15] 165	[29] 388	Oct	309	
Minsmere	[29] 250	[29] 143	[29] 150	[29] 500	[29] 350	Dec	279	▲
Morecambe Bay	286	282	191	239	245	Dec	249	
Grafham Water	506	197	272	150	98	Jan	245	
Wraysbury Gravel Pits	263	246	289	202	167	Dec	233	
Stour Estuary	261	185	196	[30] 290	[30] 222	Dec	231	
Cotswold Water Park (West)	181	175	245	225	306	Jan	226	
Pitsford Reservoir	304	147	(218)	195	241	Sep	222	
Cardigan Bay	[11] 311	[11] 177	(58)	(29)	147	Jan	212	
Blithfield Reservoir	169	105	198	240	231	Aug	189	
Lee Valley Gravel Pits	164	175	148	201	191	Oct	176	

	96–97	97–98	98–99	99–00	00–01	Mon	Mean	
Abberton Reservoir	248	149	185	207	77	Nov	173	
Bough Beech Reservoir	-	-	-	(21)	160	Aug	160	
Draycote Water	93	84	133	200	219	Nov	146	
Swansea Bay	80	128	76	204	201	Dec	138	▲
Thanet Coast	166	15	5	[29] 202	[29] 299	Jan	137	▲
Bewl Water	73	111	136	104	261	Aug	137	
Attenborough Gravel Pits	155	135	107	135	(90)	Aug	133	
Loch Ryan	[29] 145	54	58	258	147	Oct	132	
Blagdon Lake	270	73	89	(98)	80	Oct	128	
Loch Leven	98	112	119	170	131	Nov	126	
Pegwell Bay	8	137	28	68	370	Jan	122	▲
Alton Water	109	73	139	143	147	Sep	122	
Southampton Water	94	169	[30] 127	106	71	Jan	113	
Clyde Estuary	80	109	110	116	143	Jan	112	▲
Ardleigh Reservoir	84	171	112	98	90	Feb	111	
Rye Harbour & Pett Level	22	88	68	299	68	Dec	109	
Blackwater Estuary	118	99	100	71	151	Oct	108	
Thrapston Gravel Pits	88	(82)	76	(179)	84	Aug	107	
Hanningfield Reservoir	59	123	80	130	132	Nov	105	
Queen Elizabeth II Reservoir	118	168	88	90	42	Jul	101	
Cotswold Water Park (East)	118	86	80	116	102	Feb	100	▲

Sites of all-Ireland importance in Northern Ireland

	96–97	97–98	98–99	99–00	00–01	Mon	Mean
Loughs Neagh & Beg	1,537	863	1,596	847	1,547	Sep	1,278
Carlingford Lough	364	231	270	249	326	Dec	288
Upper Lough Erne	276	304	144	243	-		242
Larne Lough	124	76	124	140	204	Sep	134
Strangford Lough	83	64	69	111	141	Sep	94
Lough Foyle	116	86	[29] 189	24	38	Dec	91

	96–97	97–98	98–99	99–00	00–01	Mon	Mean
Outer Ards	1	3	3	1	199	Feb	41

Important sites not counted in last five years
Craigalea to Newcastle

Sites no longer meeting table qualifying levels
Eyebrook Reservoir
King George VI Reservoir
Mersey Estuary

Other sites surpassing table qualifying levels in 2000–01

King George VI Reservoir	348	Sep	Middle Tame Valley Gravel Pits	102	Jul
Poole Harbour	151	Dec	Walthamstow Reservoirs	101	Aug
Fen Drayton Gravel Pits	117	Aug	Lower Windrush Valley GP	100	Nov

---

RED-NECKED GREBE
Podiceps grisegena

International threshold:	150
Great Britain threshold:	1[*†]
All-Ireland threshold:	?

GB Max: 37 Jan
NI Max: 0

[*] *50 is normally used as a minimum threshold*

The national total for Britain was lower than average; small numbers are expected in such mild winters. The September count for the Forth Estuary was 38% lower than the most recent five-year peak mean. There is large variation in the timing of peak numbers at this site, which has occurred during mid and late winter in the past. This was, however, the only site to support more than five birds in 2000–01. Largely because this species tends to inhabit sheltered coastal habitats during mild winters and can be widely dispersed, it remains inadequately surveyed by WeBS.

	96–97	97–98	98–99	99–00	00–01	Mon	Mean

Sites of national importance in Great Britain							
Forth Estuary	44	64	41	55	29	Sep	47
Scapa Flow	-	-	[31] 23	-	-		23
Bay of Sandoyne to Holme Sound	-	-	-	[29] 8	-		8 ▲
North Norfolk Coast	2	17	8	6	3	Nov/Dec	7

†   *as the British threshold for national importance is so small, and as no all-Ireland threshold has been set, a qualifying level of five has been chosen to select sites for presentation in this report*

SLAVONIAN GREBE
Podiceps auritus

International threshold:	**50**
Great Britain threshold:	**4[*]**
All-Ireland threshold:	**?**

GB Max:	**307 Jan**
NI Max:	**9 Dec**

[*] *50 is normally used as a minimum threshold*

The British peak was higher than average for recent winters and occurred during the mid winter. In most winters the national peak is in late winter or early spring when passage birds gather at key sites.

Wintering Slavonian Grebes remain at favoured sites for extended periods, with numbers relatively stable at sites through the winter. This makes this species particularly susceptible to oil spills. Between 8% and 16% of the birds wintering in Shetland died as a result of the *Esso Bernicla* spill in the 1970s (Heubeck & Richardson 1980).

The most notable count in 2000–01 was from Traigh Luskentyre in Harris where the peak was 140% higher than the five-year peak mean. Peak counts at most other sites were about average though with markedly low maxima at the Forth Estuary, 47% below average and the lowest count at the site during the most recent five-year period, and Pagham Harbour. Peak numbers in Northern Ireland remained low for the second year running.

	96–97	97–98	98–99	99–00	00–01	Mon	Mean
Sites of international importance in the UK							
Scapa Flow	-	-	[31] 124	-	-		124
Moray Firth	(22)	[24] 163	[24] 98	29	86	Jan	94
Forth Estuary	107	75	57	67	44	Jan	70
Sites of national importance in Great Britain							
Loch Ashie	-	-	-	-	[29] 41	Sep	41 ▲
Whiteness to Scarvister	-	-	[28] 33	-	-		33
Loch Indaal	(13)	32	21	27	23	Jan	26
Traigh Luskentyre	13	8	19	38	48	Nov	25
Pagham Harbour	29	39	22	34	1	Dec	25
Clyde Estuary	32	25	5	22	20	Jan	21
Loch Ryan	[29] 21	11	9	10	19	Nov	14
Bay of Sandoyne to Holme Sound	-	-	-	[29] 14	-		14 ▲
Loch of Harray	6	14	14	24	8	Oct	13
Blackwater Estuary	14	18	10	8	9	Jan	12
North West Solent	12	(16)	14	8	8	Feb	12
North Norfolk Coast	17	9	11	5	5	Nov	9
Lindisfarne	2	12	19	1	9	Dec	9
Chichester Harbour	13	[30] 9	[30] 6	2	11	Jan	8
Poole Harbour	10	9	10	3	7	Jan	8
Exe Estuary	2	11	7	12	3	Jan	7
Upper Loch Torridon	-	-	9	0	9	Feb	6
Loch of Swannay	10	5	4	3	7	Nov/Dec	6
Tamar Complex	7	5	4	4	5	Jan	5
Loch Eriboll	-	-	-	5	(1)	Feb	5
St Andrews Bay	2	4	0	15	0		4 ▲
Loch Linnhe: Corran Ferry - Onich	-	-	-	-	4	Nov	4 ▲

Lough Foyle	20	6	[29] 48	2	9	Dec	17

Important sites not counted in last five years
Sound of Taransay
Studland Bay

Sites no longer meeting table qualifying levels
Strangford Lough

Other sites surpassing table qualifying levels in 2000–01

Traeth Lafan	6	Dec
Inland Sea	5	Jan
Jersey Shore	5	Jan
Mere Sands Wood NR	5	Aug/Sep
Loch of Boardhouse	4	Oct
Renishaw Lakes	4	Jun

†   *as no all-Ireland threshold has been set, a qualifying level of four has been chosen to select sites for presentation in this report*

BLACK-NECKED GREBE
Podiceps nigricollis

International threshold:	1,000
Great Britain threshold:	1 [*†]
All-Ireland threshold:	?

GB Max:	**52 Dec**
NI Max:	**0**

* *50 is normally used as a minimum threshold*

The peak count for Britain was the highest recorded in the past five years, and a reasonable proportion of the 120 birds estimated to be wintering in Britain by Chandler (1986). WeBS data show that the distribution is more southerly and westerly than that of the other grebe species.

The peak count at the Fal Estuary was very low for the third year running, as a consequence of the absence of counts from the Carrick Roads area. The peak count from Holme Pierrepont Gravel Pits in June was more than double the average count for this site. Unfortunately, Studland Bay has not been counted in the last five years and therefore currently fails to qualify for the list of sites regularly supporting more than five birds. Up to 14 birds were recorded at this site in the mid 1990s.

	96–97	97–98	98–99	99–00	00–01	Mon	Mean	
Sites of national importance in Great Britain [†]								
Fal Complex	23	33	(0)	(0)	(1)	Feb	28	
Woolston Eyes	(6)	17	25	15	11	Jun	17	
Langstone Harbour	19	9	17	12	15	Dec	14	
William Girling Reservoir	3	4	11	11	14	Oct-Dec	9	
Fleet/Wey	3	(2)	2	11	9	Feb	6	▲
Tamar Complex	4	6	6	6	9	Feb	6	
Poole Harbour	7	12	2	1	5	Jan	5	
Holme Pierrepont Gravel Pits	0	3	5	5	14	Jun	5	▲
Kilconquhar Loch	5	4	5	4	6	Jul	5	▲

Important sites not counted in last five years
Studland Bay

Other sites surpassing table qualifying levels in 2000–01

Hilfield Park Reservoir	7	Jun
Walthamstow Reservoirs	6	Oct
Fairburn Ings	5	Jul

†   *as the British threshold for national importance is so small, and as no all-Ireland threshold has been set, a qualifying level of five has been chosen to select sites for presentation in this report*

CORMORANT
Phalacrocorax carbo

International threshold: 1,200
Great Britain threshold: 130
All-Ireland threshold: ?[†]

GB Max: 16,315 Oct
NI Max: 2,490 Sep

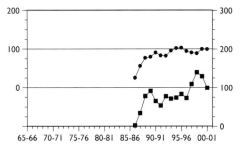

Figure 8. Annual indices for Cormorant in GB (circles, left axis) and NI (squares, right axis)

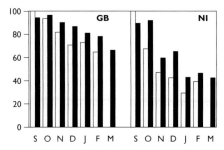

Figure 9. Monthly indices for Cormorant in GB and NI (white bars 2000–01; black bars 1995–96 to 1999–2000)

There was little change to the national index value or peak count for Britain in 2000–01. In comparison the indices for Northern Ireland fell sharply and the maximum count for the province was down on the previous year.

Five-year peak mean counts at Loughs Neagh & Beg exceeded the level of international importance for a second successive year despite a slight fall in numbers, whilst at Morecambe Bay the peak count exceeded this level for the first time in over a decade.

Staines Reservoirs qualified as nationally important due to the high count recorded in 2000–01, whereas a steady increase in the number of Cormorants at the Humber Estuary has led to the site qualifying for the same status. High numbers were noted on the Dee Estuary (Eng/Wal) and on the nearby Clwyd Estuary, while Cormorant numbers have shown sustained increases on the Solway Estuary and at Rye Harbour & Pett Level over the last five winters. Particularly low counts were recorded at several sites, including Abberton Reservoir, Grafham Water, Besthorpe & Girton Gravel Pits, Queen Elizabeth II Reservoir, William Girling Reservoir, Sonning Gravel Pit and Blithfield Reservoir.

	96–97	97–98	98–99	99–00	00–01	Mon	Mean
Sites of international importance in the UK							
Loughs Neagh & Beg	927	1,184	2,071	1,643	1,416	Sep	1,448
Sites of national importance in Great Britain							
Morecambe Bay	977	1,099	963	1,030	1,223	Sep	1,058
Forth Estuary	657	632	701	681	744	Aug	683
Abberton Reservoir	900	710	600	600	318	Sep	626
Solway Estuary	457	510	586	628	678	Sep	572
Alt Estuary	514	397	779	574	574	Nov	568
Dee Estuary (Eng/Wal)	253	374	613	541	864	Sep	529
Clyde Estuary	404	610	470	466	606	Aug	511
Loch Leven	405	[29] 400	442	608	488	Dec	469
Walthamstow Reservoirs	450	430	430	580	450	Jun	468
Tees Estuary	471	320	444	451	647	Sep	467
Hanningfield Reservoir	223	272	758	539	221	Oct	403
Queen Mary Reservoir	1,050	91	59	678	112	Jan	398
Rutland Water	391	385	350	330	425	Oct	376
Poole Harbour	375	400	440	298	338	Sep	370
The Wash	337	295	279	462	401	Sep	355
Dungeness Gravel Pits	144	330	550	344	294	Jul	332
North Norfolk Coast	492	224	310	278	294	Aug	320
Ranworth & Cockshoot Broads	254	405	308	317	[22] 298	Oct	316
Grafham Water	610	297	341	212	71	Nov	306
Thames Estuary	164	150	287	435	463	Jan	300

	96–97	97–98	98–99	99–00	00–01	Mon	Mean
Queen Mother Reservoir	600	46	7	535	-		297
Ouse Washes	391	[29]139	426	[22]287	[22]197	Dec	288
Blackwater Estuary	348	273	278	190	(209)	Dec	272
Rostherne Mere	229	270	243	273	281	Jan	259
Besthorpe/Girton Gravel Pits	262	236	453	323	10	Dec	257
Queen Elizabeth II Reservoir	380	268	360	172	90	Jul	254
Herne Bay	-	-	-	-	[29]250	Feb	250
Chichester Gravel Pits	[22]346	[22]213	[22]252	[22]216	[22]186	Sep	243
Stevenston Point	(230)	(230)	-	-	-		(230)
Lee Valley Gravel Pits	210	229	229	206	220	Oct	219
Pagham Harbour	246	183	177	234	244	Aug	217
Medway Estuary	154	179	185	298	246	Jan	212
Wraysbury Gravel Pits	169	105	180	276	264	Oct	199
Clwyd Estuary	255	84	50	146	439	Oct	195
Rye Harbour & Pett Level	61	179	187	211	324	Aug	192
Southampton Water	[30]174	150	195	[30]223	204	Oct	189
Tay Estuary	212	[30]234	134	196	165	Sep	188
South Stoke	[22]332	[22]187	[22]136	[22]138	[22]109	Nov	180
Wraysbury Reservoir	142	479	(16)	39	59	Jan	180
Swale Estuary	200	187	(128)	203	126	Nov	179
Dysynni Estuary	214	173	(59)	129	178	Aug	174
Ribble Estuary	179	123	132	163	219	Oct	163
William Girling Reservoir	(91)	(180)	(200)	210	60	Aug	163
Staines Reservoirs	32	216	26	39	499	Sep	162 ▲
Middle Tame Valley Gravel Pits	(82)	150	171	207	118	Sep	162
Sonning Gravel Pit	150	312	161	140	27	Oct	158
Humber Estuary	(131)	122	127	139	185	Jan	143 ▲
Chew Valley Lake	170	190	90	120	145	Sep	143
Blithfield Reservoir	323	77	92	146	55	Aug	139
Exe Estuary	169	125	143	113	140	Nov	138
Lindisfarne	79	76	255	84	188	Oct	136 ▲
Farmoor Reservoirs	185	120	168	109	95	Jan	135
Attenborough Gravel Pits	181	137	103	112	(46)	Sep	133
Stour Estuary	153	137	123	125	124	Oct	132

Sites with mean peak counts of 130 or more birds in Northern Ireland [†]

Belfast Lough	352	514	[30]349	321	499	Oct	407
Strangford Lough	167	164	300	285	275	Oct	238
Outer Ards	152	158	359	303	121	Nov	219
Carlingford Lough	187	174	150	209	166	Sep	177

Sites no longer meeting table qualifying levels

Ardrossan – West Kilbride
Inner Moray Firth
Breydon Water & Berney Marshes
Alde Complex
Orwell Estuary

Other sites surpassing table qualifying levels in 2000–01

R. Avon: R'wood to Christchurch [29] 205 Feb
Loch of Strathbeg 176 Dec
Hornsea Mere 157 Nov
Dengie Flats 155 Jan
Blyth Estuary (Northumberland) [22] 149 Sep
Dee Estuary (Scotland) 145 Sep
Knight & Bessborough Reservoirs 135 Sep

[†] as no all-Ireland threshold has been set, a qualifying level of 130 has been chosen to select sites for presentation in this report

BITTERN
Botaurus stellaris

International threshold:	?
Great Britain threshold:	?
All-Ireland threshold:	?

GB Max:	16 Dec
NI Max:	0

Following fluctuating totals in recent years Bittern numbers recorded by WeBS in 2000-01 were average. As in 1999–2000 several traditional sites held none or only one bird and for the second year running the most notable omission from the table is Leighton Moss, the species stronghold in Britain, from where no counts were received. Bitterns were recorded at 28 sites in total in 2000–01.

Sites with two or more birds in 2000-01

Rye Harbour & Pett Level	5	Jan
Stodmarsh & Collards Lagoon	3	Oct
Fleet Pond	2	Dec/Jan
Minsmere	2	May/Sep
North Norfolk Coast	2	Nov
Potteric Carr Nature Reserve	2	Jan
Seaton Gravel Pits	2	Nov
Trinity Broads	2	Dec

SQUACCO HERON
Ardeola ralloides

Vagrant
Native range: Southern Europe, Middle East, Africa

One was seen at Stoke Fleet on the Thames Estuary during June.

CATTLE EGRET
Bubulcus ibis

Vagrant
Native range: SW Europe, Asia, Africa, Americas

One was present in the Greater London area at Osterley Park Lakes from August to October.

LITTLE EGRET
Egretta garzetta

International threshold:	1,250
Great Britain threshold:	?[†]
All-Ireland threshold:	?[†]

GB Max:	1,373 Sep
NI Max:	0

The peak count rose by 37% from the previous winter, continuing the increase observed over the past decade. The timing of the peak count in autumn was typical, lower numbers remaining throughout the winter.

Numerous sites now regularly support double-figure counts, and with very few exceptions most have seen large increases over the past five years. It is notable that, at many, standard WeBS Core Counts recorded more birds than during roost surveys in the previous year. Information from the census in autumn 1999 produced an estimated total of around 1,700 birds, 50% more than recorded through Core Counts alone (Musgrove 2002). Applying this correction factor would suggest that numbers nationally in autumn 2000 may well have been in excess of 2,000 birds.

Whilst high counts were recorded from a number of sites, such as the Thames Estuary, of particular interest were double-figure counts from North Norfolk Marshes and increasing numbers on the Dee Estuary (Eng/Wal), Dyfi Estuary and the Wash, all at the edge of the species current range.

	96–97	97–98	98–99	99–00	00–01	Mon	Mean	
Sites with mean peak counts of 10 or more birds in Great Britain [†]								
Chichester Harbour	74	[14] 130	134	[14] 271	[22] 220	Nov	152	
Longueville Marsh	130	(98)	(125)	70	(85)	Feb	108	
Poole Harbour	57	[14] 107	61	[14] 142	118	Sep	97	
Tamar Complex	69	[14] 72	50	[19] 143	121	Aug	91	
Jersey Shore	-	-	-	-	64	Dec	64	▲
Camel Estuary	46	[14] 47	56	[14] 55	77	Aug	56	
Kingsbridge Estuary	47	45	59	58	72	Sep	56	
Exe Estuary	34	37	47	58	71	Sep	49	
Taw-Torridge Estuary	23	[22] 27	32	[14] 77	71	Sep	46	
Pagham Harbour	30	27	41	[14] 51	76	Aug	45	
Burry Inlet	[30] 11	14	32	(86)	58	Oct	40	
Langstone Harbour	32	19	36	51	51	Aug-Oct	38	
Fowey Estuary	35	27	39	[14] 40	49	Oct	38	
Fal Complex	24	21	45	34	39	Jul-Aug	33	
Newtown Estuary	21	34	26	[14] 46	38	Dec	33	
Medway Estuary	(17)	8	(21)	(71)	19	Aug/Oct	33	
Portsmouth Harbour	0	[30] 15	17	(51)	64	Sep	30	
Guernsey Shore	18	-	17	31	46	Sep	28	
Thames Estuary	11	4	11	30	83	Aug	28	
Teign Estuary	36	13	23	[14] 30	25	Aug	25	
North West Solent	16	14	27	[14] 45	30	Aug	26	
Fleet/Wey	18	(13)	6	30	37	Oct	23	
Cleddau Estuary	14	25	21	(17)	25	Oct	21	
Helford Estuary	7	7	(23)	(24)	20	Jul	16	
R. Avon: Salisbury to F'bridge	5	3	12	20	(38)	Sep	16	▲
Christchurch Harbour	-	-	-	9	(20)	Sep	15	▲
Colne Estuary	3	4	9	27	26	Feb	14	▲
Erme Estuary	13	13	12	[14] 26	17	Aug	16	▲
Avon Estuary	8	10	(12)	[14] 20	21	Aug	15	
Beaulieu Estuary	21	9	11	7	19	Feb	13	
Southampton Water	6	3	17	11	25	Dec	12	▲
Yealm Estuary	(11)	8	15	16	9	Sep	12	
Yar Estuary	9	5	12	10	19	Nov	11	▲
R. Avon: R'wood to Christchurch	(0)	1	9	(12)	26	Feb	10	▲
Hayle Estuary	7	7	10	13	13	Aug	10	▲

Sites no longer meeting table qualifying levels

Looe Estuary

Other sites surpassing table qualifying levels in 2000–01

Swale Estuary	19	Oct	Dart Estuary	12	Sep
Pegwell Bay	17	Sep	North Norfolk Coast	12	Sep
Cuckmere Estuary	15	Sep	Alde Complex	12	Nov
Crouch-Roach Estuary	15	Oct-Jan	Stour Estuary	10	Jan
Blackwater Estuary	(15)	Several	Alresford Pond	10	Feb
Wootton Creek	13	Oct	Axe Estuary (Devon)	10	Sep
Severn Estuary	13	Jul			

[†] as no British or all-Ireland thresholds have been set, a qualifying level of 10 has been chosen to select sites for presentation in this report

---

GREAT WHITE EGRET
Ardea alba

Vagrant

Native range: S Europe, Africa, Asia, N & C America

On Anglesey, singles were present at both Llynnau Y Fali and Cors Crugyll during July and at the Inland Sea during September; these records may refer to either of two birds present on Anglesey from June to September (Rogers *et al.* 2001). One was also present at Minsmere from August to October.

GREY HERON
Ardea cinerea

International threshold: 4,500
Great Britain threshold: ?[†]
All-Ireland threshold: ?[†]

GB Max: 4,269 Sep
NI Max: 459 Sep

The Great Britain maximum exceeded 4,000 for only the third time, though the peak was slightly below the record of the previous year. As usual, it occurred in autumn, numbers typically dropping by around 25% during the midwinter months. A similar pattern occurred in Northern Ireland where numbers were very similar to those of 1999–2000.

Peak counts at many key sites occur in the August to October period, presumably reflecting post-breeding gatherings as adults and juveniles leave the heronries. Of note were counts from Walthamstow Reservoirs and Besthorpe/Girton Gravel Pits, which were significantly lower than in recent years, and counts at the Dee Estuary (Eng/Wal) and the Avon Valley, counts at the latter being the second highest by WeBS at a British site in the last decade.

	96–97	97–98	98–99	99–00	00–01	Mon	Mean	
Sites with mean peak counts of 50 or more birds in Great Britain [†]								
Walthamstow Reservoirs	300	280	330	(0)	81	Mar	248	
R. Avon: Salisbury to F'bridge	72	70	92	102	326	Oct	132	
Somerset Levels	115	(119)	(105)	143	148	Oct	135	
Coombe Country Park	-	169	144	31	-		115	
Thames Estuary	98	92	105	114	137	Oct	109	
Morecambe Bay	70	88	101	88	69	Aug	83	
Taw-Torridge Estuary	125	94	47	78	69	Aug	83	
Dee Estuary (Eng/Wal)	58	76	(61)	80	124	Sep	85	
Ribble Estuary	99	95	(54)	88	48	Oct	83	
Clyde Estuary	46	86	79	90	81	Aug	76	
Ouse Washes	63	57	133	61	36	Oct	70	
Montrose Basin	71	42	42	83	87	Aug	65	
Hanningfield Reservoir	20	48	57	137	57	Sep	64	
Besthorpe/Girton Gravel Pits	102	22	107	76	2	Nov	62	
Tamar Complex	64	75	62	45	45	Sep	58	
Severn Estuary	54	59	51	51	67	Jan	56	
Durham Coast	40	58	50	60	63	Aug	54	
The Wash	(35)	45	42	91	56	Sep	54	
Tees Estuary	38	38	51	57	83	Aug	53	▲
Alde Complex	46	50	52	72	37	Jul	51	
Sites with mean peak counts of 50 or more birds in Northern Ireland [†]								
Loughs Neagh & Beg	198	217	359	269	267	Sep	262	
Strangford Lough	79	87	85	96	92	Sep	88	

Sites no longer meeting table qualifying levels
R. Avon: Fordingbridge to Ringwood
Burry Inlet

Other sites surpassing table qualifying levels in 2000–01

Mersey Estuary	56	Aug	
Forth Estuary	56	Sep	
North Norfolk Coast	51	Aug	

†   *as no British or all-Ireland thresholds have been set, a qualifying level of 50 has been chosen to select sites for presentation in this report*

PURPLE HERON
Ardea purpurea

Scarce

Single birds were recorded at the Carlton & Manby Washlands in July and at Pegwell Bay in August.

WHITE STORK
Ciconia ciconia

Vagrant & Escape
Native range: Europe, Africa, Asia

Two free-flying escapes were recorded at Harewood House throughout the year and a single was at Earls Barton Gravel Pits in August.

SPOONBILL
Platalea leucorodia

Scarce

GB Max: 14   Dec
NI Max: 0

The number of sites where two or more birds were seen reached double figures in 2000-01, the highest recorded by WeBS. Summing the site maxima, whilst not accounting for individuals recorded at more than one site, also suggests an increase in numbers, with 20 sites producing 42 birds, also the highest recorded by WeBS.

Sites with two or more birds in 2000-01

Breydon Wtr & Berney Marshes	5	Jun	Stodmarsh NNR & Collards Lagoon	3	Jun
Exe Estuary	5	Oct/Dec	Chichester Harbour	2	Oct
Taw-Torridge Estuary	5	Nov/Dec	Mersehead RSPB Reserve	2	Aug
Alde Complex	3	Sep	Ribble Estuary	2	Jul/Aug
Humber Estuary	3	Jul/Sep	Tamar Complex	2	Dec

FULVOUS WHISTLING DUCK
Dendrocygna bicolor

Escape
Native range: C & S America, Africa, S Asia

A single was present on the Tweed Estuary in April.

MUTE SWAN
Cygnus olor

International threshold:	2,400
Great Britain threshold:	**260**
All-Ireland threshold:	**55**

GB Max: 20,699 Oct
NI Max: 2,316 Sep

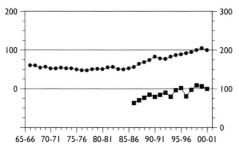

Figure 10. Annual indices for Mute Swan in GB (circles, left axis) and NI (squares, right axis).

Whilst the peak total for Northern Ireland remained average for recent years the British maximum increased for the fifth consecutive year. The British annual index, however, fell for the first time in eight years.

Several of the key Northern Ireland sites held numbers below their respective five-year peak mean, with notable low counts at the Upper Quoile River and Lough Aghery.

In Britain numbers at key sites were near or above average and six more sites qualified as nationally important. Peak counts at the Somerset Levels and Loch of Harray continued to increase and there was a sharp rise on the Avon Valley, although numbers at Abberton Reservoir fell to their lowest since the early 1980s.

	96–97	97–98	98–99	99–00	00–01	Mon	Mean	
Sites of national importance in Great Britain								
Fleet/Wey	1,185	1,313	1,141	1,177	1,150	Oct	1,193	
Somerset Levels	731	734	733	1,011	1,110	Jan	864	
Tweed Estuary	664	544	615	580	575	Jul	596	
Ouse Washes	364	432	663	662	[29] 726	Nov	569	
Rutland Water	396	485	465	617	547	Jul	502	
Abberton Reservoir	480	428	512	520	328	Aug	454	
Loch of Harray	249	413	441	495	597	Jan	439	
Hornsea Mere	-	(49)	394	364	346	Jul	368	
Loch Bee (South Uist)	-	-	-	341	343	Aug	342	▲
Montrose Basin	356	315	304	343	327	Aug	329	
Loch Leven	199	71	423	406	496	Aug	319	▲
Stour Estuary	426	307	276	274	252	Nov	307	
Tring Reservoirs	201	329	310	342	306	Dec	298	
Morecambe Bay	281	237	269	333	314	Dec	287	
Severn Estuary	239	302	299	248	337	Dec	285	▲
Humber Estuary	(158)	213	314	271	303	Dec	275	▲
R. Avon: Salisbury to F'bridge	233	215	239	263	395	Oct	269	▲
Fen Drayton Gravel Pits	286	264	228	316	249	Aug	269	▲
Sites of all-Ireland importance in Northern Ireland								
Loughs Neagh & Beg	1,844	1,612	2,422	1,887	1,931	Sep	1,939	
Upper Lough Erne	590	468	351	328	-		434	
Strangford Lough	83	96	111	225	174	Sep	138	
Lower Lough Erne	-	116	-	-	-		116	
Lough Foyle	130	110	115	115	98	Nov	114	
Broad Water Canal	78	66	71	-	113	Oct	82	
Upper Quoile River	104	116	50	88	32	Oct	78	
Dundrum Bay	67	76	81	80	68	Oct	74	
Lough Aghery	89	67	59	(54)	31	Sep	62	
Belfast Lough	[30] 60	37	42	[30] 90	57	Nov	57	

Important sites not counted in last five years
Ballyroney Lake
Christchurch Harbour

Other sites surpassing table qualifying levels in 2000–01

Nene Washes	342	Nov
Ribble Estuary	301	Jan
Stodmarsh & Collards Lagoon	289	Aug
Dungeness Gravel Pits	269	Jun
Thanet Coast	260	Nov

BLACK SWAN
Cygnus atratus

Escape
Native range: Australia

GB Max: **56 Oct**
NI Max: **1 May**

After remarkable increases over the previous two years, numbers recorded by WeBS in 2000–01 rose only slightly. Birds were seen at 81 sites, one less than the previous year, but the summed site maxima was 156, the highest recorded by WeBS.

The number of sites that held three or more birds was 16 (*cf.* 13, 9 and 5 in the preceding three years) and unusually for Northern Ireland one was present at Dundrum Bay in May.

Sites with three or more birds in 2000-01

Fleet/Wey	8	May/Jun	Exe Estuary	5	Sep/Oct
Hanningfield Reservoir	8	Aug	Thorpe Water Park	5	Nov
Deene Lake	7	Jul	Lindisfarne	4	Aug
Woburn Park Lakes	7	Sep	North Norfolk Coast	4	Dec
Fillingham Lake	6	Nov/Dec	Thorpe Water Park	3	Feb
Ramsbury Lake	6	Nov	Westport Lake	3	Sep
Cotswold Water Park (West)	5	Sep	Arlington Reservoir	3	Nov

BEWICK'S SWAN
Cygnus columbianus

International threshold:	170
Great Britain threshold:	70
All-Ireland threshold:	25*

GB Max: 5,232 Jan
NI Max: 102 Oct

* 50 is normally used as a minimum threshold

% young 14.6–23 **brood size:** n/a

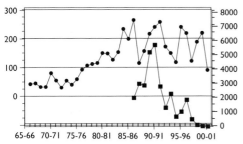

Figure 11. Annual indices for Bewick's Swan in GB (circles, left axis) and NI (squares, right axis)

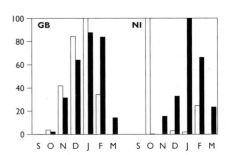

Figure 12. Monthly indices for Bewick's Swan in GB and NI (white bars 2000–01; black bars 1995–96 to 1999–2000)

In 2000–01 both the British and Northern Ireland maxima were down on the previous year and the British annual indices dropped sharply – the largest fall in one year – to a value close to those of the late 1970s.

Productivity was higher than in 1999–2000 with 23% young in flocks at WWT Slimbridge, 14.6% at WWT Welney and 21.2% at WWT Martin Mere (WWT, unpubl. data).

The majority of Bewick's Swans in Northern Ireland were recorded at Loughs Neagh & Beg where the peak count constituted the total count of the whole province.

There was a notable decrease at a private site in Kent, where numbers have continued to decline in recent years. In contrast, and despite the decline nationally, peak counts at Martin Mere/Ribble Estuary, the Dee Estuary (Eng/Wal) and the Nene Washes were higher than in the previous winter by 97%, 110% and 236%, respectively.

	96–97	97–98	98–99	99–00	00–01	Mon	Mean	
Sites of international importance in the UK								
Ouse Washes	[29] 4,977	[33] 4,257	[33] 5,129	[22] 5,649	[22] 4,693	Jan	4,941	
Nene Washes	863	2,585	723	327	1,100	Jan	1,120	
Severn Estuary	555	[33] 393	[33] 287	[33] 216	[33] 272	Jan	345	
Martin Mere/Ribble Estuary	[33] 669	368	[22] 144	[33] 163	[33] 322	Feb	333	
Breydon Wtr & Berney Marshes	476	231	210	132	186	Jan	247	
St Benet's Levels	286	161	126	209	(206)	Jan	198	
Unspecified SE England site	324	306	256	64	10	Jan	192	
Sites of national importance in Great Britain								
Somerset Levels	[22] 285	68	120	117	146	Jan	147	▼
Dee Estuary (Eng/Wal)	107	79	48	56	118	Feb	82	
Medway Estuary	[30] 32	15	302	42	0		78	
Lower Derwent Valley	139	81	21	61	-		76	▲
Arun Valley	68	98	52	78	71	Jan	73	

	96–97	97–98	98–99	99–00	00–01	Mon	Mean	
Sites of all-Ireland importance in Northern Ireland								
Loughs Neagh & Beg	117	77	53	16	102	Oct	73	
Boghill Fields (Coleraine)	48	-	-	-	-		48	▲
R. Lagan: Flatfield	²⁹ 49	38	-	-	-		44	
Upper Lough Erne	122	7	0	0	-		32	
Canary Road	-	26	-	-	-		26	
Lough Foyle	90	14	10	5	10	Feb	26	

Sites no longer meeting table qualifying levels
Alde Complex
Walmore Common
R. Avon: Fordingbridge to R'wood

WHOOPER SWAN
Cygnus cygnus

International threshold:	**160**
Great Britain threshold:	**55**
All-Ireland threshold:	**100**

GB Max: 5,429 Jan
NI Max: 1,172 Dec

% young: 15.6–19.6   **brood size:** n/a

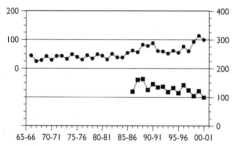

Figure 13. Annual indices for Whooper Swan in GB (circles, left axis) and NI (squares, right axis)

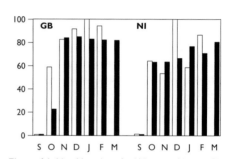

Figure 14. Monthly indices for Whooper Swan in GB and NI (white bars 2000–01; black bars 1995–96 to 1999–2000)

Although the peak in Great Britain was 19% below that of the previous winter, numbers remained relatively high compared with previous years. Correspondingly the annual index fell (-12%) but still represents the second highest value in the 35 year series and consolidates a generally rising trend; over the past decade, indices have risen by 64%. Breeding success was slightly below average, with 15.6% young on the Ouse Washes, 19.6% at Martin Mere/Ribble Estuary and 15.6% at WWT Caerlaverock.

In Northern Ireland the peak was the lowest in the province to date and indices fell similarly to the lowest ever level. Although coverage of some key swan sites is poorer than during the early and mid 1990s, annual indices, which take account of changes in coverage between years, still suggest a decline of 26% over the last 10 years.

Peak counts at Martin Mere/Ribble Estuary continued to rise, and the long-term decline in numbers of Bewick's Swans at the site may be in part attributable to competition from Whoopers. Other noteworthy counts came predominantly from Scottish sites, with numbers on the Solway Estuary, Dornoch Firth and the Lower Teviot Valley being well above average, whilst peaks at Loch a'Phuill on Tiree and at Tyninghame Estuary were down considerably compared with recent years.

	96–97	97–98	98–99	99–00	00–01	Mon	Mean
Sites of international importance in the UK							
Ouse Washes	[29] 1,211	1,299	[22] 1,623	[22] 2,120	[22] 1,797	Jan	1,610
Martin Mere/Ribble Estuary	851	[22] 1,041	[22] 1,130	[33] 1,335	1,650	Dec	1,201
Upper Lough Erne	1,094	892	989	985	-		990
Loughs Neagh & Beg	1,169	1,113	830	641	735	Dec	898
Lough Foyle	671	566	642	657	434	Oct	594
Loch of Strathbeg	158	310	476	262	424	Nov	326
Solway Estuary	[33] 350	[33] 221	[33] 188	[33] 223	[33] 466	Jan	290
River Foyle: Grange	380	150	-	-	-		265
R. Clyde: Carstairs to Thankerton/ Ravenstruther	60	(157)	125	393	354	Oct/Jan	233
Black Cart Water	[34] 163	[34] 180	[34] 244	[34] 187	299	Nov	215
Sites of national importance in Great Britain							
Loch Leven	97	98	134	144	144	Dec	123
R. Nith: K'bank to Nunholm	75	(115)	100	146	131	Feb	113
Dornoch Firth	13	73	89	84	307	Oct	113
Loch Insh and Spey Marshes	82	-	-	[29] 125	-		104
Wigtown Bay	59	75	102	134	(110)	Jan	96
Loch of Wester	98	114	(123)	45	(86)	Oct	95
R. Tweed: Kelso to Coldstream	48	(138)	105	50	47	Feb	78
Loch of Lintrathen	67	(77)	(36)	68	96	Jan	77
Loch a'Phuill	-	23	101	142	36	Nov	76
Milldam & Balfour Mains Pools	87	76	[29] 49	[29] 53	112	Nov	75
Barons Folly	123	[29] 73	0	71	107	Nov	75
Loch Eye & Cromarty Firth	120	52	28	126	39	Oct	73
Caistron Quarry	-	-	-	-	71	Feb	71 ▲
Lower Derwent Valley	96	61	45	81	-		71
Threave Estate	2	85	-	117	-		68
Tyninghame Estuary	65	44	113	76	15	Nov	63
Warkworth Lane Ponds	-	-	-	-	62	Feb	62 ▲
Lower Teviot Valley	31	4	75	0	179	Feb	58 ▲
Loch Heilen	51	99	38	33	-		55
Sites of all-Ireland importance in Northern Ireland							
Boghill Fields (Coleraine)	137	-	-	-	-		137 ▲
Strangford Lough	42	100	79	177	201	Dec	120 ▲
Bush River: Deepstown	122	114	-	-	-		118 ▲
R. Lagan: Flatfield	[29] 76	152	-	-	-		114

Important sites not counted in last five years

Easterloch/Uyeasound
Islesteps
R. Teviot: Kalemouth to Roxburgh
R. Tweed: Magdalenehall

Sites no longer meeting table qualifying levels

Loch of Spiggie
R. Tweed: Rutherford
Merryton Ponds
Humber Estuary
Linton Pond

Other sites surpassing table qualifying levels in 2000–01

Nene Washes	11	Feb
Clatto Reservoir	108	Nov
Forth Estuary	95	Jan
Carsebreck & Rhynd Lochs	90	Jan
Loch of Spiggie	73	Oct

MAGPIE GOOSE
Anseranas semipalmata

Escape

Native range: Australasia

Six were present on the River Carron from December to February.

SWAN GOOSE
Anser cygnoides

Escape

Native range: Eastern Asia

Birds were recorded at a notable 19 sites during 2000–01 (*cf.* 8, 3 and 4 in the preceding three years) with six of these holding more than one

bird. The flocks at Etherow Country Park and Esthwaite Water continue to thrive with maximum counts of 18 and 13, respectively.

BEAN GOOSE
Anser fabalis

International threshold (*fabalis*):	800
Great Britain threshold:	4[*]
All-Ireland threshold:	+[*]

GB Max:	187 Oct
NI Max:	0

[*] 50 is normally used as a minimum threshold

The only two sites holding nationally important numbers of Bean Goose, both of the Taiga *A. f. fabalis* population, were once again the Middle Yare Marshes, Norfolk and the Slamannan Plateau, Stirling. As in 1999–2000, these two flocks showed contrasting trends. Numbers at the Yare Marshes continued to decline and were the lowest since 1980–81, whereas at the Slamannan Plateau, the peak was just a few less than the record count in 1999–2000. Consequently, this site held the greatest number of Bean Geese in Britain for the first time, although the Yare Marshes remain the more important of the two based upon the mean five-year peak count.

The phenology of these two flocks was typical of recent years, with the Slamannan birds present for considerably longer than those in the Yare. The first birds arrived at Slamannan on 25 September, reaching a peak by early November.

In contrast, the first 15 birds were not detected at the Yare Marshes until 10 November, peaking in late December. In spring, the first departures at the Yare Marshes were noted in late January, although the last five remained until 22 February. At Slamannan, the departure was less protracted: the first birds left soon after 12 February and the last, some 130 birds, were seen seven days later.

Although no official age assessments were made at either of the key sites during 2000–01, Simpson & MacIver (2001) reported that the number of young identified at Slamannan was again low.

Away from the two main sites, Bean Geese were scarce, with a peak of four at the Ouse Washes (of the Tundra race *A. f. rossicus*), four Taigas on the Humber in October and two Taigas in September at Chichester Harbour.

	96–97	97–98	98–99	99–00	00–01	Mon	Mean	
Sites of national importance in Great Britain								
Middle Yare Marshes	[23] 224	[23] 266	[23] 296	[23] 227	177	Jan	238	
Slamannan Plateau	[2] 127	[2] 157	[2] 168	[2] 188	[2] 183	Nov	165	
Lower Derwent Valley	18	11	42	7	-		20	
Ouse Washes	34	[29] 9	[29] 7	[29] 9	[22] 4	Jan	13	
North Warren & Thorpeness Mere	36	12	0	0	-		12	
Holland Marshes	-	28	0	0	0		7	▲
Humber Estuary	(1)	0	17	0	4		5	▲
Sites no longer meeting table qualifying levels								
Heigham Holmes								

PINK-FOOTED GOOSE
Anser brachyrhynchus

International threshold: **2,250**
Great Britain threshold: **2,250**
All-Ireland threshold: **+***

* *50 is normally used as a minimum threshold*

| GB Max: | 242,419 Oct |
| NI Max: | 6 Oct |

% young: 18.7   **brood size: 2.15**

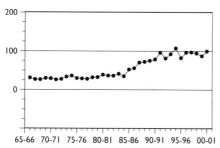

Figure 15. Annual indices for Great Crested Grebe in GB

The 41st National Census of Icelandic-breeding Grey Geese took place during October and November 2000, recording a maximum of 242,419 Pinkfeet in October (Hearn 2002). This represents an increase of 14.0% over the previous peak count (although that was considered to be an undercount as a result of the late arrival into Britain that year) and is the second highest since the census began in 1960. For the first time, an adjusted population estimate (of 245,349 birds) was calculated, which took account of key sites not covered during October 2000 (see Hearn 2002 for a full discussion of this methodology). Overall, the population has been largely stable for the past ten years.

At the site level, the Loch of Strathbeg was again the most important, with over 40,000 birds during the autumn. Nearby, the Slains Lochs (primarily Meikle) also held large numbers during the autumn. Other key sites that supported larger than average numbers included Aberlady Bay, Loch of Skene and Loch Spynie. These latter two sites are both known primarily for roosts of Icelandic Greylag Geese, but an increase in the number of Pinkfeet has been a feature of recent winters. At the same time, the number of Greylags has been more sporadic, but which of these factors is the cause and which is the effect is currently unknown; indeed, they may be completely unrelated.

Key Pinkfoot roosts that held low numbers during 2000–01 included the southwest Lancashire mosses, the Solway Estuary, Loch Eye/Cromarty Firth and Dupplin Lochs. The last site was formerly the most important roost site in Britain for this species, with a site maxima of 62,000 in October 1994. Recently, however, numbers have been considerably lower, with only 51% of the current five year peak mean recorded during 2000–01. Low counts on the Solway and at Loch Eye/Cromarty Firth are less conclusive. These locations are not known for key concentrations of Pinkfeet during the autumn, but support much higher numbers during the spring. As most monitoring of this species occurs in the autumn, low counts in a particular year may be a reflection of a lack of spring counts, rather than a lack of birds. Despite this, the decrease noted on the Solway at least is thought to be real, but the count of 12,000 on the Cromarty Firth in April 2001, highlights the difference in perceived site importance when spring counts are available.

Productivity during 2000 was 18.7% young in autumn flocks and a mean brood size of 2.15 goslings per successful pair (Hearn 2002). This is slightly above the ten-year average (1990–99) of 17.6% young, although the brood size is slightly less (mean 1990–99: 2.2 goslings per brood). Hunting mortality in Iceland was also slightly above average at 13,923 birds (mean for 1995–2000: 13,441) (Icelandic Wildlife Management Institute).

Uncertainty over proposed dam developments in central Iceland still continue. The proposal adjacent to, and partially within, þjórsárver (pronounced 'Theeorsaver'), the most important breeding site for Pinkfeet in the world and a designated Ramsar site, currently has approval from the Icelandic Government, although there remains intense public debate as to the desirability of the proposal.

	96–97	97–98	98–99	99–00	00–01	Mon	Mean	
Sites of international importance in the UK								
Loch of Strathbeg	[35] 32,000	[35] 33,556	(37,078)	31,031	[35] 42,615	Oct	35,256	
West Water Reservoir	[29] 55,000	38,700	[35] 21,670	[35] 28,000	[35] 26,500	Oct	33,974	
Holkham Bay	[35] 26,000	[35] 33,700	[35] 34,100	[35] 31,190	[35] 33,750	Jan	31,748	
SW Lancashire	[35] 41,680	[35] 28,960	[35] 36,260	[35] 29,955	[35] 16,885	Oct	30,748	
Dupplin Lochs	[35] 40,500	[35] 29,850	[35] 42,500	[35] 22,800	[35] 15,530	Sep	30,236	
Snettisham	[35] 35,930	[35] 40,350	[35] 35,555	[35] 19,450	[35] 18,250	Jan	29,907	
Scolt Head	17,900	18,800	[35] 28,510	[35] 35,180	[35] 41,000	Dec	28,278	
Montrose Basin	[35] 17,150	[35] 35,000	[35] 33,012	[35] 18,480	[35] 29,922	Oct	26,713	
Ythan Estuary/Slains Lochs	[35] 17,400	[35] 12,200	[35] 16,400	[35] 15,500	[35] 23,500	Oct	17,000	
Hule Moss	[35] 19,400	[35] 19,675	11,200	[29] 19,100	[35] 14,700	Oct	16,815	
Carsebreck & Rhynd Lochs	[35] 12,000	[35] 13,560	[35] 18,500	[35] 15,400	[35] 16,500	Oct	15,192	
Loch Leven	[35] 18,150	[35] 14,740	[35] 14,100	[35] 11,540	[35] 14,700	Oct	14,646	
Solway Estuary	[35] 19,586	[35] 17,971	[35] 3,710	[35] 6,434	[35] 2,541	Oct	10,048	
Aberlady Bay	[35] 4,650	[35] 6,540	[35] 13,260	[35] 4,840	[35] 16,750	Oct	9,208	
Tay Estuary	[35] 8,897	[35] 3,765	[35] 5,355	[35] 4,630	[35] 8,930	Nov	6,315	
Loch Long	(0)	(0)	[35] 7,200	[35] 5,417	[35] (2,450)	Nov	6,309	
Fala Flow	[35] 5,000	[35] 7,500	[35] 2,100	[35] 7,550	[35] 4,910	Oct	5,412	
Cameron Reservoir	[35] 3,460	[35] 11,280	[35] 4,104	[35] 3,168	5,000	Jan	5,402	
Loch Tullybelton	[35] 4,658	[35] 8,000	[35] 8,100	[35] 0	[35] 4,050	Oct	4,962	
R. Clyde: Carstairs to Thankerton	-	(8,000)	948	5,650	(4,850)	Dec	4,866	
Breydon Wtr & Berney Marshes	1,100	5,500	5,500	6,600	[35] 5,500	Jan	4,840	
Wigtown Bay	[35] 7,280	5,234	[35] 5,029	6,459	50	Dec	4,810	
Morecambe Bay	8,671	3,000	189	(2,347)	7,143	Jan	4,751	
Loch of Skene	[35] 1,100	[35] 600	[35] 1,500	[35] (60)	[22] 13,550	Nov	4,188	▲
Gladhouse Reservoir	[35] 6,200	[35] 5,000	[35] 1,300	[35] 6,000	[35] 1,520	Oct	4,004	
Upper Cowgill Reservoir	[35] 6,060	[35] 6,000	[35] 1,000	[35] 2,900	[35] (300)	Oct/Nov	3,990	
Loch of Lintrathen	[35] 920	[35] 2,800	[35] 3,350	[35] 10,400	[35] 2,220	Oct	3,938	
Loch Spynie	[35] 500	[35] 2,300	[35] (2,000)	[35] 1,000	[35] 8,000	Nov	2,950	▲
Holburn Moss	2,100	4,500	[35] 4,350	[35] 2,000	[35] 1,600	Oct	2,910	
Loch Eye & Cromarty Firth	[35] 1,570	465	[35] 295	[29] 12,000	[35] 126	Nov	2,891	
Loch Mahaick	[35] 2,700	[35] 6,465	[35] 1,300	[35] (600)	[35] 900	Oct	2,841	
Drummond Pond	[35] 7,000	[35] 3,300	[35] 2,644	[35] 170	[35] 930	Oct	2,809	
Strathearn (West sites)	[35] 2,730		-	-	-	-	2,730	▲
Lindisfarne	[35] 900	1,000	[35] 4,100	[35] 1,500	5,881	Oct	2,676	▲
Heigham Holmes	(2,400)	5,000	[35] 1,040	3,236	[35] 1,330	Oct	2,652	▲
Loch Mullion	[35] 0	[35] 3,000	[35] 2,000	[35] 5,500	[35] (660)	Oct	2,625	
Tay-Isla Valley	[35] 2,911	[35] 229	[35] 4,000	[35] 2,700	[35] 2,000	Nov	2,368	
Horsey Mere	-	(450)	(100)	1,027	[35] 3,620	Nov	2,324	▲

Important sites not counted in last five years

Crombie Reservoir
Forth & Teith Valleys
Carse of Stirling

Other sites surpassing table qualifying levels in 2000–01

Findhorn Bay	[35] 5,500	Nov
Lake of Menteith	[35] (4,500)	Oct
Skinflats	[35] 2,750	Dec
Humber Estuary	[35] 2,700	Nov
Clatto Reservoir	2,500	Feb

EUROPEAN WHITE-FRONTED GOOSE
Anser albifrons albifrons

International threshold:	**6,000**
Great Britain threshold:	**60**
All-Ireland threshold:	**+***

GB Max: 2,291 Jan
NI Max: 0

* 50 is normally used as a minimum threshold

% young: 13.2   **brood size:** n/a

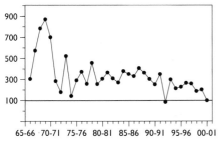

Figure 16. Annual indices for European White-fronted Goose in GB

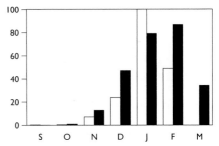

Figure 17. Monthly indices for European White-fronted Goose in GB (white bars 2000–01; black bars 1995–96 to 1999–2000)

The number of European Whitefronts in Britain during 2000–01 was the second lowest since monitoring began; only in 1992–93 were there fewer. The Severn Estuary remained the most important site, but numbers there continued to decrease; the peak count of 1,330 is just 64% of the current five-year peak mean.

The number of birds at the Swale Estuary was also very low, in this case for the second consecutive winter. This picture was mirrored elsewhere, with low counts on the North Norfolk Coast, the Alde Complex, the Thames Estuary and a confidential site in southeast England. Only at a few of the less important sites were numbers typical or greater than average: Dungeness Gravel Pits, Minsmere, Middle Yare Marshes and Breydon Water.

This population is now placed on the Amber List of Birds of Conservation Concern on account of its moderate (25–49%) decline over the past 25 years. This decline does not, however, reflect the trend shown by the whole population internationally; rather, it is a result of the shift in wintering distribution. This is likely to be a combination of the effects of the ban on goose hunting in the Netherlands, which began in 2000, and the effects of climate change and agricultural intensification – what is popularly known as 'short-stopping'. There seems little that reserve managers in the UK can do to halt this local decline, if the factors influencing it occur outside this country. The future of European Whitefronts in the UK appears uncertain, although internationally they are clearly doing well.

	96–97	97–98	98–99	99–00	00–01	Mon	Mean
Sites of national importance in Great Britain							
Severn Estuary	2,780	2,501	1,840	1,931	[29] 1,330	Jan	2,076
Swale Estuary	1,604	1,402	973	455	432	Jan	973
Heigham Holmes	(640)	475	740	(415)	-		618
North Norfolk Coast	491	290	383	343	240	Feb	349
North Warren & Thorpeness Mere	302	220	[29] 500	[29] 350	-		343
Dungeness Gravel Pits	355	240	320	[29] 340	[29] 234	Mar	298
Minsmere	215	236	196	(0)	[29] 200	Jan	212
Unspecified SE England site	328	198	198	230	26	Dec	196
Alde Complex	317	60	230	323	0		186
Middle Yare Marshes	47	107	84	155	298	Jan	138
Lower Derwent Valley	114	152	60	18	-		86
Breydon Wtr & Berney Marshes	69	90	91	51	112	Jan	83
Thames Estuary	146	69	76	7	18	Jan	63

Sites no longer meeting table qualifying levels
Crouch-Roach Estuary

Important sites not counted in last five years
Kessingland Levels

GREENLAND WHITE-FRONTED GOOSE
Anser albifrons flavirostris

International threshold:		300
Great Britain threshold:		140
All-Ireland threshold:		140

GB Max: 21,148 Nov
NI Max: 60 Feb

% young 9.1   **brood size:** 3.4

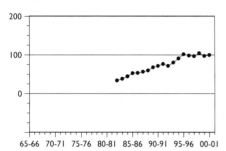

Figure 18. Annual indices for Greenland White-fronted Goose in GB

The November Census, carried out by the Greenland White-fronted Goose Study (Fox & Francis 2002), revealed a slight increase (2.4%) on the previous year, thus continuing a run of stable counts since 1995–96. Islay remained the most important site by far, although the peak count there was slightly lower than in 1999–2000 and the current five-year peak mean. Elsewhere, most sites held a typical number of birds, although the peak count on Coll was well below the recent average. South Uist held nationally important numbers for the first time in the current five-year period.

Breeding success was well below the average of the past 15 years for the second successive year. In contrast to the previous year, however, the proportion of young on Islay (8.2%) was lower than the proportion in other British locations (11.2%) (Fox & Francis 2002). Hunting

mortality in Iceland was above average at 3,515 birds (mean for 1995–2000: 3,240) (Icelandic Wildlife Management Institute).

Recently published research has demonstrated that Greenland White-fronted Geese exhibit a high degree of site loyalty to their spring and autumn staging areas in Iceland (Fox *et al.* 2002). During spring-staging in Iceland, more than 90% of goslings still associate with their parents and siblings and 96% of all within-spring movements are less than 4 km. Similarly, only 4% of sightings in subsequent springs are of geese that have moved more than 4 km from their location in the previous spring. More birds, however, show a shift in staging area between spring and autumn or autumn and spring, with 12% moving greater than 4 km. In all such cases, geese moved to Hvanneyri Agricultural College, the only hunting-free area for these birds. In addition, the geese from southern wintering areas in Ireland (Wexford) are more likely to use staging areas in the west of Iceland, while those from the Scottish wintering grounds (mainly Islay) prefer the southern lowlands of Iceland. This high degree of site loyalty and limited exchange between staging areas means that strategic refuge creation in both the western and southern lowlands is important to protect adequately the whole of this small population of geese.

	96–97	97–98	98–99	99–00	00–01	Mon	Mean	
Sites of international importance in the UK								
Islay	[26] 12,964	[26] 13,414	[26] 13,560	[13] 14,474	[13] 13,281	Nov	13,539	
Rhunahaorine	[13] 1,272	[13] 1,193	[13] 1,532	[13] 1,585	[13] 1,551	Nov	1,427	
Tiree	[13] 1,455	[13] 1,464	[13] 1,444	[13] 1,347	[13] 1,221	Mar	1,386	
Machrihanish	[13] 1,629	[13] 931	[13] 1,579	[13] 1,322	[13] 1,386	Nov	1,369	
Coll	[13] 1,047	[13] 1,052	[13] 1,122	[13] 1,014	[13] 721	Jan	991	
Stranraer Lochs		[13] 535	[13] 680	[13] 1,000	[13] 440	[13] 550	Feb	641
Keills Peninsular & Isle of Danna	[13] 333	[13] 441	[13] 425	[13] 290	[13] 443	Feb	386	
Loch Ken		[13] 318	[13] 450	[13] 357	[13] 330	[13] 311	Feb	353
Sites of national importance in Great Britain								
Appin/Eriska/Benderloch/Lismore	[13] 217	[13] 318	[13] 270	[13] 227	[13] 377	Mar	282	
Caithness Lochs	[13] 210	310	[13] 230	[13] 280	[13] 232	Jan	252	▲
Loch Heilen/Loch of Mey	[13] 199	[13] 217	[13] 215	[13] 280	232	Jan	229	
Loch Lomond	[13] 245	[13] 261	[13] 306	200	[13] 200	Nov	242	
Westfield Marshes	[13] 210	[13] 206	[13] 230	[13] 255	[13] 171	Mar	214	
Bute	[13] 224	[13] 223	[13] 219	[13] 192	[13] 200	Dec	212	
Clachan/Whitehouse	[13] 184	[13] 203	[13] 196	[13] 232	[13] 217	Dec	206	
Colonsay/Oronsay	[27] 175	[13] 288	[27] 208	[13] 204	[13] 128	Nov	201	
Orkney	126	128	[13] 125	201	[13] 153	Nov	147	▲

LESSER WHITE-FRONTED GOOSE
Anser erythropus

Vagrant and escape
Native range: SE Europe and Asia

Two birds were present at Poole Harbour in February, while singles at Ogden Reservoir (Grane) in June and nearby Holden Wood Reservoir in July almost certainly refer to the same bird.

GREYLAG GOOSE
Anser anser

ICELANDIC POPULATION

International threshold:	**1,000**
Great Britain threshold:	**1,000**
All-Ireland threshold:	**40**[*]

GB Max: 78,608 Nov
NI Max: 0

[*] *50 is normally used as a minimum threshold*

% young **20.9** **brood size:** **2.48**

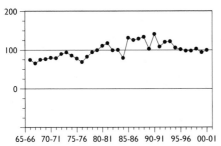

Figure 19. Annual indices for Icelandic Greylag Geese in GB

The 41st National Census of Icelandic-breeding Grey Geese took place in October and November 2000. A maximum of 81,097 Greylag Geese was recorded during November, an increase of 6.9% over the previous year (Hearn 2002). For the first time, an adjusted population estimate (of 80,324 birds) was calculated, which took account of key sites not counted during the census and estimates of the number of UK Greylags (from the re-established and Northwest Scotland populations) counted during the census (see Hearn 2002 for a full discussion of this methodology). The index shows a slight increase over the previous year and it now appears that this population has been largely stable for the past six years. The trend calculated by Hearn (2002), however, using five-year running means, lends a little more support for a continued slow but steady decline, the current five-year peak mean being the lowest since 1978.

The Orkney Isles have now replaced Dinnet Lochs as the most important site for wintering Icelandic Greylags, based upon the current five year peak mean. The total there, however, is likely to include a significant proportion of locally breeding birds, possibly as much as 10%, this population having also increased considerably in recent years. The peak count for 1999–2000 given in last year's report has now been replaced by a higher count of 20,475; the highest for the archipelago to date.

Away from Orkney, most other sites supported numbers lower or similar to their current five year peak mean, with a particularly low peak count at Dinnet Lochs for the second time in the past three years. Notable exceptions to this trend were Loch Garten and the Gadloch/Summerston area near Glasgow. Six other sites also held internationally important numbers during 2000–01 for the first time in the current five-year period.

Productivity in 2000 was 20.9% young in autumn flocks and a mean brood size of 2.48 goslings per successful pair (Hearn 2002) which compares with the ten-year average (1990–99) of 16.7% young and 2.47 goslings per brood. Hunting mortality in Iceland decreased for the third consecutive year, although remained high at 31,821 birds (mean for 1995–2000: 36,398) (Icelandic Wildlife Management Institute).

Census difficulties caused by the presence of UK Greylag Geese (principally re-established birds) in the wintering areas of Icelandic migrants has been highlighted in previous reports and continues to limit the understanding of trends in abundance in this population. At a local scale, UK Greylag Geese could cause either under- or over-estimation of Icelandic Greylags, depending on whether birds at a particular site are thought to be Icelandic or not. In order to measure the abundance of Icelandic and other Greylag Geese more accurately, a suite of projects that clarify the status of wintering Greylags is needed. This work is made more urgent by the concern regarding the conservation status of the Icelandic Greylag population.

Through the resighting of marked individuals, it is now apparent that Icelandic Greylag Geese have a wider distribution than previously thought, or have recently expanded their wintering range. They are now known to be present in mid winter in southwestern Norway, as well as Iceland and the Faeroes. In addition, marked Icelandic Greylag Geese have regularly been sighted as far south as North Yorkshire in recent winters. This highlights the need for an improved understanding of delimitation in these populations, and greater international co-ordination of this census.

	96–97	97–98	98–99	99–00	00–01	Mon	Mean	
Sites of international importance in the UK								
Orkney	[35] 9,338	[35] 13,361	[35] 18,110	[35] 20,475	[35] 15,914	Nov	15,440	
Dinnet Lochs	[35] 26,185	[35] 24,346	[35] 4,400	[35] (10,000)	[35] 4,560	Nov	14,873	
Loch of Skene	[35] 12,876	[35] 11,200	9,890	[35] 6,110	[35] 9,660	Nov	9,947	
Caithness Lochs	[35] 5,378	[35] 7,200	[35] (12,731)	[35] 10,017	[35] 8,326	Nov	8,730	
Loch Eye & Cromarty Firth	[35] 5,320	[35] 5,416	[35] 9,181	[35] 5,674	6,192	Oct	6,357	
Loch Spynie	[35] 5,500	[35] 3,000	[35] (6,500)	[29] 3,000	[35] 5,500	Nov	4,700	
Loch of Lintrathen	[35] 960	[35] 7,200	[35] 2,750	[35] 1,440	[35] (905)	Nov	3,088	
Dornoch Firth	1,132	3,211	2,352	[35] 3,351	3,339	Jan	2,677	
Tay-Isla Valley	2,096	[35] 1,155	[35] 4,640	[35] 2,075	[35] 2,553	Nov	2,504	
Killimster Loch	2,500	-	-	-	-		2,500	▲
R. Earn: Lawhill Oxbows	-	-	-	-	2,316	Dec	2,316	▲
Haddo House Lakes	[35] 4,360	[35] 1,110	[35] 3,000	[35] 670	[35] 1,100	Nov	2,048	
R. Eden: Warcop to Little Salkeld	-	-	-	-	1,900	Dec	1,900	▲
Tay Estuary	[35] 1,080	[35] 650	4,350	[35] 2,221	[35] 1,116	Nov	1,883	
Findhorn Bay	[35] 1,860	[35] 2,350	[35] 1,760	[35] 2,600	[35] 620	Nov	1,838	
Lower Teviot Valley	1,200	550	-	-	[29] 3,500	Dec	1,750	▲
Drummond Pond	[35] 1,021	[35] 1,834	[35] 2,350	[35] 1,900	[35] 1,075	Nov	1,636	
Munlochy Bay	600	945	3,702	[35] 1,050	-		1,574	
Loch Fleet Complex	[35] 1,200	[35] 843	[35] 2,970	980	[35] 1,700	Oct	1,539	
Threipmuir & Harlaw Reservoirs	620	397	219	(5,000)	1,390	Nov	1,525	
Bute	[35] 1,797	[35] 1,200	[35] 1,055	[35] 1,780	[35] 1,530	Apr	1,472	
Lochs Garten & Mallachie	[35] 587	[35] 735	-	[35] 1,650	[35] 2,700	Nov	1,418	
Loch Ken	(422)	(995)	[35] 871	(1,742)	(971)	Feb	1,307	▲
Loch of the Clans	[35] 1,942	[35] 300	-	-	-		1,121	
Stranraer Lochs	-	[35] 645	2,717	[35] 176	[35] 750	Oct	1,072	
R. Eamont & Eden: H'pot to E'hall	601	1,023	1,344	1,300	(920)	Feb	1,067	
Kilconquhar Loch	1,300	1,216	797	[35] 844	1,096	Jan	1,051	
Birgham Haugh	1,035	-	-	-	-		1,035	
Upper Tay	[35] 971	[35] 1,333	[35] 1,227	[35] 376	[35] 1,189	Nov	1,019	▲

Important sites not counted in last five years
Fincastle Loch
R. Spey: Boat of Balliefirth
R. Earmont: Watersmeet to Pooley Bridge
R. Tay: Dunkeld
Corby Loch

Sites no longer meeting table qualifying levels
Strathearn (West sites)
Bridge of Earn
Carse of Stirling

Other sites surpassing table qualifying levels in 2000–01

Beauly Firth	[35] 2,980	Nov	Carsebreck & Rhynd Lochs	[35] 1,160	Nov
Gadloch	1,550	Nov	R. Clyde: Carstairs to Thankerton	1,100	Nov
Summerston	1,500	Nov	West Myre	1,070	Feb
Clatto Reservoir	1,500	Feb	Lindisfarne	[35] 1,050	Nov

NORTHWEST SCOTLAND POPULATION

International threshold: **50**
Great Britain threshold: **50**

GB Max: **8,366 Aug**

% young **25.4**   brood size: **3.6**

High counts were recorded from both North and South Uist during the co-ordinated August census undertaken there each year. The late summer count on Islay was also considerably higher than average and reflects the increasing use being made of this island as a moulting site. Soon after this late summer peak, birds rapidly disperse and numbers on the island decrease again. Numbers on Tiree continued to increase while the count at Melbost Sands & Tong Saltings was markedly above average.

Productivity data came only from Tiree (A J Leitch/J Bowler). It suggests another successful breeding season, although data on the proportion of young and brood size data between May and July. They are therefore collected considerably earlier than the estimates for the Icelandic population (for which assessment is made after the autumn shooting season in Iceland) which is likely to explain much of the apparent disparity between the two populations.

Sites of international importance in the UK	96–97	97–98	98–99	99–00	00–01	Mon	Mean	
Tiree	[27] 2,475	[25] 2,417	[1] 3,137	[27] 3,109	[27] 3,535	Jan	2,935	
North Uist	[21] 1,630	[21] 1,670	[21] 1,318	[21] 1,808	[21] 2,877	Aug	1,861	
South Uist	[21] 1,270	[21] 1,046	[21] 1,336	[21] 1,362	[21] 1,862	Aug	1,375	
Coll	[27] 1,016	[27] 953	[27] 912	[27] 587	[27] 679	Nov	829	
Benbecula	[21] 440	[21] 595	[21] 567	[21] 374	[21] 431	Feb	481	
Machrihanish	[27] 410	[27] 74	[27] 442	[27] 434	[27] 0		272	▲
Moine Mhor	[27] 254	[27] 254	[27] 203	[27] 165	[27] 137	Nov	203	▲
Loch Broom	-	-	-	-	(197)	Nov	(197)	▲
Rhunahaorine	[27] 252	[27] 143	[27] 165	[27] 269	[27] 141	Nov	194	▲
Colonsay/Oronsay	[27] 175	[27] 226	[27] 208	[27] 174	[27] 137	Nov	184	
Loch Ordais & Port Mhor Bragar	(150)	(28)	-	[29] (7)	(130)	Oct/Jan	(150)	▲
Melbost Sands & Tong Saltings	-	51	40	64	394	Feb	137	▲
Loch Urrahag	(62)	100	130	40	(167)	Nov	109	▲
Islay	[27] 129	[27] 20	[27] 32	[27] 79	206	Sep	93	▲
Loch Kishorn	-	-	-	-	58	Feb	58	▲
Loch Sheil: West	24	39	75	59	79	Dec	55	▲
Clachan/Whitehouse	[27] 81	[27] 0	[27] 139	[27] 30	[27] 0		50	▲

Other sites surpassing table qualifying levels in 2000–01
Back Pools   51   Feb

RE-ESTABLISHED POPULATION

Naturalised re-establishment [†]

GB Max: **25,550 Sep**
NI Max: **1,168 Feb**

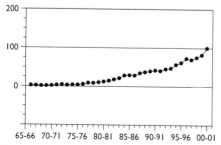

Figure 20. Annual indices for naturalised Greylag Geese in GB

The long-term trend upward of re-established Greylag Geese showed a large increase during 2000, reaching a third consecutive all-time high. Most notable was the very large count at the North Norfolk Marshes in August: an increase of 1,594 (87%) over the previous year and 155% of the current five-year peak mean. It is also the largest single count of re-established Greylags to be made in Britain.

Notable increases were apparent at a number of sites, distributed widely across the country: Bolton-on-Swale Gravel Pits, Tophill Low Reservoirs, the Swale Estuary, the Ouse

Washes, Hornsea Mere, Llyn Traffwll, Watermill Broad, the Thames Estuary, Ardleigh Reservoir, Stodmarsh NNR & Collards Lagoon and Loughs Neagh & Beg. The continuing growth and expansion of this population is demonstrated by the addition of a further 11 sites to the table. A further 13 sites also surpassed table qualifying levels in 2000–01. Small declines were recorded at some sites, although none were particularly noteworthy.

	96–97	97–98	98–99	99–00	00–01	Mon	Mean	
Sites with mean peak counts of 300 or more birds in Great Britain [†]								
North Norfolk Coast	1,669	2,177	1,892	1,837	3,431	Aug	2,201	
Lower Derwent Valley	(1,200)	1,063	1,200	763	-		1,057	
Bolton-on-Swale Gravel Pits	955	635	508	880	1,110	Oct	818	
Tophill Low Reservoirs	561	450	990	850	1,126	Aug	795	
Sutton & Lound Gravel Pits	570	650	-	800	-		673	
Heigham Holmes	538	(410)	577	865	-		660	
Nosterfield Gravel Pits	129	771	682	993	678	Nov	651	
Orwell Estuary	440	[30] 799	563	[30] 989	449	Feb	648	
Swale Estuary	456	589	574	653	907	Jan	636	
Humber Estuary	(459)	854	419	443	590	Sep	577	
Alton Water	514	647	542	550	624	Jan	575	
Ouse Washes	521	453	276	[29] 596	964	Oct	562	
Tattershall Pits	700	340	[29] 770	570	403	Jan	557	
The Wash	747	314	683	476	563	Aug	557	
Bough Beech Reservoir	-	-	-	(11)	543	Aug	543	
Eccup Reservoir	393	368	550	600	742	Nov	531	
Kirby-on-Bain Gravel Pits	(64)	627	376	541	562	Sep	527	
Hornsea Mere	-	98	441	714	834	Jun	522	
Llyn Traffwll	349	646	464	252	746	Jun	491	
Little Paxton Gravel Pits	518	655	300	399	457	Nov	466	
Hay-a-Park Gravel Pits	190	-	-	501	696	Sep	462	▲
Dungeness Gravel Pits	381	473	440	517	472	Aug	457	
Abberton Reservoir	307	297	537	589	469	Oct	440	
Martin Mere	420	419	435	460	440	Nov	435	
Langtoft West End Gravel Pits	420	490	635	165	401	Dec	422	
Livermere	330	300	334	655	-		405	
Earls Barton Gravel Pits	542	284	363	398	(379)	Jan	397	
Watermill Broad	-	257	274	328	(722)	Sep	395	▲
Buckden/Stirtloe Pits	506	149	649	330	304	Sep	388	
Bardney Pits	290	350	450	350	490	Jan	386	
Thrapston Gravel Pits	417	(520)	370	276	324	Sep	381	
Willen Lake	569	280	392	295	367	Jun	381	
Emberton Gravel Pits	315	602	420	280	280	Feb	379	
Morecambe Bay	370	401	351	411	327	Dec	372	
Llyn Alaw	445	312	376	384	328	Jan	369	
Wynyard Lake	224	710	376	280	205	Oct	359	
Dee Flood Meadows	230	430	521	310	295	Oct	357	
Ranworth & Cockshoot Broads	125	290	565	230	[29] 504	Oct	343	▲
Derwent Reservoir	198	442	360	128	530	Jan	332	
Windermere	199	(464)	-	-	-		332	▲
Baston Langtoft Gravel Pits	349	320	450	380	152	Dec	330	
Thames Estuary	293	252	319	310	465	Dec	328	▲
Beaulieu Estuary	345	239	270	381	392	Dec	325	
Ardleigh Reservoir	184	312	226	271	610	Nov	321	▲
Middle Yare Marshes	247	481	83	340	442	Sep	319	▲
Revesby Reservoir	273	571	(385)	302	41	Jun	314	
Stodmarsh & Collards Lagoon	175	(190)	273	276	521	Sep	311	▲
Hardley Flood	-	-	-	-	307	Nov	307	▲
Huntingdon Racecourse Gravel Pits	-	-	-	-	300	Oct	300	▲

Sites with mean peak counts of 50 or more birds in Northern Ireland [†]	96–97	97–98	98–99	99–00	00–01	Mon	Mean
Loughs Neagh & Beg	448	510	296	71	785	Feb	422
Lough Foyle	88	383	[29] 190	1,282	0		389
Strangford Lough	351	379	489	367	166	Dec	350
Belfast Lough	86	86	122	112	242	Oct	130
Bann Estuary	60	-	-	-	-		60 ▲

Sites no longer meeting table qualifying levels

Medway Estuary
Linford Gravel Pits
St Benet's Levels
Temple Water

Other sites surpassing table qualifying levels in 2000–01

Traeth Lafan	903	Sep	Rostherne Mere	333	Aug
Southill Lake	520	Oct	Colemans Reservoir	320	Dec
Radwell Gravel Pits	454	Aug	Newport Pagnell Gravel Pits	318	Oct
Blatherwyke Lake	401	Sep	St Benet's Levels	312	Nov
Fen Drayton Gravel Pits	343	Jun	Nene Washes	305	Nov
Llyn Maelog	341	Dec	Wykeham Lakes	300	Sep
Breydon Wtr & Berney Marshes	335	Oct			

†   *as site designation does not occur and the 1% criterion is not applied, qualifying levels of 300 and 50 have been chosen to select sites in Great Britain and Northern Ireland, respectively, for presentation in this report*

BAR-HEADED GOOSE

Anser indicus

Escape
Native range: Southern Asia

Following increases in the previous two years, the 2000–01 summed site maxima fell to 75 birds, the same as the 1998–99 value. Birds were recorded at 49 sites and 15 of these held more than one bird, the most notable being eight at Stodmarsh, six at Stratfield Saye and four at Edington Lake.

SNOW GOOSE

Anser caerulescens

Escape and vagrant
Native range: N America

GB Max:	57	Dec
NI Max:	1	various

Numbers recorded were similar to the pervious year, with 35 sites producing a summed site maxima of 121 birds. Ten sites held three or more birds and double figure counts were as follows: 19 at Stratfield Saye, 18 at Eversley Cross & Yateley Gravel Pits and 13 at Blenheim Park Lake. The bird recorded in Northern Ireland at Belfast Lough in 1999–2000 was present throughout the winter in 2000–01.

ROSS'S GOOSE

Anser rossii

Escape and possible vagrant
Native range: Alaska and NE Siberia

Single birds were recorded at Drakelow Gravel Pits in October and again in January, on the Severn Estuary in November and at Barton Pits in December.

EMPEROR GOOSE

Anser canagicus

Escape
Native range: N America

Birds were recorded at seven sites with a maximum of five in January and February. All involved single birds except four at Morecambe Bay in September and three at Ramsbury Lake in December.

CANADA GOOSE
Branta canadensis

Naturalised introduction[†]
Native range: N America

GB Max:	54,557 Sep
NI Max:	310 Dec

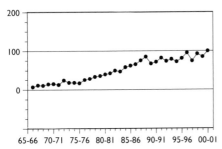

Figure 21. Annual indices for Canada Goose in GB

The index value and peak national total for Britain in 2000–01 were the highest yet recorded by WeBS. In contrast, the Northern Ireland peak was relatively low compared to those in recent years. Indices indicate that the species has increased by 24% over the last ten years and by an incredible five-fold over the last 30 years. Most key sites for the species are freshwater habitats in lowland England and Wales, many of which are man-made, e.g. reservoirs and gravel pit complexes, and increasing in number.

Numbers were higher than average at two-thirds of the sites regularly supporting at least 600 birds. There were notably large counts at the Dyfi Estuary (115% higher than the previous five-year peak mean), the Mersey Estuary (259%), Colliford Reservoir (91%) and the Cleddau Estuary (96%). The only particularly low count was at Blithfield Reservoir where the peak was 35% lower than average with 570 birds fewer than were recorded in the previous year. Peak counts were recorded during the late summer or early winter at most key sites.

It has been suggested that much of the population growth of Canada Geese in Britain and Northern Ireland might be occurring on new or small sites not usually surveyed by WeBS or that have not been surveyed for long enough to contribute to the national indices. To address this, a survey using a randomised stratified sampling technique was used to estimate the change in numbers more closely. The results of this 1999 survey indicated that there may be a minimum of 82,000 birds in southern England alone (Rehfisch *et al.* 2002).

	96–97	97–98	98–99	99–00	00–01	Mon	Mean	
Sites with mean peak counts of 600 or more birds in Great Britain [†]								
Rutland Water	1,266	1,395	1,374	1,255	1,539	Sep	1,366	
Dyfi Estuary	682	1,020	899	1,676	2,137	Sep	1,283	
Dee Estuary (Eng/Wal)	877	875	1,150	1,347	1,664	Dec	1,183	
Arun Valley	796	1,490	1,298	967	1,139	Nov	1,138	
Fairburn Ings	[29] 1,091	1,340	711	630	1,177	Jun	990	
Blithfield Reservoir	916	850	1,120	1,140	570	Aug	919	
Lower Derwent Valley	841	1,170	980	627	-		905	
Bewl Water	[29] (1,000)	548	592	1,200	1,078	Aug	884	
Middle Tame Valley Gravel Pits	[29] 539	(750)	(630)	1,173	889	Aug	867	
Abberton Reservoir	433	608	989	928	1,217	Aug	835	
Southampton Water	693	1,067	745	675	735	Nov	783	
Walthamstow Reservoirs	1,030	816	784	(500)	454	Jun	771	
King's Bromley Gravel Pits	726	641	804	814	850	Aug	767	
Mersey Estuary	550	442	680	308	1,738	Aug	744	▲
Cleddau Estuary	482	450	469	1,108	1,080	Dec	718	▲
Harewood Lake	620	560	670	943	750	Feb	709	
Chew Valley Lake	740	780	631	660	720	Jul	706	
Ellesmere Lakes	574	269	692	737	912	Sep	637	▲
Stour Estuary	492	608	795	785	485	Jan	633	
Croxall Pits	423	793	550	577	760	Sep	621	▲
Colliford Reservoir	445	492	460	759	946	Jul	620	▲
Kedleston Park Lake	360	650	650	800	607	Sep	613	
Tundry Pond	255	840	730	815	410	Nov	610	
Port Meadow	700	500	710	[29] 490	(450)	Dec	600	

	96–97	97–98	98–99	99–00	00–01	Mon	Mean
Sites with mean peak counts of 50 or more birds in Northern Ireland [†]							
Upper Lough Erne	451	170	96	222	-		235
Strangford Lough	257	[30] 204	161	153	310	Dec	217
Drumgay Lough	236	172	260	110	-		195

Important sites not counted in last five years
Woodford River

Sites no longer meeting table qualifying levels
Holme Pierrepont Gravel Pits

Other sites surpassing table qualifying levels in 2000–01

Exe Estuary	753	Nov
Netherfield Gravel Pits	(750)	Sep
Somerset Levels	704	Dec
Old Moor Wetlands	670	Dec
Cuckmere Estuary	669	Nov
Ouse Washes	654	Oct
Colne Valley Gravel Pits	(646)	Sep
Tring Reservoirs	626	Oct
Watermead Gravel Pits	615	Jun

†   as site designation does not occur and the 1% criterion is not applied, qualifying levels of 600 and 50 have been chosen to select sites in Great Britain and Northern Ireland, respectively, for presentation in this report

---

BARNACLE GOOSE
Branta leucopsis

GREENLAND POPULATION

International threshold:	**320**
Great Britain threshold:	**270**
All-Ireland threshold:	**75**

GB Max:	39,757 Nov			
NI Max:	0	**% young** 10.1	**brood size:**	**2.1**

Numbers on Islay, the most important site numerically, were lower than the total recorded in the previous winter, but were 2% higher than the five-year peak mean. Higher than average numbers were also recorded at North Uist and Tiree. In contrast, the peak counts for Coll, the Keills Peninsula & Isle of Danna and Colonsay/Oronsay were much lower than those recorded in recent winters.

Breeding success, as measured on Islay, was slightly above average for the last decade (Ogilvie 2001). The last really productive years were in 1989 (19.8%) and 1990 (23.7%).

The peak total for Britain was relatively high compared to those in previous winters and comprised counts from the co-ordinated census of main locations in Argyll plus that from South Walls, Orkney. These are the key accessible sites used by this population. The remainder of the population is dispersed across a large number of small Hebridean islands. These sites are counted periodically, generally once every five years, along with sites in the Republic of Ireland, as part of a complete international census.

	96–97	97–98	98–99	99–00	00–01	Mon	Mean
Sites of international importance in the UK							
Islay	[25] 35,013	[25] 32,812	[26] 35,172	[26] 35,429	[27] 35,332	Nov	34,752
North Uist	[9] 600	[21] 1,414	[21] 1,648	[21] 1,491	[21] 1,957	Feb	1,422
Tiree	[1] 1,479	[1] 1,158	[1] 1,572	[27] 1,123	[27] 1,442	Mar	1,355
Sound of Harris	[9] 1,351	-	-	-	-		1,351
South Walls	[18] 1,170	[18] 1,180	[18] 1,140	-	-		1,163
North Sutherland	[9] 792	-	-	-	-		792
Monach Isles	[9] 760	-	-	-	-		760
Coll	[1] 861	[1] 715	[27] 931	[27] 667	[27] 380	Nov	711
Keills Peninsular & Isle of Danna	[1] 341	[1] 469	[27] 720	[27] 610	[27] 280	Nov	484
Colonsay/Oronsay	[1] 429	[1] 436	[27] 463	[27] 600	[27] 244	Nov	434

SVALBARD POPULATION

International threshold: 120
Great Britain threshold: 120

GB Max: 24,047 Dec

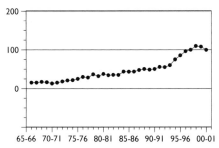

Figure 22. Annual indices for Svalbard Barnacle Geese in GB

% young 3.0   **brood size:** 1.4

Annual indices indicate that this population has more than doubled in size over the last ten years. The peak for 2000–01, however, was 7% lower than that recorded in the previous year. Productivity was notably low; a comparable figure has not been noted since 1992 and continues a trend of decreasing breeding success from 20.9% young recorded in 1995 (Griffin & Coath 2001). Brood size was also low, following a decreasing trend from a mean of 2.05 in 1995. Low breeding success in 2000–01 was attributed to poor grass growth and high predation from Arctic Foxes on the breeding grounds in Svalbard (Maarten Loonen pers. comm.).

The first birds arrived at Loch of Strathbeg, an autumn staging site, on 13 September, rising to a peak by the end of the month, before declining rapidly to just over 100 by the end of the first week in October. This is the only site away from the Solway Estuary that regularly supports internationally important numbers of these birds in Britain.

The first arrivals on the Solway Estuary were recorded on 23 September, three days later than in the previous year, with numbers rising to a peak in December. The distribution of birds in the area followed a similar pattern to that recorded in recent years with the majority of birds using the Caerlaverock, Mersehead, Southerness and Rockliffe/Burgh Marshes areas. One bird from the Greenland population was recorded in the Caerlaverock area in early March.

	96–97	97–98	98–99	99–00	00–01	Mon	Mean
Sites of international importance in the UK							
Solway Estuary	[33] 24,360	[33] 23,754	[33] 26,040	[33] 25,750	[33] 23,783	Dec	24,737
Loch of Strathbeg	(165)	353	[23] 6,200	[22] (513)	[29] 3,700	Sep	3,418

NATURALISED POPULATION

Naturalised establishment [†]

GB Max: 947 Dec
NI Max: 158 Oct

The numbers of naturalised Barnacle Geese in Britain and Northern Ireland have remained relatively stable over the last five winters with annual fluctuations being explained, in part, by infrequent coverage at some key sites. After another high count in 2000–01, Hornsea Mere returns to the top of the table of sites regularly supporting 50 or more birds. Of those sites with regularly counted flocks, higher than average numbers were recorded at the Duddon Estuary and Stratfield Saye.

There is, as always, some uncertainty about the origin of Barnacle Geese away from the sites known to support birds from the Svalbard and Greenland populations. Those birds recorded at sites along the east and northwest coasts of Britain are considered as naturalised in this report, but some may be wandering individuals from the migratory populations.

	96–97	97–98	98–99	99–00	00–01	Mon	Mean	
Sites with mean peak counts of 50 or more birds in Great Britain [†]								
Hornsea Mere	-	0	314	(326)	241	Dec	220	
Eversley Cross & Yateley GP	311	184	220	187	183	Nov	217	
Thwaite Flat & Roanhead Pond	-	-	-	-	[29] 152	Dec	152	▲
Duddon Estuary	0	1	150	155	150	Feb	91	
Stratfield Saye	141	142	1	28	120	Dec	86	
Hardley Flood	-	-	-	-	58	Oct	58	▲
Middle Yare Marshes	56	56	70	80	20	Dec	56	
Sites with mean peak counts of 50 or more birds in Northern Ireland								
Strangford Lough	129	148	122	136	158	Oct	139	
Sites no longer meeting table qualifying levels								
Severn Estuary								
Other sites surpassing table qualifying levels in 2000–01								
Dyfi Estuary	63	Jan						
Barcombe Mills Reservoir	60	Oct						
Severn Estuary	53	Feb						

[†] as site designation does not occur and the 1% criterion is not applied, a qualifying level of 50 has been chosen to select sites for presentation in this report

---

DARK-BELLIED BRENT GOOSE
Branta bernicla bernicla

International threshold:	3,000
Great Britain threshold:	1,000
All-Ireland threshold:	+[*]

GB Max:	92,600 Jan
NI Max:	1 Feb

[*] 50 is normally used as a minimum threshold

% young	0.6	brood size:	1.74

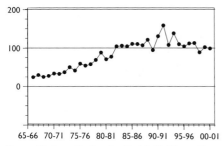

Figure 23. Annual indices for Dark-bellied Brent Goose in GB

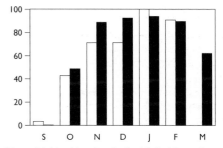

Figure 24. Monthly indices for Dark-bellied Brent Goose in GB (white bars 2000–01; black bars 1995–96 to 1999–2000)

The majority of Dark-bellied Brent Geese occur at a small number of well-watched estuarine sites in southern and eastern England and are, therefore, well surveyed by WeBS. The British peak count was 2% higher than that of the previous year yet remained much lower than the totals recorded in the early to mid 1990s. The annual index also showed little change. Although the annual index has increased by 228% over the last 30 years, it has declined by 16% over the last ten years. The number of birds wintering in Britain is affected by severity of winter temperatures and food availability on the continent, as well as productivity.

According to the three-year cycle of good, poor and variable breeding success (Dhondt 1987), breeding success was expected to be high in 2000. However, the cycle missed a year

in the mid 1990s as the peak years for lemming abundance occurred in 1991, 1994, 1996 and 1999. Therefore, as observations confirm, 2000 was year of poor breeding success, following high lemming abundance and breeding success in summer 1999 (Hearn 2001).

Nine sites regularly support numbers surpassing the threshold for international importance and the list remains unchanged from 1999–2000. Lower than average numbers were recorded at all but one site: the peak count at the Blackwater Estuary was 8% higher than the most recent five-year peak mean. Nevertheless, the continuing very low numbers on the Thames Estuary, less than half the totals in some recent winters, give some cause for concern. The list of nationally important sites also remained relatively unchanged. Lower than average numbers were, however, recorded at 59% of these sites.

The draft International Action Plan for this population of Brent Geese was discussed by the second Meeting of Parties to the African-Eurasian Waterbird Agreement in September 2001. The final draft of the plan will be finalised and sent to the Range States for consultation and endorsement. It will be formally adopted at the next Meeting of Parties in three years time. The Action Plan has been designed to engender flyway-scale collaboration to secure the future for this population.

	96–97	97–98	98–99	99–00	00–01	Mon	Mean
Sites of international importance in the UK							
The Wash	23,001	23,797	17,736	28,811	19,518	Feb	22,573
Thames Estuary	15,393	17,014	14,100	7,346	7,371	Oct	12,245
North Norfolk Coast	8,793	14,088	[22] 10,100	[22] 12,969	10,201	Jan	11,230
Blackwater Estuary	10,641	10,290	5,160	9,838	9,860	Jan	9,158
Chichester Harbour	8,997	8,427	8,142	9,267	7,412	Jan	8,449
Langstone Harbour	5,520	6,344	[30] 6,230	6,928	5,080	Dec	6,020
Hamford Water	9,286	4,194	2,320	3,879	4,047	Feb	4,745
Crouch-Roach Estuary	5,292	5,644	2,452	5,488	4,446	Jan	4,664
Colne Estuary	3,493	4,263	(2,685)	(3,614)	3,310	Jan	3,689
Sites of national importance in Great Britain							
Fleet/Wey	3,529	3,048	2,290	1,404	1,813	Oct	2,417
Portsmouth Harbour	2,785	[30] 2,505	2,169	2,661	1,827	Jan	2,389
Deben Estuary	3,306	2,094	1,268	2,139	2,890	Feb	2,339
North West Solent	2,279	(2,810)	2,659	2,114	1,616	Jan	2,296
Swale Estuary	3,141	1,803	2,215	1,800	2,149	Oct	2,222
Dengie Flats	2,000	2,290	2,600	1,550	2,455	Feb	2,179
Medway Estuary	2,526	2,725	2,580	1,845	1,041	Jan	2,143
Humber Estuary	(2,366)	1,532	2,540	2,404	1,649	Feb	2,098
Pagham Harbour	2,879	1,071	1,260	[30] 2,438	2,520	Jan	2,034
Stour Estuary	1,757	2,173	2,367	1,769	[30] 1,716	Nov	1,956
Southampton Water	1,821	2,160	[30] 1,533	[30] 2,480	[30] 1,742	Dec	1,947
Beaulieu Estuary	2,480	2,283	1,682	1,458	1,334	Jan	1,847
Exe Estuary	1,832	1,768	1,647	1,806	1,345	Oct	1,680
Newtown Estuary	1,676	1,472	1,180	(1,727)	1,800	Jan	1,571
Poole Harbour	1,644	1,449	1,297	1,354	1,708	Dec	1,490
Orwell Estuary	[30] 1,000	[30] 878	[30] 1,129	[30] 1,799	[30] 1,228	Dec	1,207
Burry Inlet	1,014	1,165	1,043	1,195	1,158	Nov	1,115
Other sites surpassing table qualifying levels in 2000–01							
Thanet Coast	1,020	Dec					
Jersey Shore	1,002	Jan					

BLACK BRANT

Branta bernicla nigricans

Vagrant

Native range: N America and E Asia

Two were present on the Deben Estuary in February and singles were recorded on the North Norfolk Coast in October and January, in Chichester Harbour in January and February, and on the Crouch-Roach Estuary in January and February.

LIGHT-BELLIED BRENT GOOSE
Branta bernicla hrota

EAST CANADIAN HIGH ARCTIC POPULATION

International threshold:	**200**
Great Britain threshold:	**+***[*†]
All-Ireland threshold:	**200**

GB Max: 178 Jan
NI Max: 18,591 Nov

[*] 50 is normally used as a minimum threshold

% young 30 **brood size:** 3.4

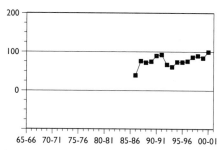

Figure 25. Annual indices for Light-bellied Brent Goose in NI

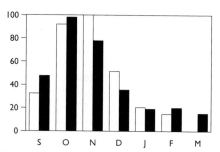

Figure 26. Monthly indices for Light-bellied Brent Goose in NI (white bars 2000–01; black bars 1995–96 to 1999–2000)

The fifth all-Ireland census recorded 20,225 individuals in October 2000. This was the highest total since the census began in 1994–95. Just over 74% were at Strangford Lough, where the 2000–01 peak was particularly impressive, and 16% at Lough Foyle, both key staging areas during the autumn. The census total follows an increasing upward trend of around 5% per annum since 1997–98. This can partly be attributed to high productivity during this period.

As usual, monthly indices indicate that numbers peaked in the province during October and November 2000. Away from Northern Ireland, small flocks were recorded staging at Loch Gruinart and South Ford in western Scotland and later in the winter at the Dee Estuary (Eng/Wal) and traditional wintering sites on Jersey, while the count at Inland Sea was also notably higher than average, so that four sites in Great Britain now regularly support in excess of 25 birds.

	96–97	97–98	98–99	99–00	00–01	Mon	Mean	
Sites of international importance in the UK								
Strangford Lough	11,614	11,184	13,196	13,376	16,162	Nov	13,106	
Lough Foyle	4,757	3,820	2,766	1,934	3,469	Oct	3,349	
Carlingford Lough	242	317	642	437	498	Dec	427	
Killough Harbour	254	-	[16] 557	-	-		406	
Larne Lough	177	232	218	253	266	Jan	229	
Sites with mean peak counts of 25 or more birds in Great Britain [†]								
Inland Sea	63	17	23	51	95	Dec	50	
Loch Gruinart	[29] 16	0	107	46	60	Sep	46	▲
Jersey Shore	13	29	14	0	86	Dec	28	▲

Sites no longer meeting table qualifying levels
Outer Ards

Other sites surpassing table qualifying levels in 2000–01

Belfast Lough	[30] 40	Feb	
Dee Estuary (Eng/Wal)	(39)	Jan	
South Ford	30	Sep	

†   as no British threshold has been set, a qualifying level of 25 has been chosen to select sites for presentation in this report

SVALBARD POPULATION

International threshold: **50**
Great Britain threshold: **25***

GB Max: 3,196
NI Max: 0

* 50 is normally used as a minimum threshold

% young 13 **brood size:**

Lindisfarne is the most important site in Great Britain for the Svalbard population of Light-bellied Brent Geese. Smaller numbers often occur along the Northumberland coast between Seahouses and Budle Point but were not recorded by WeBS in 2000–01. The international population estimate of 6,600 was the highest recorded since the 1950s (P. Clausen, M.J.H. Denny & S.M. Percival pers. comm.). The peak number recorded at Lindisfarne in 2000–01 was slightly higher than average and represented 48% of the population estimate, a marked increase over recent winters and the highest since the cold weather influx from the other key wintering area in Denmark in January 1997. Reproductive success was about average, yet higher than in the previous two years.

	96–97	97–98	98–99	99–00	00–01	Mon	Mean
Sites of international importance in the UK							
Lindisfarne	4,092	2,567	2,812	1,767	3,184	Nov	2,884
Sites of national importance in Great Britain							
Seahouses to Budle Point	107	0	(22)	0	0		27

RED-BREASTED GOOSE
Branta ruficollis

Vagrant and escape
Native range: SE Europe and Asia

Single birds, possibly of wild origin, were at Loch of Strathbeg in November and Loch Leven in January. It is possible these records relate to the same individual. Birds considered to be escapes were also recorded at Lee Valley Gravel Pits, Bolton-on-Swale Gravel Pits and Harewood Lake.

EGYPTIAN GOOSE
Alopochen aegyptiacus

Naturalised introduction†
Native range: Africa

GB Max: 329 Sep
NI Max: 0

The Great Britain peak, although some 20% down on the record 1999-2000 figure, was around average for recent years. The September peak, and similarly high counts in August, were typical of this species whose numbers, unusually amongst wildfowl, peak in late summer and decline during the winter months. To date the species is yet to be recorded by WeBS in Northern Ireland.

Although national totals were not exceptional, the August count on the North Norfolk Coast represents the highest count from an individual WeBS site to date. Numbers at Rutland Water, the only site regularly holding significant numbers outside East Anglia, continued to rise.

	96–97	97–98	98–99	99–00	00–01	Mon	Mean	
Sites with mean peak counts of 10 or more birds in Great Britain †								
North Norfolk Coast	113	198	170	197	218	Aug	179	
St Benet's Levels	85	56	66	0	51	Oct	52	
Rutland Water	35	46	40	52	54	Oct	45	
Watermill Broad	-	8	26	92	(23)	Aug	42	▲
Lynford Gravel Pit	0	76	52	32	(33)	Jun	40	
Middle Yare Marshes	4	52	16	44	45	Sep	32	
Trinity Broads	-	13	15	58	17	Jun	26	
Nunnery Lakes	11	19	26	21	(22)	Jun	20	
Snetterton Gravel Pits	-	-	2	29	(24)	Sep	18	

	96–97	97–98	98–99	99–00	00–01	Mon	Mean
Stanford Training Area	8	15	16	[29] 30	7	Jan	15
Didlington Lakes	4	41	6	6	17	Sep	15
Livermere	13	14	15	9	-		13

Sites not counted in last five years
Blickling Lake
Gunton Park Lake
Pentney Gravel Pits
R. Wensum: Fakenham to Great Ryburgh
Sennowe Park Lakes

Other sites surpassing table qualifying levels in 2000–01

Spade Oak Gravel Pit	18	Nov
Barton Broad	13	Oct
Ranworth & Cockshoot Broads	[29] 12	Oct

†   *as site designation does not occur and the 1% criterion is not applied, a qualifying level of 10 has been chosen to select sites for presentation in this report*

RUDDY SHELDUCK
Tadorna ferruginea

Escape and possible vagrant
Native range: Asia, N Africa & S Europe

GB Max: 10 Aug
NI Max: 0

The summed site maxima for the 25 sites at which the species was found in 2000–01 was 31, compared with 34, 26 and 40 in the preceding three years.

All sites held single birds with the exception of three at Chew Valley Lake in August and on the North Norfolk Coast in February and two at Clennon Valley, Mersey Estuary and on the River Cam.

CAPE SHELDUCK
Tadorna cana

Escape
Native range: S Africa

One was present at Alveston Lake from October through to January.

AUSTRALIAN SHELDUCK
Tadorna tadornoides

Escape
Native range: Southern Asia

A single was at Benacre Broad in September.

SHELDUCK
Tadorna tadorna

International threshold: **3,000**
Great Britain threshold: **750**
All-Ireland threshold: **70**

GB Max: 60,692 Jan
NI Max: 4,353 Jan

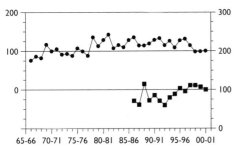

Figure 27. Annual indices for Shelduck in GB (circles, left axis) and NI (squares, right axis)

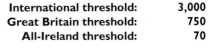
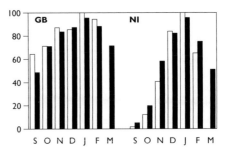

Figure 28. Monthly indices for Shelduck in GB and NI (white bars 2000–01; black bars 1995–96 to 1999–2000)

Following successive falls in the previous three winters, numbers in Great Britain peaked slightly above the 1999-2000 figure. Counts throughout the midwinter months still, however, remain well below those recorded throughout most of the 1990s when totals exceeding 70,000 were not uncommon in two or three different months in a single winter. The annual index value remained almost unchanged from the previous year. Monthly indices largely followed the trend for recent years, although early autumn values were above average.

In Northern Ireland, numbers have fared considerably better over the last decade, rising steadily in the early 1990s and stabilising in the latter half of the decade. The peak count in 2000-01 was the lowest since winter 1995–96, though annual indices, down by 7%, still remain

similar to those of recent years and well above former levels.

Continued high counts of moulting birds on the Mersey Estuary saw the Wash eclipsed as the premier Shelduck site in the UK for the first time since comparative tables were produced in WeBS reports. The steady decline in numbers at the Wash in recent years was, at least temporarily, halted, although the peak count was still amongst the lowest at the site in the last thirty years (15–20,000 was a more normal count in the 1980s and early 1990s). At other sites, notably large counts were recorded on the Dee Estuary (Eng/Wal), Humber and Solway Estuaries and Lindisfarne whilst counts on the Forth Estuary, Medway Estuary and Poole Harbour were well below average. At the last site numbers have fallen by over 60% in the last 5 years.

	96–97	97–98	98–99	99–00	00–01	Mon	Mean
Sites of international importance in the UK							
Mersey Estuary	7,025	14,516	10,600	15,070	10,084	Jul	11,459
The Wash	10,352	12,368	11,430	7,608	10,074	Jan	10,366
Dee Estuary (Eng/Wal)	8,047	10,418	5,634	8,814	11,563	Oct	8,895
Morecambe Bay	5,632	8,426	8,030	6,225	(6,707)	Oct	7,078
Humber Estuary	(3,900)	(4,843)	5,262	4,020	6,918	Aug	5,400
Forth Estuary	5,065	5,507	4,684	3,775	3,009	Sep	4,408
Solway Estuary	3,450	3,370	4,049	30 3,270	4,606	Nov	3,749
Medway Estuary	30 5,618	4,160	1,951	2,629	1,920	Jan	3,256
Ribble Estuary	3,788	4,106	2,644	2,908	2,536	Sep	3,196
Strangford Lough	30 3,493	30 4,142	3,574	3,193	2,634	Jan	3,407
Severn Estuary	4,117	2,371	30 3,730	2,281	2,912	Feb	3,082
Blackwater Estuary	4,129	2,123	(1,777)	3,093	2,873	Jan	3,055
Sites of national importance in Great Britain							
Swale Estuary	2,760	3,027	3,015	2,929	2,013	Jan	2,749
Poole Harbour	4,650	2,662	2,318	2,192	1,748	Feb	2,714 ▼
Thames Estuary	3,094	2,089	2,363	2,387	2,537	Feb	2,494
Hamford Water	3,006	2,781	1,791	1,369	2,003	Feb	2,190

	96–97	97–98	98–99	99–00	00–01	Mon	Mean
Stour Estuary	[30] 2,247	(2,029)	1,956	[30] 2,351	[30] 2,164	Jan	2,180
Alde Complex	765	1,935	2,129	1,707	1,328	Jan	1,573
North Norfolk Coast	1,335	[30] 1,876	1,310	955	938	Jan	1,283
Burry Inlet	1,282	883	1,327	1,557	1,233	Jan	1,256
Lindisfarne	1,295	927	973	1,224	1,751	Dec	1,234
Chichester Harbour	[30] 1,800	[30] 1,063	[30] 836	1,040	990	Jan	1,146
Colne Estuary	1,338	977	799	963	773	Jan	970
Montrose Basin	596	[30] 1,174	973	1,071	907	Jan	944
Eden Estuary	(942)	1,088	(717)	768	680	Oct	870
Deben Estuary	824	875	895	952	772	Feb	864
Cleddau Estuary	1,023	939	921	696	655	Feb	847
Orwell Estuary	1,039	[30] 939	[30] 645	846	681	Feb	830
Duddon Estuary	853	900	821	814	554	Nov	788
Tees Estuary	893	837	755	784	556	Jan	765
Sites of all-Ireland importance in Northern Ireland							
Larne Lough	440	505	711	414	710	Jan	556
Lough Foyle	527	439	446	419	278	Jan	422
Belfast Lough	[30] 775	497	[30] 184	250	[30] 319	Feb	405
Carlingford Lough	165	198	213	321	326	Feb	245
Loughs Neagh & Beg	188	240	211	157	74	Feb	174
Dundrum Bay	[30] 131	64	98	104	79	Mar	95

Sites no longer meeting table qualifying levels
Crouch-Roach Estuary
Langstone Harbour

MUSCOVY DUCK
Cairina moschata

Escape
Native range: S America

GB Max:	**91 Oct**
NI Max:	**0**

The peak national total rose this year following low figures in the previous two years, although it is some way off the peaks recorded in the mid/late 1990s (e.g. 127 in 1997–1998 and 137 in 1996–1997). However, the 41 sites where this species was seen was the highest ever recorded by WeBS.

Sites with more than five birds in 2000–01
Buxton Pavilion Gardens	25	Mar
Derwent Water	21	Jan/Dec
Fort Henry Ponds & Exton Pk Lake	15	Oct
R. Devon: Kersiepow Ponds	13	Nov
Nafferton Mere	12	Nov
Dart Estuary	11	Feb
R. Devon: Kersiepow Ponds	7	Oct
Blair Drummond Safari Park Loch	6	Oct

WOOD DUCK
Aix sponsa

Escape
Native range: N America

GB Max:	**10 Oct**
NI Max:	**0**

Birds were recorded at 14 sites with a peak national total of ten birds. Apart from five at Wellington Gravel Pits, four at Middle Tame Gravel Pits and two at Middle Pool, Eglwys Nunydd and the Stour Estuary, all other sites held single birds.

MANDARIN
Aix galericulata

Naturalised introduction[†]
Native range: Eastern Asia

GB Max: 491 Dec
NI Max: 4 Apr

A combination of welcomed improvements in coverage and high counts at many regular sites produced record totals in Great Britain. The previous high (315 in November 1997) was eclipsed in all months from September to February. In Northern Ireland, Dundrum Bay remains the only site to regularly record birds. The species' secretive nature and localised movements to sites not covered by WeBS can cause considerable fluctuations from year to year. In a winter with excellent coverage of key WeBS sites, more than half held above average numbers, most notable being those at Busbridge Lakes and Darwell Reservoir. Others, including Osterley Park Lakes and Panshanger Flash supported relatively few birds. Wraysbury Pond, counted for the first time for WeBS, was a prominent addition to the table.

	96–97	97–98	98–99	99–00	00–01	Mon	Mean	
Sites with mean peak counts of 10 or more birds in Great Britain [†]								
Forest of Dean Ponds	-	[20] 146	[20] 221	[20] 195	-		187	
Wraysbury Pond	-	-	-	-	83	Feb	83	▲
Cuttmil Ponds	106	44	41	65	104	Dec	72	
Severn Estuary	113	40	102	32	72	Sep	72	
Stockgrove Country Park	-	-	34	66	80	Jan	60	
Passfield Lake	48	15	66	(10)	61	Jan	48	
Arun Valley	48	59	45	46	31	several	46	
Bough Beech Reservoir	-	-	-	(2)	[29] 40	Sep	40	▲
Connaught Water	28	39	51	27	54	Nov	40	
Dee Flood Meadows	34	[29] 38	38	36	31	Dec	35	
Bradley Pools	-	-	-	26	43	Jan	35	
Lost/G'ding Hill/B'dwins Hill Ponds	-	-	-	6	45	Dec	26	▲
Overstone Park Lakes	18	32	-	-	-		25	
Osterley Park Lakes	24	27	20	41	8	Jun/Sep	24	
Panshanger Flash	51	-	22	6	8	Sep	22	
Bramshill Park Lake	7	60	5	19	14	Sep	21	
Busbridge Lakes	0	22	0	-	57	Feb	20	▲
Fonthill Lake	18	(12)	5	23	23	Feb	17	
Woburn Park Lakes	16	9	13	18	25	Oct	16	
Headley Mill Pond	4	16	12	18	16	Feb	13	
Darwell Reservoir	1	4	4	6	46	Oct	12	▲
Norbury Pond	-	-	-	20	2	Nov/Mar	11	

Important sites not counted in last five years
Frenchess Road Pond
Hammer Wood Pond
Paultons Bird Park
Virginia Water

Sites no longer meeting table qualifying levels
Epsom Common Ponds
Thursley Lake

Other sites surpassing table qualifying levels in 2000–01

Gatton Park	15	Nov
Radnor Mere	13	Nov/Jan
Harewood Lake	10	Sep
Echna Loch	10	Nov

† as site designation does not occur and the 1% criterion is not applied, a qualifying level of 10 has been chosen to select sites for presentation in this report

WIGEON
Anas penelope

International threshold:		12,500
Great Britain threshold:		2,800
All-Ireland threshold:		1,250

GB Max: 382,015 Jan
NI Max: 11,747 Oct

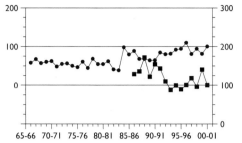

Figure 29. Annual indices for Wigeon in GB (circles, left axis) and NI (squares, right axis)

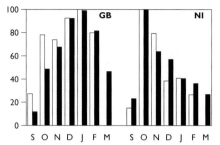

Figure 30. Monthly indices for Wigeon in GB and NI (white bars 2000–01; black bars 1995–96 to 1999–2000)

Numbers in Great Britain were the second highest recorded by WeBS, surpassed only by a count of over 400,000 in 1996–97. This was all the more noteworthy given the relatively low counts on the Ribble Estuary, a site which has, on occasion, held over a quarter of the national total. The annual index rose accordingly whilst monthly indices showed a larger than average proportion of birds were present in the autumn months. In Northern Ireland, the peak count was around average for recent winters, the annual index returning to a level near similar to those of the last nine years

Whilst the number of key sites supporting above average numbers was not exceptional, several recorded counts that were particularly noteworthy. The Somerset Levels held record numbers for the site, whilst sustained high counts at Breydon Water & Berney Marshes for a further year will see the site added to the list of those supporting internationally important numbers following a steady increase in recent winters. A large count at Lindisfarne in September was unusual for recent years, although numbers there exceeded 20,000 on several occasions in the 1980s. Both Cromarty and Dornoch Firths held above average numbers, whilst a count of over 9,000 birds on Loch of Harray was exceptional for recent years. Numbers at the Blackwater Estuary, a site which qualified as nationally important only the previous year, continued to rise whilst a count of almost 5,000 birds was sufficient to see the River Avon: Ringwood to Christchurch become the only addition to the table in 2000-01.

	96–97	97–98	98–99	99–00	00–01	Mon	Mean
Sites of international importance in the UK							
Ribble Estuary	74,068	66,197	96,855	50,678	63,921	Oct	70,344
Ouse Washes	[29] 31,980	26,922	[29] 16,999	24,540	[29] 14,874	Jan	23,063
Swale Estuary	40,090	13,292	13,837	11,725	17,637	Jan	19,316
Somerset Levels	11,000	16,010	14,523	[29] (21,965)	28,366	Dec	18,373
North Norfolk Coast	14,247	12,423	16,398	18,950	20,083	Nov	16,420
Dornoch Firth	11,615	17,240	13,282	9,305	17,445	Oct	13,777
Sites of national importance in Great Britain							
Breydon Wtr & Berney Marshes	6,500	10,200	11,200	14,130	15,700	Dec	11,546
Cromarty Firth	8,516	11,199	9,338	[30] 14,956	14,027	Oct	11,607
Nene Washes	8,090	12,699	13,533	6,994	10,808	Feb	10,425
Mersey Estuary	[30] 12,133	10,520	12,013	[30] 8,731	8,279	Jan	10,335
Lower Derwent Valley	10,600	7,900	8,100	8,600	-		8,800
Inner Moray Firth	10,097	7,964	8,208	9,746	7,260	Oct	8,655
Alde Complex	8,181	6,810	7,247	6,676	7,145	Jan	7,212
Lindisfarne	4,368	5,600	4,612	5,006	14,141	Sep	6,745
Morecambe Bay	6,432	6,002	4,783	5,289	7,746	Dec	6,050
Severn Estuary	11,548	5,304	4,011	3,559	5,789	Jan	6,042
Middle Yare Marshes	7,189	6,306	5,460	5,387	4,794	Dec	5,827

	96–97	97–98	98–99	99–00	00–01	Mon	Mean
Loch of Harray	2,384	5,070	5,263	5,092	9,476	Jan	5,457
Humber Estuary	(5,803)	7,668	4,439	3,315	3,969	Oct	5,039
Arun Valley	4,411	5,155	4,421	4,173	5,343	Dec	4,701
Unspecified SE England site	8,600	5,400	3,900	3,200	1,200	Jan	4,460
Rutland Water	4,968	4,669	3,611	3,630	3,484	Jan	4,072
Dee Estuary (Eng/Wal)	3,682	5,366	3,302	2,751	4,681	Feb	3,956
Blackwater Estuary	2,534	3,031	3,401	4,296	6,507	Feb	3,954
Hamford Water	9,511	2,668	2,825	1,959	2,543	Jan	3,901
Martin Mere	2,460	3,620	6,000	5,430	750	Mar	3,652
Thames Estuary	5,146	1,260	3,407	2,951	5,116	Jan	3,576
Cleddau Estuary	3,351	3,058	4,009	3,532	3,604	Nov	3,511
Montrose Basin	2,735	3,170	3,503	4,402	3,446	Oct	3,451
Exe Estuary	3,184	4,344	4,231	3,143	2,031	Oct	3,387
Stour Estuary	[30] 3,847	3,628	2,277	[30] 2,518	[30] 4,218	Jan	3,298
Southampton Water	3,233	2,791	2,830	3,924	3,351	Jan	3,226
Dyfi Estuary	4,681	2,911	2,489	2,900	2,451	Oct	3,086
Burry Inlet	4,436	3,144	2,514	2,821	2,492	Nov	3,081
Foryd Bay	2,330	1,980	4,140	3,350	3,170	Oct	2,994
Fleet/Wey	3,021	2,637	4,262	1,889	3,062	Oct	2,974
R. Avon: R'wood to Christchurch	1,570	3,000	2,138	3,051	[29] 4,945	Jan	2,941 ▲
Medway Estuary	2,951	3,736	4,592	1,751	1,424	Dec	2,891

Sites of all-Ireland importance in Northern Ireland

	96–97	97–98	98–99	99–00	00–01	Mon	Mean
Lough Foyle	6,850	9,440	8,829	11,496	8,051	Oct	8,933
Loughs Neagh & Beg	2,398	3,052	2,333	5,743	2,375	Dec	3,180
Strangford Lough	1,900	1,937	2,153	2,469	2,509	Nov	2,194

Sites no longer meeting table qualifying levels
Dungeness Gravel Pits

Other sites surpassing table qualifying levels in 2000–01
Fen Drayton Gravel Pits   3,314   Dec

AMERICAN WIGEON
Anas americana

Vagrant
Native range: N & Central America

Apart from the long staying bird, considered to be an escape, at Dorchester Gravel Pits and singles at Foryd Bay in September and October and at Cors Caron in January, all other records were from Scotland.

On Shetland peaks of three, two and two were recorded at Loch of Gards, Loch of Hilwell,

and Loch of Spiggie, respectively. These may relate to the same individuals but ten birds were present at Loch of Hilwell in October (Nightingale & McGeehan 2000). Singles were also recorded along the Moray Coast, at Loch Bee, Loch Spynie and the Lossie Estuary.

CHILOE WIGEON
Anas sibilatrix

Escape
Native range: S America

Two were at Chew Valley Lake in July and singles were seen at the Cotswold Water Park, Radley Gravel Pits and on the Ouse Washes.

GADWALL
Anas strepera

International threshold: **300**
Great Britain threshold: **80**
All-Ireland threshold: **+*†**

* 50 is normally used as a minimum threshold

GB Max: 13,562 Jan
NI Max: 217 Oct

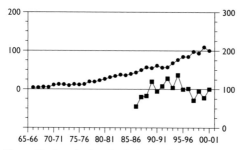

Figure 31. Annual indices for Gadwall in GB (circles, left axis) and NI (squares, right axis)

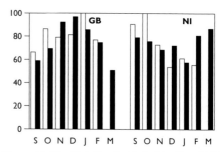

Figure 32. Monthly indices for Gadwall in GB and NI (white bars 2000–01; black bars 1995–96 to 1999–2000)

For the first time in many years the peak number of Gadwall in Great Britain failed to rise to record levels; indeed, it was some 12% lower than the previous winter. As in 1999–2000, the peak occurred in January, slightly later than usual, and monthly indices suggest lower than average numbers in November and December following a peak earlier in the autumn.

The number of birds in Northern Ireland is prone to considerable fluctuations between years, and typically dip in the midwinter period. The peak counts in 2000–01 occurred early, falling markedly by midwinter.

More sites qualify as nationally or internationally important for Gadwall than for any other species of waterbird, partly a consequence of international and national population estimates no longer reflecting the true population status. Relatively few sites hold very large congregations of birds, and numbers at each site may fluctuate considerably between years. Counts on the River Avon: Fordingbridge to Ringwood (inc. Blashford Lakes), Abberton Reservoir, Brent Reservoir and Lower Windrush Valley Gravel Pits were well above normal.

	96–97	97–98	98–99	99–00	00–01	Mon	Mean	
Sites of international importance in the UK								
Rutland Water	733	2,181	961	1,529	967	Sep	1,274	
Wraysbury Gravel Pits	528	734	1,397	612	713	Oct	797	
Ouse Washes	942	[29] 1,250	[29] 337	[29] 808	393	Oct	746	
R. Avon: Fordingbridge to R'wood[29]	516	580	611	612	[29] 897	Jan	643	
Lee Valley Gravel Pits	576	609	448	764	526	Sep	585	
Thrapston Gravel Pits	(895)	(567)	195	668	531	Jan	572	
Somerset Levels	342	[29] 433	[4] 819	527	453	Jan	515	
Abberton Reservoir	338	120	(460)	549	746	Aug	443	
Loch Leven	235	248	526	544	270	Sep	365	
Hornsea Mere	-	(17)	(315)	(380)	265	Jul	323	
Fen Drayton Gravel Pits	251	388	393	186	345	Jan	313	▲
Thames Estuary	190	198	387	439	346	Feb	312	▲
Sites of national importance in Great Britain								
Pitsford Reservoir	362	355	(169)	204	259	Sep	295	▲
Colne Valley Gravel Pits	434	150	270	155	412	Jan	284	
Lower Derwent Valley	271	283	317	255	-		282	
Eversley Cross & Yateley GP	376	236	183	248	323	Jan	273	
Severn Estuary	281	250	208	294	298	Feb	266	
Fairburn Ings	202	191	358	342	220	Sep	263	
Hoveton Great Broad	-	-	-	230	283	Dec	257	
Buckden/Stirtloe Pits	163	277	277	257	284	Oct	252	
North Norfolk Coast	163	232	258	294	250	Aug	239	
Chichester Gravel Pits	284	188	69	(289)	307	Jan	227	

	96–97	97–98	98–99	99–00	00–01	Mon	Mean	
Chew Valley Lake	175	200	305	145	310	Aug	227	
Stodmarsh & Collards Lagoon	274	122	240	276	222	Dec	227	
Cotswold Water Park (West)	217	147	272	282	194	Jan	222	
Little Paxton Gravel Pits	287	132	193	132	360	Jan	221	
Earls Barton Gravel Pits	121	264	266	279	159	Sep	218	
Minsmere	240	130	92	(0)	[29] 366	Feb	207	
Burghfield Gravel Pits	209	178	236	175	-		200	
Hampton & Kempton Reservoirs	153	198	250	273	113	Sep	197	
Sutton & Lound Gravel Pits	96	150	-	274	-		173	
Hickling Broad	-	-	82	198	229	Feb	170	
Crome's Broad	-	-	-	-	168	Dec	168	▲
Horsey Mere	-	15	(20)	316	-		166	▲
Dinton Pastures	191	64	193	204			163	
Hanningfield Reservoir	156	216	105	159	159	Aug	159	
Thorpe Water Park	96	102	178	249	157	Jan	156	
Brent Reservoir	54	121	115	180	306	Oct	155	
Breydon Wtr & Berney Marshes	129	161	258	109	117	Feb	155	
Alton Water	80	312	108	168	92	Dec	152	
Ditchford Gravel Pits	115	118	184	230	104	Jan	150	
Whitlingham Country Park	-	(9)	115	187	145	Jan	149	
North Warren & Thorpness Mere	141	200	[29] 123	[29] 131	-		149	
Grafham Water	82	223	192	153	76	Nov	145	
Reedham Water	-	-	-	-	141	Jan	141	▲
Meadow Lane Gravel Pits	157	111	178	59	195	Dec	140	
Twyford Gravel Pits	156	89	134	166	-		136	
Sonning Gravel Pit	127	143	132	137	106	Feb	129	
Dungeness Gravel Pits	76	85	169	174	140	Nov	129	
Middle Tame Valley Gravel Pits	(196)	108	99	127	113	Oct	129	
Orwell Estuary	[30] 147	59	120	[30] 165	150	Sep	128	
Swale Estuary	52	106	251	94	119	Feb	124	
Woolston Eyes	87	79	92	147	211	Nov	123	
Blagdon Lake	164	53	46	175	178	Jul	123	
Tophill Low Reservoirs	40	190	86	[29] (141)	158	Nov	123	
Blunham Gravel Pit	-	-	(15)	111	118	Dec	115	
Bewl Water	[29] 121	72	122	150	100	Oct	113	
Belvide Reservoir	43	(79)	202	86	116	Aug	112	
Hollowell Reservoir	45	12	124	330	39	Sep	110	
Leybourne/New Hythe Gravel Pits	-	-	-	-	110	Jan	110	▲
Swanholme Lakes	105	99	135	126	83	Feb	110	
Lower Windrush Valley GP	82	130	74	55	(188)	Jan	106	
Crichel Lake	(47)	100	91	149	82	Jan	106	
Fort Henry Ponds & Exton Pk Lake	179	85	119	82	60	Oct	105	
Seaton Gravel Pits	201	109	80	[29] 58	74	Feb	104	
Allington Gravel Pit	(40)	-	74	152	86	Nov	104	
Holme Pierrepont Gravel Pits	152	110	140	72	40	Oct	103	
Longside Lake	5	123	178	-	-		102	
Kirby-on-Bain Gravel Pits	(18)	48	123	54	179	Jan	101	▲
Clifford Hill Gravel Pits	115	69	52	201	65	Dec	100	
Stanford Reservoir	(267)	(100)	94	4	33	Oct	100	
Eyebrook Reservoir	56	29	211	-	101	Sep	99	▲
Bainton Pits	71	48	232	96	47	Jan	99	
Nene Washes	63	151	100	138	42	Nov	99	
Langtoft West End Gravel Pits	166	87	66	74	101	Dec	99	
Middle Yare Marshes	85	129	37	143	(77)	Feb	99	
Rye Harbour & Pett Level	113	69	108	73	127	Oct	98	
Unspecified SE England site	27	111	125	110	103	Jan	95	
Tring Reservoirs	79	146	77	68	102	Dec	94	
Blatherwyke Lake	21	15	22	236	174	Sep	94	▲
Thompson Water	-	30	223	26	-		93	▲
Swithland Reservoir	66	61	161	59	117	Nov	93	

	96–97	97–98	98–99	99–00	00–01	Mon	Mean
Cotswold Water Park (East)	[29] 129	92	63	(41)	87	Dec	93
Wellington Country Park	154	152	26	34	(25)	Nov	92
Swillington Ings	113	52	116	111	53	Aug	89
Otmoor	-	-	-	-	[29] 87	Feb	87 ▲
North West Solent	63	(26)	133	95	55	Jan	87
The Wash	53	100	135	36	105	Jan	86
Marsh Lane Gravel Pits	100	55	130	54	-		85

Sites with mean peak counts of 10 or more birds in Northern Ireland [†]

	96–97	97–98	98–99	99–00	00–01	Mon	Mean
Loughs Neagh & Beg	124	108	182	138	155	Oct	141
Strangford Lough	118	63	83	62	72	Sep	80
Upper Quoile River	58	4	0	6	2	Feb	14
Hillsborough Lakes	4	3	0	53	3	Jan	13

Important sites not counted in last five years

Deeping St James Gravel Pits
Lackford Gravel Pits
Shrigley Lakes
Clea Lakes
South Iver Gravel Pits
Sennowe Park Lakes
Gunton Park Lake

Sites no longer meeting table qualifying levels

Broomfleet Brick Ponds
Stanford Training Area
Dingle Marshes & Walberswick NNR
Barons Haugh
Fleet/Wey
Roseherne Mere
Linford Gravel Pits

Other sites surpassing table qualifying levels in 2000–01

Potteric Carr Nature Reserve	(96)	Oct	Old Moor Wetlands	111	Sep
Godmanchester Gravel Pit	105	Jan	Ixworth Thorpe	89	Dec
Pen Ponds	86	Dec	Leventhorpe Flood Meadows	86	Sep
Arun Valley	98	Feb	R. Cam: Kingfishers Bridge	106	Feb
Welbeck Estate	106	Oct	North Cave Gravel Pits	106	Jan
Frampton Pools	120	Jan	Lowther Lake	87	Jan
Harrold-Odell Country Park	91	Jan	Colne Estuary	145	Feb
Didlington Lakes	108	Nov	Walthamstow Reservoirs	82	Nov
London Wetland Centre	144	Feb	R. Avon: Salisbury to F'bridge	82	Feb
Alde Complex	106	Jan			

[†]   as no all-Ireland threshold has been set, a qualifying level of 10 has been chosen to select sites for presentation in this report

TEAL
Anas crecca

International threshold: **4,000**
Great Britain threshold: **1,400**
All-Ireland threshold: **650**

GB Max: 149,276 Jan
NI Max: 4,590 Sep

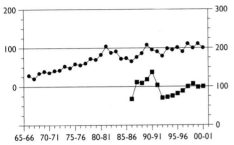

Figure 33. Annual indices for Teal in GB (circles, left axis) and NI (squares, right axis)

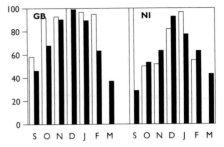

Figure 34. Monthly indices for Teal in GB and NI (white bars 2000–01; black bars 1995–96 to 1999–2000)

National totals in Great Britain reached an all time high in December and rose further to peak in January. Despite these high counts, and sustained higher than average numbers throughout the October to February period. The annual index in Britain fell slightly from the record level of the previous winter. In Northern Ireland, the count was typical for recent years and the annual index remained almost unchanged.

The Somerset Levels, the UK's most important site for Teal, recorded the highest count from any site since the count there in January 1996. Interestingly both of these high counts occurred shortly after cold snaps perhaps suggesting a displacement from other sites during cold weather. There was a record site count at Martin Mere (like the nearby Ribble Estuary, peaking in late autumn) which raised the site to internationally important status. Elsewhere, the Arun Valley and Blackwater and Swale Estuaries also recorded greatly elevated peaks, while the early autumn count at Lough Foyle was exceptional, more than three times the average of the previous five years. The steady increase in counts at Breydon Water & Berney Marshes was sustained, numbers having risen by almost 750% over the five-year period. The low count at Abberton Reservoir was extraordinary, numbers over 90% below the typical peak.

	96-97	97-98	98-99	99-00	00-01	Mon	Mean	
Sites of international importance in the UK								
Somerset Levels	3,305	16,156	16,037	13,641	[29] 19,040	Jan	13,636	
Mersey Estuary	14,120	12,065	9,393	11,700	8,777	Feb	11,211	
Ribble Estuary	7,833	6,209	5,114	5,748	7,874	Oct	6,556	
Dee Estuary (Eng/Wal)	6,545	6,254	4,544	5,185	5,622	Feb	5,630	
Abberton Reservoir	6,756	9,381	(3,593)	5,450	488	Oct	5,519	
Lower Derwent Valley	3,875	5,900	4,300	4,100	-		4,544	
Martin Mere	2,560	5,750	3,170	3,710	6,700	Oct	4,378	▲
Sites of national importance in Great Britain								
Severn Estuary	2,665	2,880	3,772	4,939	5,151	Dec	3,881	
Loch Leven	3,250	3,288	5,055	4,320	2,940	Oct	3,771	
North Norfolk Coast	2,668	3,992	3,721	3,133	4,186	Nov	3,540	
Hamford Water	6,563	2,633	3,266	1,514	2,510	Jan	3,297	▼
Ouse Washes	3,661	[29] 3,830	[29] 2,970	3,212	2,429	Oct	3,220	
Blackwater Estuary	2,593	2,522	(2,131)	2,598	4,867	Feb	3,145	
Inner Moray Firth	3,407	3,428	[30] 3,028	2,921	2,794	Jan	3,116	
Thames Estuary	2,575	1,971	3,346	3,718	3,659	Dec	3,054	
Swale Estuary	2,868	2,457	2,672	2,388	4,385	Oct	2,954	
Cleddau Estuary	2,220	2,637	2,138	2,438	2,427	Jan	2,372	
Horsey Mere	-	2,400	(2,500)	2,143	-		2,348	
Arun Valley	655	1,385	2,695	2,438	4,276	Dec	2,290	

	96–97	97–98	98–99	99–00	00–01	Mon	Mean	
Humber Estuary	(785)	1,528	1,438	2,765	3,370	Oct	2,275	
Southampton Water	2,356	2,493	[30] 2,058	[30] 1,727	2,366	Jan	2,200	
Dornoch Firth	1,476	(2,073)	2,272	2,039	2,261	Jan	2,024	
Mersehead RSPB Reserve	825	-	-	970	4,180	Dec	1,992	▲
Breydon Wtr & Berney Marshes	500	779	1,284	3,150	4,237	Dec	1,990	▲
Alde Complex	1,793	2,078	1,863	1,837	2,234	Jan	1,961	
Morecambe Bay	1,439	2,114	1,528	1,719	2,956	Nov	1,951	
Nene Washes	1,648	2,054	2,129	1,548	1,592	Dec	1,794	
Mere Sands Wood NR	2,525	1,025	1,350	2,245	1,600	Nov	1,749	
Burry Inlet	2,734	759	2,566	1,471	1,152	Dec	1,736	
Chichester Harbour	2,037	1,649	2,141	1,444	1,359	Jan	1,726	
Woolston Eyes	900	1,500	2,000	1,800	2,100	Feb	1,660	
Poole Harbour	2,297	972	1,623	1,059	2,086	Feb	1,607	
Forth Estuary	929	1,411	1,484	1,419	2,353	Jan	1,519	▲
Rutland Water	1,954	1,402	980	1,876	1,250	Sep	1,492	
Minsmere	779	2,336	1,029	(21)	[29] 1,700	Nov	1,461	▲
Medway Estuary	[30] 1,968	1,466	1,804	679	1,236	Dec	1,431	
Pagham Harbour	[30] 1,660	969	1,716	812	1,849	Feb	1,401	
Sites of all-Ireland importance in Northern Ireland								
Strangford Lough	2,302	1,978	2,519	1,627	1,189	Jan	1,923	
Loughs Neagh & Beg	1,076	2,270	2,388	1,487	2,002	Dec	1,845	
Lough Foyle	837	575	[29] 1,500	577	2,888	Sep	1,275	
Upper Lough Erne	368	405	631	1,379	-		696	

Other sites surpassing table qualifying levels in 2000–01

Holburn Moss	3,920	Sep
Stour Estuary	[30] 2,413	Jan
R. Avon: R'wood to Christchurch[29]	2,178	Jan
Solway Estuary	2,101	Dec
Beaulieu Estuary	2,045	Dec
Dungeness Gravel Pits	1,615	Nov
Ashleworth Ham	1,559	Jan
Cotswold Water Park (West)	1,465	Jan
Caerlaverock WWT	1,420	Nov

GREEN-WINGED TEAL
Anas carolinensis

Vagrant
Native range: N America

Two individuals were recorded on the Severn Estuary, at different locations in April and January. Singles were noted at Acre Nook Sand Quarry, Inner Moray Firth, Larne Lough, Loch Bee (South Uist), Loch Scarmclate, Loch of Gards, Loe Pool, Inner Moray Firth, Maer Lake, Morecambe Bay, Poole Harbour and Sandbach Flashes.

SPECKLED TEAL
Anas flavirostris

Escape
Native range: S America

Birds were present at two sites during the winter, Bramshill Park Lake and Woburn Park Lakes, with maxima of three and two respectively.

MALLARD
Anas platyrhynchos

International threshold: 20,000[**]
Great Britain threshold: 5,000[†]
All-Ireland threshold: 500

GB Max: 147,684 Jan
NI Max: 10,028 Sep

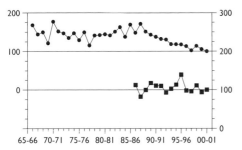

Figure 35. Annual indices for Mallard in GB (circles, left axis) and NI (squares, right axis)

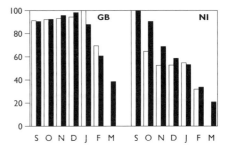

Figure 36. Monthly indices for Mallard in GB and NI (white bars 2000–01; black bars 1995–96 to 1999–2000)

Although the peak Great Britain count was around average for recent years, suppressed numbers in other winter months saw the annual index fall to its lowest ever level. The eleventh fall in 13 years serves to heighten concern for this species in Britain, particularly given that the factors affecting wintering numbers are largely unknown. Although smaller in scale and restricted in habitats covered, results from other surveys such as the Waterways Bird Survey suggest that breeding populations show no decline in numbers and may even be increasing (Marchant, 2001). Monthly indices followed a typical pattern, although values in January and February were above normal.

In Northern Ireland, the September peak, although not exceptional, was the highest recorded since September 1995. Monthly indices suggest that this was short lived, the proportion of birds present over the following three months being lower than usual. The annual trend showed little change from the previous year, and has remained relatively stable throughout the period of WeBS monitoring in the province.

Of the key sites for Mallard, only the Humber Estuary recorded counts significantly above the five-year peak mean, although counts in excess of 3,000 birds were recorded at more sites than at any time since 1994–95. Notably, however, three sites no longer surpass the table qualifying levels following counts in 2000–01.

	96–97	97–98	98–99	99–00	00–01	Mon	Mean
Sites with mean peak counts of 2,000 or more birds in Great Britain [†]							
Lower Derwent Valley	3,655	2,400	3,450	4,250	-		3,439
Morecambe Bay	3,116	3,615	3,045	3,334	3,126	Sep	3,247
Ouse Washes	2,149	2,582	2,402	[29] 4,168	3,657	Oct	2,992
Severn Estuary	3,088	2,101	2,465	2,767	3,265	Dec	2,737
The Wash	2,636	2,771	1,956	2,350	3,264	Jan	2,595
Tring Reservoirs	2,956	2,200	(2,040)	(1,500)	(1,700)	Nov	2,578
Martin Mere	2,885	2,520	2,440	2,230	2,400	Sep	2,495
Humber Estuary	(2,112)	2,215	2,089	2,001	3,460	Dec	2,441
Inner Moray Firth	1,582	2,044	3,325	1,819	1,825	Jan	2,119
Sites of all-Ireland importance in Northern Ireland							
Loughs Neagh & Beg	5,399	5,463	6,176	3,828	6,431	Sep	5,459
Lough Foyle	1,795	1,592	1,696	1,336	1,298	Oct	1,543
Strangford Lough	1,238	1,753	1,198	1,514	1,807	Sep	1,502

Sites no longer meeting table qualifying levels
Solway Estuary
Abberton Reservoir
Upper Lough Erne

Other sites surpassing table qualifying levels in 2000–01

Somerset Levels	2,681	Jan
Dee Estuary (Eng/Wal)	2,237	Nov

†   *as no sites exceed the British threshold, a qualifying level of 2,000 has been chosen to select sites for presentation in this report*

BLACK DUCK   Vagrant
Anas rubripes   **Native range: N America**

Long-staying birds first recorded by WeBS in 1999–2000 were still present at Stithians Reservoir and Loch Fleet during the winter.

Another was seen at Colliford Reservoir in October.

CHESTNUT TEAL   Escape
Anas castanea   **Native range: S Australia**

One was present on the Dee Estuary (Eng/Wal) at Inner Marsh Farm in February.

PINTAIL
Anas acuta

International threshold:	**600**
Great Britain threshold:	**280**
All-Ireland threshold:	**60**

GB Max:	**20,052**	**Dec**
NI Max:	**326**	**Feb**

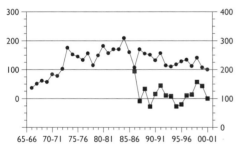

Figure 37. Annual indices for Pintail in GB (circles, left axis) and NI (squares, right axis)

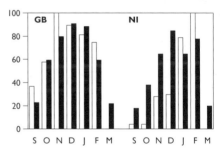

Figure 38. Monthly indices for Pintail in GB and NI (white bars 2000–01; black bars 1995–96 to 1999–2000)

Although higher than the peak of 1999-2000, the December peak of 20,000 in Great Britain was amongst the lowest in the last 25 years. The annual index correspondingly fell to the lowest level since 1971-72. Monthly indices showed a slightly earlier peak than normal in November, whilst the higher than average proportion of birds present in September and February may be a result of the lower than normal peak.

In comparison, Northern Ireland holds relatively small numbers which represent 5–10% of the all-Ireland wintering population. The peak was typical for recent years, although relatively low numbers in early winter saw annual index values fall. Given the small number of birds involved, the trend can fluctuate considerably between years and no clear pattern is evident.

The low totals in Great Britain were reflected in counts at key sites, the peaks of the top six being well below the recent five-year averages. Despite this, several other sites held unusually high numbers, many being inland floodland sites which can be rapidly exploited by Pintail when conditions become suitable. Amongst the new additions to the table are several such sites, most noteworthy being the following which all supported over 1,000 birds: Somerset Levels, Arun Valley and the River Avon: Ringwood to Christchurch.

	96–97	97–98	98–99	99–00	00–01	Mon	Mean	
Sites of international importance in the UK								
Dee Estuary (Eng/Wal)	5,749	5,954	5,018	2,356	4,216	Oct	4,659	
Morecambe Bay	3,207	4,411	4,795	4,161	2,387	Sep	3,792	
Solway Estuary	3,852	2,677	4,436	3,067	2,389	Dec	3,284	
Ouse Washes	2,055	3,271	2,082	3,804	[29] 1,509	Feb	2,544	
Burry Inlet	2,889	1,093	2,782	3,609	1,328	Jan	2,340	
Ribble Estuary	4,073	1,271	3,894	747	819	Jan	2,161	
Nene Washes	264	1,668	1,487	353	2,671	Feb	1,289	
North Norfolk Coast	1,177	1,668	1,075	1,235	987	Nov	1,228	
Medway Estuary	2,047	489	807	463	475	Nov	856	
Mersey Estuary	904	813	882	1,100	491	Nov	838	
Duddon Estuary	1,349	464	918	810	628	Dec	834	
Severn Estuary	698	709	510	898	966	Jan	756	
Pagham Harbour	1,210	1,087	683	[30] 434	340	Dec	751	
Stour Estuary	[30] 718	638	569	[30] 629	691	Feb	649	▲
Sites of national importance in Great Britain								
Swale Estuary	277	570	556	395	952	Dec	550	
Somerset Levels	76	118	171	570	1,546	Dec	496	▲
Arun Valley	167	359	447	199	1,171	Feb	469	▲
Alde Complex	147	340	673	495	506	Jan	432	
Dee Flood Meadows	122	328	94	472	990	Dec	401	
Otmoor	-	-	-	-	[29] 396	Feb	396	▲
Tottenhill Gravel Pits	415	397	203	410	-		356	
Hamford Water	1,117	54	315	103	102	Jan	338	
Poole Harbour	375	451	285	227	296	Feb	327	
R. Avon: R'wood to Christchurch	0	20	[29] 90	30	[29] 1,385	Jan	305	▲
Mersehead RSPB Reserve	375	-	-	46	480	Dec	300	▲
Fleet/Wey	414	276	270	233	241	Oct	287	
Martin Mere	231	239	294	313	344	Nov	284	
Sites of all-Ireland importance in Northern Ireland								
Strangford Lough	242	304	313	303	249	Feb	282	
Sites no longer meeting table qualifying levels								
Inner Moray Firth								
Abberton Reservoir								
Orwell Estuary								
Cromarty Firth								
Lower Derwent Valley								
Blackwater Estuary								

Other sites surpassing table qualifying levels in 2000–01

Blackwater Estuary	325	Feb	Ashleworth Ham	291	Jan
Inner Moray Firth	307	Feb	Fen Drayton Gravel Pits	404	Feb
Breydon Wtr & Berney Marshes	446	Dec	Lough Foyle	75	Feb
R. Severn/Vyrnwy Confluence	320	Nov			

YELLOW-BILLED PINTAIL   Escape
Anas georgica   **Native range: S America**

A single was at Liden Lagoon in August.

BAHAMA PINTAIL   Escape
Anas bahamensis   **Native range: S America**

Single birds were recorded at Avon Estuary, Cowdenknowes Reservoir, Harrow Lodge Park, Llyn Coed-y-dinas and the Taw-Torridge Estuary.

RED-BILLED TEAL
Anas erythrorhyncha

Escape
Native range: Africa

One present at Connaught Water in May, August and September was presumably the same bird as recorded there in 1999–2000.

GARGANEY
Anas querquedula

International threshold:	20,000**
Great Britain threshold:	?[†]
All-Ireland threshold:	?[†]

GB Max: 56 May
NI Max: 0

The peak, around average for recent years, occurred in early summer rather than the usual August peak which failed to materialise in 2000. Birds were recorded at only 37 sites (*cf.* 55–74 in previous four years). Four birds were still present in November, singles remaining through December and January.

Whilst peak national counts occurred during the spring, most site peaks typically occurred during mid-late summer. Five or more birds were recorded at seven sites, each during the July/August period, most notable being 12 at Stodmarsh NNR & Collards Lagoon.

	96–97	97–98	98–99	99–00	00–01	Mon	Mean	
Sites with mean peak counts of four or more birds in Great Britain [†]								
Fairburn Ings	11	3	4	10	4	Aug	6	
Wraysbury Gravel Pits	6	3	7	10	2	Aug	6	
Breydon Wtr & Berney Marshes	0	6	7	8	6	Jun	5	
Stodmarsh & Collards Lagoon	3	0	7	3	12	Jul	5	▲
Ouse Washes	[29] 3	[29] 6	[29] 7	9	0		5	
Chew Valley Lake	3	4	9	3	5	Sep	5	
Unspecified SE England site	2	7	5	7	3	Sep	5	
Rutland Water	8	3	3	7	0		4	
Thames Estuary	1	1	3	6	9	Aug	4	▲

Sites no longer meeting table qualifying levels
North Norfolk Coast

Other sites surpassing table qualifying levels in 2000–01

Millbrook Clay Pit	10	Jul/Aug
Earls Barton Gravel Pits	6	Aug
Morecambe Bay	5	Jul
Old Moor Wetlands	4	Aug
Severn Estuary	4	Sep
Dee Estuary (Eng/Wal)	4	Sep

[†] *as no British or all-Ireland thresholds have been set, a qualifying level of four has been chosen to select sites for presentation in this report*

BLUE-WINGED TEAL
Anas discors

Vagrant & escape
Native range: Americas

The bird at Stodmarsh & Collards Lagoon first recorded in 1998–1999 was still present in May. Two other singles were seen in August, at Blithfield Reservoir and on the North Norfolk Coast at Cley.

SHOVELER
Anas clypeata

International threshold: **400**
Great Britain threshold: **100**
All-Ireland threshold: **65**

GB Max: 11,501 Nov
NI Max: 212 Jan

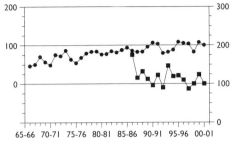

Figure 39. Annual indices for Shoveler in GB (circles, left axis) and NI (squares, right axis)

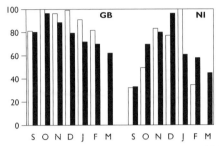

Figure 40. Monthly indices for Shoveler in GB and NI (white bars 2000–01; black bars 1995–96 to 1999–2000)

The late autumn peak in Great Britain was the second highest on record, exceeded only in November 1995 by a count of over 12,000 birds. The timing of the peak, in late autumn, is typical and is reflected in the pattern of monthly indices which show an October or November peak followed by a gradual decline throughout the winter. Interestingly, higher than average numbers persisted throughout the midwinter months, and closer examination of numbers in recent years also suggests that the number of birds staying later in the winter may be increasing. Annual index values in Britain remain on a par with recent years. For a species that occurs only in small numbers in Northern Ireland, peak totals and index values for Shoveler in the province fluctuate relatively little between years.

The number of sites supporting important numbers is higher than for any other species of waterbird with the exception of Gadwall. Concentrations of more than 3–400 birds are very infrequent and occur only on a handful of sites, making the count on the Somerset Levels, the second highest ever recorded by WeBS at any site, all the more noteworthy. Other sites holding well above average numbers included Breydon Water & Berney Marshes, Llynnau Y Fali, the Ribble Estuary, Fen Drayton Gravel Pits and Minsmere. Peak counts at many sites fluctuate considerably between years probably a result of the large turnover during the autumn period and their ability to exploit favourable conditions at sites when they occur (Cranswick *et al.* 1997).

	96–97	97–98	98–99	99–00	00–01	Mon	Mean	
Sites of international importance in the UK								
Ouse Washes	663	[29] 925	[29] 574	[29] 980	287	Oct	686	
Somerset Levels	435	504	485	635	1,343	Dec	680	
Rutland Water	704	531	430	1,154	401	Sep	644	
Burry Inlet	490	363	826	573	368	Nov	524	
Swale Estuary	411	551	468	498	511	Feb	488	
Abberton Reservoir	628	541	(488)	375	352	Oct	477	
Loch Leven	541	426	318	420	480	Sep	437	
Sites of national importance in Great Britain								
Nene Washes	143	689	482	406	190	Dec	382	▼
Breydon Wtr & Berney Marshes	172	183	319	356	620	Nov	330	
Staines Reservoirs	210	490	251	312	(130)	Feb	316	
Blithfield Reservoir	77	436	266	443	341	Aug	313	
Chew Valley Lake	225	405	235	425	270	Sep	312	▼
Dungeness Gravel Pits	421	260	197	269	398	Nov	309	
Unspecified SE England site	359	325	360	320	164	Jan	306	
Stodmarsh & Collards Lagoon	265	328	230	280	409	Nov	302	
Lee Valley Gravel Pits	288	275	228	241	374	Oct	281	
Thames Estuary	197	173	374	187	452	Jan	277	

	96–97	97–98	98–99	99–00	00–01	Mon	Mean	
Fairburn Ings	352	272	200	144	289	Oct	251	
Lower Derwent Valley	221	310	341	122	-		249	
Severn Estuary	169	150	259	206	306	Feb	218	
Arun Valley	146	176	203	163	392	Dec	216	
Grafham Water	290	160	171	265	128	Nov	203	
Llynnau Y Fali	57	205	178	92	464	Jan	199	
Wraysbury Gravel Pits	157	169	84	399	154	Sep	193	
King George VI Reservoir	310	248	119	114	141	Nov	186	
Tees Estuary	202	201	107	131	260	Sep	180	
Brent Reservoir	100	103	185	241	183	Sep	162	
Woolston Eyes	152	152	104	176	210	Sep	159	
Hanningfield Reservoir	211	304	51	184	42	Nov	158	
Rye Harbour & Pett Level	238	135	126	130	160	Feb	158	
Ribble Estuary	46	92	73	173	(393)	Nov	155	▲
Leighton Moss	188	95	185	146	-		154	
Medway Estuary	[30] 264	(80)	156	122	71	Nov	153	
Blagdon Lake	404	64	52	95	145	Oct	152	
North Norfolk Coast	135	121	138	153	203	Oct	150	
Rostherne Mere	103	157	121	278	86	Sep	149	
Alde Complex	120	119	141	161	181	Dec	144	
Humber Estuary	(13)	(78)	92	195	146	Oct	144	
North West Solent	138	(110)	178	110	150	Dec	144	
Fen Drayton Gravel Pits	26	56	155	92	378	Dec	141	▲
Pitsford Reservoir	236	157	(32)	47	114	Oct	139	
Hampton & Kempton Reservoirs	234	88	105	147	118	Oct	138	
Knight & Bessborough Reservoirs	185	160	73	110	159	Aug	137	
Middle Tame Valley Gravel Pits	(186)	116	127	141	102	Sep	134	
Minsmere	69	128	98	(0)	[29] 241	Dec	134	
Otmoor	-	-	-	-	[29] 134	Dec	134	▲
Walthamstow Reservoirs	144	143	78	143	157	Oct	133	
Swithland Reservoir	98	116	51	203	182	Sep	130	
Fleet/Wey	133	107	217	118	73	Sep	130	
R. Avon: Fordingbridge to R'wood[29]	238	52	67	81	182	Feb	124	
Malltraeth Marsh RSPB	89	92	125	145	157	Feb	122	
Willen Lake	25	138	123	128	177	Sep	118	▲
Beddington Sewage Farm	170	95	85	115	125	Sep	118	
Aqualate Mere	358	50	47	(3)	3	Aug	115	
Coombe Country Park	-	(4)	107	(111)	-		109	▲
Middle Yare Marshes	67	106	67	123	175	Oct	108	▲
Dee Estuary (Eng/Wal)	67	91	143	80	157	Nov	108	▲
Poole Harbour	64	103	159	51	158	Jan	107	
Belvide Reservoir	136	(59)	187	21	81	Aug	106	▲
Stanford Reservoir	145	276	19	54	37	Sep	106	
Wraysbury Reservoir	325	69	(41)	18	11	Jan	106	
Reedham Water	-	-	-	-	105	Jan	105	▲
Loch of Strathbeg	(213)	75	19	(65)	(46)	Oct	102	▲

Sites of all-Ireland importance in Northern Ireland

Strangford Lough	108	101	126	168	159	Jan	132	
Loughs Neagh & Beg	89	84	103	72	53	Sep	80	

Important sites not counted in last five years
Lackford Gravel Pits
Ashford Common Waterworks

Sites no longer meeting table qualifying levels
Hornsea Mere
Thrapston Gravel Pits
Colne Valley Gravel Pits

North Warren & Thorpeness Mere
Blackwater Estuary

R. Avon: R'wood to Christchurch[29]	264	Jan	Hornsea Mere	118	Nov
Cotswold Water Park (West)	188	Dec	Hollowell Reservoir	117	Nov
Solway Estuary	174	Dec	Walmore Common	112	Nov
Shinewater Lake	172	Dec	Southampton Water	106	Jan
Chichester Gravel Pits	160	Jan	Mersehead RSPB Reserve	105	Dec
Seaton Gravel Pits	140	Jan/Feb	Martin Mere	103	Sep
Colne Estuary	128	Feb	Crouch-Roach Estuary	100	Dec
Blyth Estuary (Suffolk)	126	Feb	Rush Bog	(100)	Nov
Great Pool Westwood Park	120	Feb			

RINGED TEAL
Callonetta leucophrys

Escape
Native range: S America

Singles were at Valentines Park in July and Tundry Park in September.

RED-CRESTED POCHARD
Netta rufina

Vagrant & escape[†]
Native range: Europe & Asia

GB Max: 110 Jan
NI Max: 0

Despite the absence of counts for a number of formerly important sites, national totals were amongst the highest recorded by WeBS. Birds were recorded at 42 sites, around average for recent years. The key location remains the Cotswold Water Park, situated on the Gloucestershire/Wiltshire/Oxfordshire border. Combined counts from the two groupings of flooded gravel pits in the area reached their

highest level to date in January (89), though with no combined counts in other months approaching this number the possibility of birds moving between lakes and being recorded twice remains. It is worth noting, however, that despite their striking appearance, birds can be surprisingly elusive. A count of 17 birds at Baston/Langtoft Gravel Pits was also noteworthy.

	96–97	97–98	98–99	99–00	00–01	Mon	Mean
Sites with mean peak counts of 10 or more birds in Great Britain [†]							
Cotswold Water Park (West)	54	62	60	63	56	Jan	59
Cotswold Water Park (East)	15	12	25	22	33	Jan	21
Sites not counted in last five years							
Paultons Bird Park							
R. Wensum: Fakenham to Great Ryburgh							
Other sites surpassing table qualifying levels in 2000–01							
Baston/Langtoft Gravel Pits	17	Dec					

† *as site designation does not occur and the 1% criterion is not applied, a qualifying level of 10 has been chosen to select sites for presentation in this report*

ROSYBILL
Netta peposaca

Escape
Native range: S America

One was present in the Cotswold Water Park (East) from October to February.

POCHARD
Aythya ferina

International threshold: **3,500**
Great Britain threshold: **440**
All-Ireland threshold: **400**

GB Max: **34,240 Jan**
NI Max: **24,430 Dec**

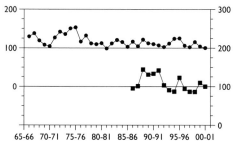

Figure 41. Annual indices for Pochard in GB (circles, left axis) and NI (squares, right axis)

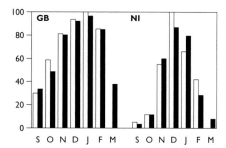

Figure 42. Monthly indices for Pochard in GB and NI (white bars 2000–01; black bars 1995–96 to 1999–2000)

National totals in Great Britain dipped below 35,000 for only the second time since the early 1980s. Consequently, annual indices also fell to their lowest level since this time, although viewed over the long term, numbers appear relatively stable.

Amongst key British sites, sustained high numbers of presumably moulting birds at Abberton Reservoir has seen mean peak counts surpass the level of internationally importance. Exceptional counts on the Nene Washes, where numbers fluctuate greatly from one year to the next according to the depth of floodwater, were in stark contrast to totals in the previous winter.

In Northern Ireland, totals are influenced almost solely by counts at Loughs Neagh & Beg which, which in the absence of counts from Upper Lough Erne, accounted for over 99% of the birds recorded in the province in some months. The peak count was typical for recent years, and annual indices have remained relatively stable over the last nine years.

	96–97	97–98	98–99	99–00	00–01	Mon	Mean	
Sites of international importance in the UK								
Loughs Neagh & Beg	25,230	19,205	29,683	22,681	24,388	Dec	24,237	
Ouse Washes	1,413	5,737	5,383	[29] 6,345	[29] 4,602	Jan	4,696	
Abberton Reservoir	3,079	2,518	(2,569)	4,744	5,296	Aug	3,909	▲
Sites of national importance in Great Britain								
Middle Tame Valley Gravel Pits	(1,899)	1,236	(1,447)	1,167	1,733	Jan	1,509	
Loch Leven	1,692	1,125	1,544	1,320	1,330	Oct	1,402	
Nene Washes	185	435	1,943	27	4,102	Feb	1,338	
Severn Estuary	1,576	1,248	1,154	1,473	997	Feb	1,290	
Cotswold Water Park (East)	1,235	1,151	1,382	(1,225)	723	Nov	1,143	
Fleet/Wey	853	848	1,320	850	928	Jan	960	
Lower Derwent Valley	750	2,350	311	113	-		881	
Martin Mere	1,111	747	767	905	861	Feb	878	
Hornsea Mere	-	(64)	806	1,065	580	Jan	817	
Cotswold Water Park (West)	562	922	876	670	988	Dec	804	
Lower Windrush Valley GP	622	780	655	1,150	(681)	Dec	802	
Dungeness Gravel Pits	633	836	659	889	669	Jul	737	
Rostherne Mere	2,616	152	133	129	576	Jan	721	
Humber Estuary	(2,505)	205	323	317	216	Feb	713	
Loch of Boardhouse	913	613	123	1,156	711	Oct	703	
Rutland Water	855	680	784	620	318	Jul	651	
Wraysbury Gravel Pits	513	697	759	596	494	Dec	612	
Loch of Harray	1,119	506	473	416	457	Oct	594	
Loch Gelly	1,518	490	-	18	330	Dec	589	
Pitsford Reservoir	410	254	1,134	654	357	Sep	562	
Poole Harbour	1,386	298	244	363	359	Feb	530	

	96–97	97–98	98–99	99–00	00–01	Mon	Mean	
Hickling Broad	-	-	250	945	390	Dec	528	
Woolston Eyes	365	362	710	630	537	Feb	521	
Chew Valley Lake	865	440	400	520	290	Sep	503	
St Johns Loch	(470)	-	(200)	-	-		(470)	
Loch Ore	540	(410)	496	105	702	Dec	461	▲
R. Avon: Fordingbridge to R'wood[29]	665	356	303	377	588	Jan	458	▲
Hanningfield Reservoir	467	377	617	430	397	Feb	458	
Shustoke Reservoirs	740	685	9	340	-		444	▲

Important sites not counted in last five years
Walton Lock

Sites no longer meeting table qualifying levels
R. Irwell
Cheddar Reservoir

Other sites surpassing table qualifying levels in 2000–01
Thames Estuary	677	Jan
Somerset Levels	677	Dec
Fen Drayton Gravel Pits	662	Feb
Eyebrook Reservoir	475	Sep

RING-NECKED DUCK
Aythya collaris

Vagrant
Native range: N America

A maximum of twelve individuals was recorded by WeBS during the winter but this does not allow for birds moving between and being recorded at more than one site. Apart from two at Bough Beech Reservoir in April and Wellington Gravel Pits in December, single birds were noted at Burrator Reservoir, Blagdon Lake, Astley Lake, Barcombe Mills Reservoir, Uskmouth Reedbed Lagoons, Heathfield Gravel Pits and Loch Ore.

FERRUGINOUS DUCK
Aythya nyroca

Vagrant & escape
Native range: Europe, N Africa & Asia

Singles were recorded at nine sites, with one present on the Somerset Levels for the third consecutive winter. Elsewhere, birds were seen at Godmanchester Gravel Pit, Luckford Lake, Lough Money, Minsmere, Morden Park Lake, Ouse Washes, Ribble Estuary and Sinah Gravel Pit.

NEW ZEALAND SCAUP
Aythya novaeseelandiae

Escape
Native range: New Zealand

One was present on Connaught Water in October and November.

TUFTED DUCK
Aythya fuligula

International threshold:	10,000
Great Britain threshold:	600
All-Ireland threshold:	400

GB Max: 57,207 Jan
NI Max: 26,598 Dec

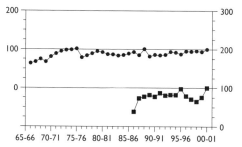

Figure 43. Annual indices for Tufted Duck in GB (circles, left axis) and NI (squares, right axis)

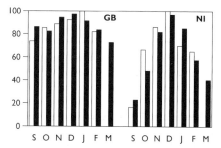

Figure 44. Monthly indices for Tufted Duck in GB and NI (white bars 2000–01; black bars 1995–96 to 1999–2000)

The January 2001 count marked the fourth successive rise in the Great Britain peak. The national total topped 57,000 for the first time ever, and saw the annual index rise to its the third highest level. Long-term trends in numbers are perhaps more stable for Tufted Duck than for any other wildfowl species; typically only small fluctuations occur from one year to the next. Interestingly, annual indices in recent years suggest a small but steady rise since the late 1980s.

In Northern Ireland, annual indices are similarly more stable than for most other species. With the peak count at Loughs Neagh & Beg being the third highest recorded and a higher than usual proportion of birds present in most months away from the peak, the annual index rose by 33% to reach its highest ever level.

Amongst other key sites, high late summer numbers at Abberton Reservoir were again present. The Ouse Washes and Hanningfield Reservoir held above average numbers, whilst numbers at Wraysbury Gravel Pits were the lowest for a decade.

	96–97	97–98	98–99	99–00	00–01	Mon	Mean
Sites of international importance in the UK							
Loughs Neagh & Beg	27,368	18,697	20,324	20,039	26,360	Dec	22,558
Sites of national importance in Great Britain							
Loch Leven	4,589	3,310	3,434	3,550	3,900	Nov	3,757
Abberton Reservoir	3,218	2,268	(2,602)	4,654	4,414	Aug	3,639
Rutland Water	3,159	3,557	4,692	3,325	3,313	Sep	3,609
Middle Tame Valley Gravel Pits	(2,384)	2,422	1,645	2,370	2,547	Jan	2,274
Wraysbury Gravel Pits	1,709	2,868	1,667	1,812	781	Oct	1,767
Pitsford Reservoir	2,034	1,129	(2,585)	1,312	1,202	Sep	1,652
Hanningfield Reservoir	1,600	1,747	851	1,534	2,183	Nov	1,583
Ouse Washes	391	1,165	1,662	1,361	2,214	Jan	1,359
Walthamstow Reservoirs	1,083	1,368	1,217	1,194	1,691	Aug	1,311
Staines Reservoirs	1,405	1,283	1,251	1,250	1,243	Aug	1,286
Alton Water	1,536	783	922	736	1,389	Jan	1,073
Lee Valley Gravel Pits	1,163	930	1,053	1,065	1,085	Dec	1,059
Besthorpe/Girton Gravel Pits	1,122	637	847	983	462	Jan	810
Draycote Water	475	645	1,010	1,007	744	Nov	776
Fen Drayton Gravel Pits	646	679	863	755	929	Aug	774
Chasewater	809	744	702	-	-		752
Chew Valley Lake	520	750	735	965	785	Sep	751
Lower Windrush Valley GP	544	624	771	1,020	737	Feb	739
King George V Reservoirs	1,020	700	740	230	970	Aug	732
William Girling Reservoir	738	807	617	859	576	Aug	719
Tophill Low Reservoirs	554	395	514	1,208	920	Aug	718

	96–97	97–98	98–99	99–00	00–01	Mon	Mean	
Cotswold Water Park (West)	483	521	829	748	753	Dec	667	
Thames Estuary	769	444	791	566	653	Jan	645	▲
Cotswold Water Park (East)	647	707	753	529	581	Nov	643	
Severn Estuary	610	382	662	906	625	Dec	637	
Dungeness Gravel Pits	558	760	641	645	523	Jul	625	
Loch of Harray	524	713	946	534	368	Nov	617	
Windermere	565	637	-	-	-		601	

Sites of all-Ireland importance in Northern Ireland

	96–97	97–98	98–99	99–00	00–01	Mon	Mean
Upper Lough Erne	644	542	255	546	-		497

Sites no longer meeting table qualifying levels
Hickling Broad
Little Paxton Gravel Pits
Loch Watten

Other sites surpassing table qualifying levels in 2000–01

Hamilton Low Parks & S'clyde Park	1,088	Jan
King George VI Reservoir	718	Aug
Millbrook Clay Pit	691	Oct
Nene Washes	747	Feb
Grafham Water	765	Nov
Somerset Levels	642	Jan

SCAUP
Aythya marila

International threshold:	3,100
Great Britain threshold:	110
All-Ireland threshold:	30*

* 50 is normally used as a minimum threshold

GB Max:	4,122 Jan
NI Max:	3,711 Feb

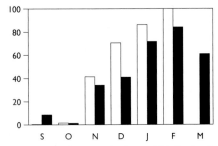

Figure 45. Monthly indices for Scaup in NI (white bars 2000–01; black bars 1995–96 to 1999–2000)

Although somewhat lower than average, the peak total of Scaup in Britain fell within the range of counts for recent winters. Correspondingly, counts at around half the nationally important sites were below their respective five-year peak means, although they were greatly elevated in the Cromarty Firth while recent winters have seen the consistent presence of around two hundred birds in Rough Firth. The most notable decline was in the Solway Estuary, where counts were amongst the lowest at the site in the last decade. There was no corresponding increase at adjacent or other sites — for example, it has been suggested that there may be interchange with Loughs Neagh & Beg during the course of a winter — indicating a genuine decline in numbers in 2000–01.

Numbers in Northern Ireland were around average, although counts at Loughs Neagh & Beg were, with the exception of just one fewer bird in 1993–94, the lowest there since 1989–90. Numbers at other sites in the province were well above average.

	96–97	97–98	98–99	99–00	00–01	Mon	Mean
Sites of international importance in the UK							
Loughs Neagh & Beg	4,222	3,671	4,426	3,874	2,633	Feb	3,765
Sites of national importance in Great Britain							
Solway Estuary	2,341	4,533	2,006	3,001	[30] 1,818	Dec	2,740
Loch Indaal	732	1,110	1,120	900	1,200	Jan	1,012
Loch Ryan	[29] 1,320	1,249	200	(637)	631	Jan	850
Inner Moray Firth	332	[24] 416	[24] 392	480	313	Dec	387
Forth Estuary	1,031	145	342	157	240	Jan	383
Loch of Stenness	318	258	268	250	211	Oct	261
Loch of Harray	[29] 20	208	198	201	311	Dec	188
Cromarty Firth	115	45	132	[24] 117	424	Jan	167
Humber Estuary	(594)	21	12	2	6	Feb	127
Rough Firth	1	0	170	204	204	Feb	116
Sites of all-Ireland importance in Northern Ireland							
Carlingford Lough	404	572	700	700	800	Dec	635
Belfast Lough	[30] 254	95	[30] 78	244	493	Feb	233

Sites no longer meeting table qualifying levels
North Norfolk Coast

LESSER SCAUP
Aythya affinis

Vagrant
Native range: N America

Four birds were recorded during 2000–01. In April and May different individuals were recorded at Blagdon Lake, Rutland Water and Fen Drayton Gravel Pits. During November one was at Meadow Lane Gravel Pits, a site visited by this species in February and March 1999.

EIDER
Somateria mollissima

International threshold:	**20,000**[**]
Great Britain threshold:	**750**
All-Ireland threshold:	**20**[*]

GB Max:	24,198 Aug
NI Max:	1,833 Oct

[*] *50 is normally used as a minimum threshold*

The British peak, whilst low for the second year, remained within the relatively narrow range of variation for this species. By contrast, that for Northern Ireland was the highest on record, easily surpassing the previous peak of 1,382 in December 1990.

Counts at individual sites may fluctuate to a fair degree between years. This may, in part, be a consequence of the difficulties of recording seaducks, but Eiders are located relatively close to shore at many sites and, with a degree of patience, and luck with suitable weather, reasonably accurate counts may be obtained. Counts in the Clyde Estuary, Gare Loch, Loch Ryan and Belfast Loch were all notably higher than normal. By contrast, several sites held markedly fewer birds in 2000–01, including Ayr to North Troon, where counts remained very low for the second winter in succession, and at Girvan to Turnberry. Co-ordinated early winter surveys throughout the Firth of Clyde (Waltho 2002) suggest that this area should be treated as a single site for Eider, with declines in some areas being matched by local increases elsewhere. The survey in September in 2001 recorded rather fewer birds than in recent years, though still totalling 15,692 and similar to the five-year peak mean. Treated as a single site, the Clyde is by far the most important area in the UK for this species, greatly exceeding recent numbers on the Tay. Coverage of the latter site however is problematic, requiring counts to be undertaken at the appropriate point in the tidal cycle which pushes the flock within sight of a suitable vantage point, and then only when suitable viewing conditions prevail. Few appropriate counts have been made at that site in the last five years, the only count to exceed 10,000 having been made during WeBS Low Tide Counts.

A mass mortality of over 20,000 Eiders occurred in the Wadden Sea in winter 1999-2000 (Camphuysen *et al.* 2002). Analyses of dissected birds showed most were severely emaciated and suffering from parasite infestation. Over-exploitation by commercial cockle and mussel fisheries in the early 1990s, and in particular intense fisheries in summer 1999, are thought to be key factors in the mortality event.

	96–97	97–98	98–99	99–00	00–01	Mon	Mean
Sites of national importance in Great Britain							
Tay Estuary	[30] 12,255	[29] 9,500	6,030	(32)	(190)	Jul	9,262
Forth Estuary	9,166	6,937	7,171	6,283	8,893	Aug	7,690
Morecambe Bay	6,073	8,200	8,131	6,713	5,306	Jul	6,885
Clyde Estuary	5,779	3,299	3,944	4,454	6,126	Aug	4,720
Ythan Estuary	3,216	3,366	3,116	3,944	-		3,411
Gare Loch	[10] 3,037	[10] 2,419	[10] 2,156	[10] 2,261	[10] 3,877	Sep	2,750
Montrose Basin	2,100	2,163	3,365	2,214	(2,500)	Sep/Jan	2,468
Scapa Flow	-	-	[31] 2,308	-	-		2,308
Ayr to North Troon	[10] 1,359	3,767	4,355	[10] 775	[10] 504	Sep	2,152
Loch Long/Loch Goil	[10] 1,285	[10] 1,331	[10] 2,960	[10] 2,164	[10] 1,539	Sep	1,856
Girvan to Turnberry	2,835	2,645	1,589	1,083	957	Feb	1,822
Farne Islands	-	-	2,500	200	2,434	Nov	1,711
Lindisfarne	1,255	1,209	2,106	1,258	[30] 1,841	Nov	1,534
Loch Fyne	-	[10] 1,499	[10] 1,558	[10] 1,510	[10] 1,297	Sep	1,466
Loch Ryan	[29] 1,161	228	1,202	1,400	2,037	Jul	1,206
Don Mouth to Ythan Mouth	1,215	2,159	360	634	224	Sep	918
Bute	[10] 571	[10] 763	[10] 949	[10] 1,367	[10] 771	Sep	884
Ardrossan to Farland Head	-	-	-	937	803	Aug	870
The Wash	1,569	638	266	258	1,370	Jan	820
Isle of Cumbrae	941	833	909	577	-		815
Stevenston Point	[10] 1,400	(1,550)	[10] 67	[10] 789	[10] 243	Sep	810
Sites of all-Ireland importance in Northern Ireland							
Belfast Lough	448	922	[30] 913	1,076	[30] 2,219	Nov	1,116
Outer Ards	709	470	716	382	241	Feb	504
Lough Foyle	452	161	[29] 130	11	28	Sep	156
Strangford Lough	61	52	95	122	279	Sep	122
Larne Lough	96	39	100	157	128	Sep	104
Sites no longer meeting table qualifying levels							
Seahouses to Budle Point							
Irvine/Garnock Estuary							
Dee Estuary (Scotland)							
Other sites surpassing table qualifying levels in 2000–01							
Inner Moray Firth	[24] 1,243	Jan					
Alnmouth to Boulmer	757	Jun					

KING EIDER
Somateria spectabilis

Vagrant
Native range: Arctic

On the Forth Estuary one was recorded at Aberlady & Gullane Bays during May.

LONG-TAILED DUCK
Clangula hyemalis

International threshold:	20,000**
Great Britain threshold:	230[†]
All-Ireland threshold:	+*[†]

GB Max: 4,693 Jan
NI Max: 182 Nov

* 50 is normally used as a minimum threshold

WeBS totals in both Britain and Northern Ireland in 2000–01 were particularly impressive, around twice the norm for recent years. For this species in particular, usually located well offshore, counts may vary considerably should conditions mean that flocks present at traditional sites are, for whatever reason, brought in sight of land. The count of almost 4,000 birds in the Moray Firth, obtained during WeBS Core Counts, is noteworthy not just for this reason, but because it greatly exceeds the counts obtained using dedicated survey in recent years and demonstrates a genuine increase in 2000–01.

Fortuitous circumstances will no doubt also have contributed to the notably large counts at Loch Indaal and Lough Foyle, but the marked jumps are presumably indicative of a genuine influx of birds to both sites. By contrast, numbers in the Forth were considerably reduced — matching a decline in Common Scoter at this site — and remained low also at nearby St Andrews Bay for a second year in succession.

	96–97	97–98	98–99	99–00	00–01	Mon	Mean	
Sites of national importance in Great Britain								
Moray Firth	(735)	[24] 2,006	[24] 2,482	[24] 1,389	3,991	Jan	2,467	
Scapa Flow	-	-	[31] 1,582	-	-		1,582	
Forth Estuary	975	660	772	783	319	Jan	702	
Hacosay, B'mull & C'grave Sounds[28]	421	[28] 383	-	-	-		402	
South Yell Sound	[28] 157	[28] 270	[28] 191	[28] 317	-		234	
Sites with mean peak counts of 30 or more birds in Great Britain [†]								
Water Sound	88	(96)	135	120	(179)	Feb	131	
Traigh Luskentyre	146	152	(75)	49	49	Jan	99	
Loch of Stenness	108	48	88	173	75	Jan	98	
Loch Indaal	(4)	3	4	8	231	Sep	62	▲
Thurso Bay	-	-	-	60	-		60	
Aberdeen Beach	-	-	12	88	-		50	▲
St Andrews Bay	106	29	72	16	7	Jan	46	
Seahouses to Budle Point	150	20	0	19	5	Feb	39	
Loch of Harray	22	21	85	20	31	Jan	36	
Sites with mean peak counts of 30 or more birds in Northern Ireland [†]								
Lough Foyle	0	0	0	4	161	Nov	33	▲
Sites no longer meeting table qualifying levels								
Grutness to Quendale								
Whiteness to Scarvister								
North Norfolk Coast								
Other sites surpassing table qualifying levels in 2000–01								
North Norfolk Coast	31	Feb						

[†] as few sites exceed the British threshold, and as no all-Ireland threshold has been set, a qualifying level of 30 has been chosen to select sites for presentation in this report

COMMON SCOTER
Melanitta nigra

International threshold:	16,000
Great Britain threshold:	275
All-Ireland threshold:	40[*]

GB Max:	5,569 Feb
NI Max:	4 Oct

[*] 50 is normally used as a minimum threshold

Total counts in 2000–01 by WeBS were within the range of normal values for recent years though, as ever, for this species and Long-tailed Duck more so than any other wildfowl, probably the least representative of the true numbers and trends in the country. Nevertheless, the count from the Forth, perhaps one of the key sites where reasonably accurate survey can be made from land, was markedly low, and although numbers in nearby St Andrews Bay were slightly above normal, WeBS counts suggest a genuine fall in the area in 2000–01. Counts off North Norfolk were higher than usual, but all the more remarkable given that they were made in June. The timing of this count suggests that many of these birds may oversummer in British waters, although a dedicated survey would be required to establish this. It was, presumably, local movements of the wintering flock in this area that resulted in the much higher than average count in the Wash.

Interest in Common Scoter in the UK has increased markedly in recent years with the development of a Biodiversity Action Plan for this species. Land and aerial survey have continued in Carmarthen Bay, marking the recovery of numbers at this site following the *Sea Empress* oil spill and noting the regular presence of internationally important numbers. Accordingly, it is hoped that this site will shortly become the UK's first marine Special Protection Area.

In winter 2000–01, CCW extended the programme of aerial surveys in for Common Scoter to Liverpool Bay (Oliver, Robinson & Howard 2001). Monthly surveys were made between November and February, centred around Conwy and Red Wharf Bays, Colwyn Bay and off Blackpool, sites known or suspected to be important for scoter, using a 'total count' method, whereby transects were flown at 1-km intervals, with observers aiming to count all birds out to a distance of 500 m either side of the plane. The results quickly justified the use of this approach, establishing that large flocks of Common Scoter were present at these sites throughout the winter (land-based counts, such as WeBS, had only previously recorded large numbers during clement conditions), with peaks of 865 in the Conwy/Red Wharf Bay area and 4,460 in Colwyn. Particularly remarkable

was a count of 11,701 birds off Blackpool, especially since the majority was found between five and 15 kilometres offshore. These birds were strongly associated with a shallow sandbank and this distribution explains why previous land-based counts from Blackpool had recorded only 2–3,000 birds. This site was quickly established as the most important for Common Scoter in England and a programme for repeat survey has been established.

International interest in scoters saw the convening of an international workshop in Denmark in November 2000 to collate information on numbers and trends in each country, and review real and perceived threats and monitoring needs. A review of numbers for the UK, aided by the improved survey of key sites in recent winters, suggests that the true number of Common Scoter wintering in the UK is likely to be in the region of 50–65,000 (Cranswick in press).

	96–97	97–98	98–99	99–00	00–01	Mon	Mean
Sites of national importance in Great Britain							
Carmarthen Bay	[12] 5,800	[6] 6,240	[32] 18,243	[32] 21,592	[32] 19,506	Feb	14,276
Cardigan Bay	(636)	[11] 5,220	(477)	(126)	(280)	Feb	5,220
Solway Firth	(43)	[3] (5,000)	[3] (1,450)	(3)	(0)		(5,000)
Moray Firth	(609)	[24] 2,061	[24] 3,543	[24] 2,281	3,848	Feb	2,933
North Norfolk Coast	2,070	1,860	1,552	2,182	3,014	Jun	2,136
Forth Estuary	2,320	1,205	1,663	3,764	783	Nov	1,947
St Andrews Bay	1,704	2,771	1,105	880	2,300	Oct	1,752
The Wash	351	200	468	166	2,650	Jan	767
Alt Estuary	12	811	454	572	399	Jan	450
Lindisfarne	300	192	1,512	220	0		445
Colwyn Bay	11	386	363	735	500	Mar	399
Traeth Coch	15	500	550	150	(20)	Sep	304 ▲
Sites of all-Ireland importance in Northern Ireland							
Dundrum Bay	(0)	(0)	755	(0)	(0)		755

Important sites not counted in last five years
Earlsferry Links to Anstruther
Craigalea to Newcastle
Tyrella Shore

Sites no longer meeting table qualifying levels
Rough Firth & Auchencairn Bay
Clwyd Estuary
Don Mouth to Ythan Mouth

SURF SCOTER
Melanitta perspicillata

Vagrant
Native range: N America

Birds were recorded on the Forth Estuary and Inner Moray Firth during the year, with maxima of four in April and three in February respectively.

VELVET SCOTER
Melanitta fusca

International threshold: 10,000
Great Britain threshold: 30[*]
All-Ireland threshold: +[*]

GB Max:	2,464 Dec
NI Max:	0

[*] 50 is normally used as a minimum threshold

The national total of Velvet Scoter in 2000–01 was particularly impressive, arising largely from the much higher than normal count at St Andrews Bay; national totals in recent winters have barely exceeded 1,000. Although large compared with recent years, numbers at St Andrews have previously been higher still, with counts of 2,400 and 2,200 in the late 1980s and early 1990s. Numbers at the other two key were around average. Together, these three sites comprise the only sites in the UK where Velvet

Scoter occur in significant numbers with any regularity. Not since 1995–96, when 108 were recorded on the North Norfolk Coast, have WeBS counts at any other site in the UK recorded more than 30 birds; small numbers there in 2000–01 saw this site drop from the list of nationally important sites.

In a recent review of scoters in the UK, the estimate of numbers of Velvet Scoter was put at 2,500 to 3,500 birds (Cranswick in press).

	96–97	97–98	98–99	99–00	00–01	Mon	Mean
Sites of national importance in Great Britain							
St Andrews Bay	942	520	840	845	(1,870)	Dec	1,003
Moray Firth	(81)	[24] 804	[24] 1,090	[24] 401	[24] 744	Dec	760
Forth Estuary	868	528	433	751	542	Dec	624
Sites no longer meeting table qualifying levels							
North Norfolk Coast							

GOLDENEYE
Bucephala clangula

International threshold: 3,000
Great Britain threshold: 170
All-Ireland threshold: 110

GB Max:	14,826 Jan
NI Max:	9,309 Feb

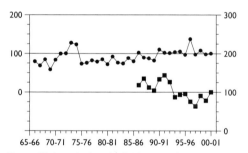

Figure 46. Annual indices for Goldeneye in GB (circles, left axis) and NI (squares, right axis)

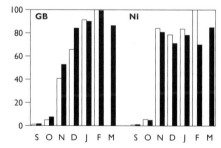

Figure 47. Monthly indices for Goldeneye in GB and NI (white bars 2000–01; black bars 1995–96 to 1999–2000)

The absence of a large proportion of March counts due to the onset of Foot and Mouth Disease perhaps has more significance for Goldeneye than for most other waterbirds. Numbers in Great Britain typically peak late in the winter and a large proportion of birds are still present in March, the last month of the WeBS recording year, and when a number of key sites support their highest numbers (Musgrove *et al.* 2001). In Northern Ireland, the pattern of occurrence varies considerably

between years; any month from November through to March can hold peak numbers.

Peak totals in Great Britain and Northern Ireland in 2000–01 were, respectively, slightly lower and slightly higher than normal, the former usually surpassing 16,000, the latter having varied in the region of 6–10,000 birds. Index values for both Britain and the province, however, rose slightly – that in Northern Ireland being the highest for eight winters.

Counts at most key sites were unremarkable, though numbers on the Tweed

Estuary, Hornsea Mere and on the Ayrshire coast from Girvan to Turnberry were well below normal. The count on the Stour Estuary was noteworthy, and contrasts with the relatively small numbers at nearby Abberton Reservoir. Numbers at the UK's only internationally important site, Loughs Neagh & Beg, were the highest at the site since winter 1995–96.

	96–97	97–98	98–99	99–00	00–01	Mon	Mean
Sites of international importance in the UK							
Loughs Neagh & Beg	8,081	5,587	7,611	7,026	8,482	Feb	7,357
Sites of national importance in Great Britain							
Forth Estuary	2,892	4,864	2,445	1,653	2,414	Feb	2,854
Inner Moray Firth	921	[24] 895	[30] 964	894	1,141	Jan	963
Abberton Reservoir	839	426	631	651	448	Feb	599
Clyde Estuary	562	509	496	858	468	Jan	579
Tweed Estuary	804	570	585	302	151	Dec	482
Humber Estuary	(558)	287	581	410	498	Dec	467
Rutland Water	427	424	366	354	353	Jan/Feb	385
Kilconquhar Loch	322	253	305	424	298	Feb	320
Morecambe Bay	329	310	314	288	346	Feb	317
Blackwater Estuary	353	(242)	279	265	341	Jan	310
Girvan to Turnberry	672	315	241	131	122	Jan	296
Loch Leven	314	301	382	256	215	Nov	294
Windermere	296	269	-	-	-		283
Scapa Flow	-	-	[31] 282	-	-		282
Doon Estuary	505	118	134	300	(283)	Nov	268
R. Tweed: Kelso to Coldstream	268	334	198	220	285	Dec	261
Loch of Stenness	259	222	215	310	261	Jan	253
Loch of Skene	202	(356)	231	244	225	Feb	252
Poole Harbour	232	405	182	273	155	Jan	249
Hornsea Mere	-	117	185	(505)	85	Jan	223
Fleet/Wey	254	248	183	202	179	Feb	213
North Norfolk Coast	218	[30] 193	199	231	198	Feb	208
Stour Estuary	[30] 191	139	154	146	291	Jan	184
Loch Ryan	[29] (166)	89	90	271	247	Dec	174 ▲
Sites of all-Ireland importance in Northern Ireland							
Belfast Lough	400	259	[30] 337	161	276	Feb	287
Strangford Lough	192	302	298	238	108	Jan	228
Larne Lough	284	238	173	247	136	Feb	216
Carlingford Lough	257	227	154	139	163	Jan	188
Lough Money	136	85	99	128	129	Jan	115
Upper Lough Erne	161	91	77	118	-		112

Sites no longer meeting table qualifying levels
Stevenston Point
Solway Estuary
Outer Ards

Other sites surpassing table qualifying levels in 2000–01

Loch Gairloch	[29] 223	Feb	
Tay Estuary	186	Jan	
Hamilton Low Parks & S'clyde Park	181	Jan	

SMEW
Mergellus albellus

			International threshold:	**250**
			Great Britain threshold:	**2**[*†]
			All-Ireland threshold:	**+**[*]

| GB Max: | 224 Jan |
| NI Max: | 0 |

[*] *50 is normally used as a minimum threshold*

The peak national total in Britain fell further from the relative low in 1999–2000. Correspondingly, several sites held rather fewer Smew than normal — the count of 10 at Hickling Broad is thus significant in being double the recent mean. Nevertheless, the most important sites continued to attract average numbers, despite the relatively mild winter, presumably a reflection of the same individuals returning to traditional sites. Typically, peaks at most occurred in January or February.

A striking feature of the table of key sites is the number of gravel pits. Eight of the top 10 sites and 15 of the 22 listed in total are not just man-made wetlands, but those resulting from specifically from mineral excavation. Quite why this habitat is so favoured in the UK is worthy of further research.

	96–97	97–98	98–99	99–00	00–01	Mon	Mean	
Sites of national importance in Great Britain [†]								
Wraysbury Gravel Pits	43	61	53	56	53	Jan	53	
Dungeness Gravel Pits	16	18	38	29	27	Jan	26	
Lee Valley Gravel Pits	31	23	30	22	20	Feb	25	
Cotswold Water Park (West)	[29] 10	[29] 8	19	28	17	Jan	16	
Fen Drayton Gravel Pits	22	15	17	14	7	Jan	15	
Rutland Water	14	18	19	8	8	Feb	13	
Thorpe Water Park	11	13	26	9	6	Jan	13	
Twyford Gravel Pits	13	11	9	17	-		13	
Earls Barton Gravel Pits	13	15	15	3	(2)	Jan	12	
Chew Valley Lake	14	7	15	5	11	Feb	10	
Middle Tame Valley Gravel Pits	(6)	5	21	5	8	Jan	10	
Eyebrook Reservoir	12	5	12	-	7	Jan	9	
Seaton Gravel Pits	3	9	16	[29] 9	7	Jan	9	
Rye Harbour & Pett Level	14	4	11	7	2	Oct	8	
Hornsea Mere	-	0	19	(1)	3	Jan	7	
Leybourne/ New Hythe Gravel Pits	-	-	-	-	7	Jan	7	
Loch of Strathbeg	9	5	8	(3)	5	Feb	7	
Little Paxton Gravel Pits	9	5	4	5	10	Feb	7	
Fairburn Ings	2	8	5	6	8	Feb	6	▲
Bedfont & Ashford Gravel Pits	16	5	1	1	5	Feb	6	
Hickling Broad	-	-	4	2	10	Feb	5	▲
Chichester Gravel Pits	12	5	2	(2)	2	Dec	5	▲

Important sites not counted in last five years
Staines Moor Gravel Pits

Sites no longer meeting table qualifying levels
Hoveringham Gravel Pits
Croxall Pits
Colne Valley Gravel Pits
Pitsford Reservoir
Eglwys Nunydd Reservoir

Other sites surpassing table qualifying levels in 2000-01
Stour Estuary   [30] 9   Jan

[†]   *as the British threshold for national importance is so small, and as no all-Ireland threshold has been set, a qualifying level of five has been chosen to select sites for presentation in this report*

RED-BREASTED MERGANSER
Mergus serrator

International threshold: 1,250
Great Britain threshold: 100
All-Ireland threshold: 20*

GB Max: 3,438 Feb
NI Max: 447 Sep

* 50 is normally used as a minimum threshold

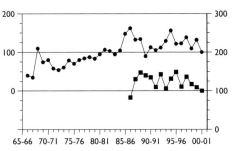

Figure 48. Annual indices for Red-breasted Merganser in GB (circles, left axis) and NI (squares, right axis)

The 2000–01 peak in Britain represents a marked fall compared with recent winters, when numbers have consistently been around 4,250. Accordingly, the national index value dropped markedly to its lowest value for 11 years and, whilst fluctuating, suggesting a decline over the last six years of around one third. There was a similar pattern in Northern Ireland, with declines in both the peak total count and the annual index value, the latter being the lowest since the first year for which indices were calculated and which, due to the relative paucity of data at that time, may, in any case, be an artefact.

This picture is reflected generally in counts at most key sites for Red-breasted Merganser: lower than average numbers were recorded at 14 of the 17 nationally important sites in Great Britain and at six of the eight sites of all-Ireland importance in Northern Ireland. Numbers have fallen markedly on the Inner Moray Firth and the Duddon Estuary, whilst counts at Lough Foyle represent just five per cent of the figure recorded three years previously.

	96–97	97–98	98–99	99–00	00–01	Mon	Mean
Sites of national importance in Great Britain							
Scapa Flow	-	-	[31] 628	-	-		628
Forth Estuary	715	675	622	601	459	Sep	614
Poole Harbour	333	502	385	466	336	Feb	404
Fleet/Wey	344	440	269	530	283	Feb	373
Inner Moray Firth	746	[24] 239	[24] 431	224	144	Feb	357
Morecambe Bay	323	312	309	475	338	Nov	351
Traeth Lafan	[15] 330	234	[15] 453	[15] 255	317	Aug	318
Duddon Estuary	382	394	378	240	148	Oct	308
Cromarty Firth	193	[24] 508	[24] 135	[30] 168	[29] 221	Jul	245
Clyde Estuary	230	186	230	159	125	Jul	186
Loch Indaal	159	157	191	185	163	Aug	171
Chichester Harbour	[30] 124	184	[30] 141	212	180	Feb	168
Langstone Harbour	182	199	185	116	122	Jan	161
Stevenston Point	(135)	148	-	-	-		148
North Norfolk Coast	166	[30] 121	100	128	103	Nov	124
Solway Estuary	130	181	66	122	109	Jan	122
Montrose Basin	52	204	113	100	120	Aug	118
Exe Estuary	67	133	93	130	139	Feb	112
The Wash	132	109	104	75	(16)	Oct	105
Sites of all-Ireland importance in Northern Ireland							
Strangford Lough	276	191	285	211	148	Sep	222
Larne Lough	201	171	195	243	188	Sep	200
Belfast Lough	[30] 123	270	[30] 123	166	169	Oct	170
Lough Foyle	130	296	[29] 99	27	15	Dec	113
Outer Ards	65	50	41	52	35	Feb	49
Carlingford Lough	36	44	46	41	44	Dec	42
Loughs Neagh & Beg	27	23	42	9	21	Sep	24
Bann Estuary	23	24	22	18	17	Feb	21

Important sites not counted in last five years
Craigalea to Newcastle
Tyrella Shore

Sites no longer meeting table qualifying levels
Irvine/Garnock Estuary
Loch Lomond
Dundrum Bay

Other sites surpassing table qualifying levels in 2000–01

Tay Estuary	127	Feb
Arran	108	Sep
Eden Estuary	104	Aug

GOOSANDER
Mergus merganser

International threshold:	**2,000**
Great Britain threshold:	**90**
All-Ireland threshold:	**+***

* 50 is normally used as a minimum threshold

GB Max: 2,413 Feb
NI Max: 1 various

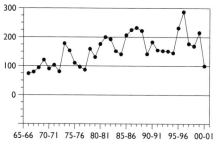

Figure 49. Annual indices for Goosander in GB (circles, left axis) and NI (squares, right axis)

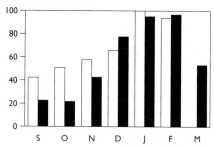

Figure 50. Monthly indices for Goosander in GB (white bars 2000–01; black bars 1995–96 to 1999–2000)

The peak 2000–01 total was the lowest count of Goosander since 1987–88. Although only a few hundred below totals in the early 1990s, the national index value dropped sharply, representing the biggest fall in an individual year and suggesting that abundance now matches the low levels of the 1960s and 1970s. The decline, by around two thirds, since the mid 1990s may reflect in part the severity of the winter. It is likely that counts in the mid 1990s were boosted by the arrival of continental birds during particularly cold winters at that time. Nevertheless, birds in Britain are believed to represent a largely discrete population, and it might be expected that counts should remain similar in mild winters in the absence of any notable declines in British breeding stock. Although counts at key sites may vary considerably between years, the low counts on Loch Lomond and Hamilton Low Parks & Strathclyde Park are notable, particularly so far north in the range since these presumably comprise solely locally bred birds. The post-breeding gathering on Tyninghame Estuary is in marked contrast to the general picture in 2000–01 and represents the second highest count at any site of Goosander during the last five years. Notable also was the fall from the table of the Inner Moray Firth, for many years the most important site in the country for this species.

	96–97	97–98	98–99	99–00	00–01	Mon	Mean
Sites of national importance in Great Britain							
Tay Estuary	225	240	160	268	230	Sep	225
Hirsel Lake	210	13	[29] 490	[29] 87	145	Oct	189
Lower Derwent Valley	298	182	111	51	-		161
Loch Lomond	184	226	129	176	11	Oct/Dec	145
Eccup Reservoir	163	163	131	154	95	Feb	141
Tyninghame Estuary	98	107	62	130	(300)	Aug	139
R. Tweed: Kelso to Coldstream	158	84	129	158	111	Feb	128
Hay-a-Park Gravel Pits	209	-	-	[22] 58	[22] 80	Dec	116
Hamilton Low Parks & S'clyde Park	-	170	140	73	48	Mar	108
Montrose Basin	89	136	129	67	88	Aug	102
Castle Loch (Lochmaben)	[29] 132	77	97	76	(0)		96
Blithfield Reservoir	165	74	102	(35)	38	Jan	95

Important sites not counted in last five years
Lochs Garten & Mallachie
Spey Mouth
Castle Howard Lake

Sites no longer meeting table qualifying levels
Inner Moray Firth
Eversley Cross & Yateley GP

Other sites surpassing table qualifying levels in 2000–01

Talkin Tarn	111	Jan
Dyfi Estuary	93	Aug

RUDDY DUCK
Oxyura jamaicensis

Naturalised introduction[†]
Native range: North and South America

GB Max:	3,760 Jan
NI Max:	53 Feb

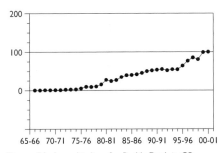

Figure 51. Annual indices for Ruddy Duck in GB

The peak British total fell by 17%, surpassing 3,000 in only two winter months (*cf.* five in winter 1999–2000). Despite the low counts, the annual index remained almost unchanged from the previous winter. In Northern Ireland, where numbers in some months reflect solely those at Loughs Neagh & Beg, counts were typical for recent years.

The results of the regional Ruddy Duck Control Trial were published in 2002 (Central Science Laboratory 2002). The trial was established to determine the feasibility, costs and access requirements necessary to reduce the UK population by 95%. The trial took place on Anglesey, in the Western Midlands and Fife. Modelling suggests that eradication could be achieved using year-round control in between four and six years if access is available to the principal wintering sites. The likely cost of this reduction would be between £3.6m and £5.4m.

The influence of control trials is reflected in the counts at some key sites, most notably low numbers on the Middle Tame Valley Gravel Pits, Llyn Traffwll, Llyn Alaw and Llynnau Y Fali. Notably high counts occurred at several sites in southeast England, including Staines, Hanningfield and Abberton Reservoirs, the Blackwater Estuary and Dungeness Gravel Pits, and the east coast on the Humber and Tees estuaries. Counts at the Cotswold Water Park (West) were also the highest at the site to date.

A detailed analysis of WeBS data up to the beginning of the control trial (Kershaw & Hughes 2002) revealed that wintering Ruddy Ducks were widely distributed within the UK, having been recorded on 742 WeBS sites between 1990–91 and 1999–2000. However, the majority of birds were concentrated on relatively few sites: in January 2000, the top ten sites held approximately 67% of the wintering population and the top 25 held 83%. The most important site (Rutland Water, Leicestershire) held 1,345 birds or 27% of the total population. The annual population increase had declined from 39% between 1966–67 and 1979–80, to 8–9% during the 1980s, and to 6–7% subsequently. During the 1980s and 1990s, Ruddy Ducks had increased most on estuarine/coastal habitats (by 29% per annum). This is illustrated by the increasing trends at four estuarine sites in the table below. Although the number of birds on estuarine/coastal habitats is still small, Ruddy Ducks in the UK may now be developing a marine wintering habit typical of their north American counterparts.

	96–97	97–98	98–99	99–00	00–01	Mon	Mean	
Sites with mean peak counts of 30 or more birds in Great Britain [†]								
Rutland Water	1,078	727	1,170	1,345	1,187	Jan	1,101	
Chew Valley Lake	[29] 789	[29] 700	[29] (255)	[29] 390	[29] 543	Dec	606	
Blithfield Reservoir	566	327	462	449	(420)	Nov	451	
Middle Tame Valley Gravel Pits	(501)	457	260	120	125	Jan	293	
Blagdon Lake	296	213	426	360	68	Sep	273	
Abberton Reservoir	88	99	(217)	443	389	Sep	255	
Hilfield Park Reservoir	306	186	216	298	206	Jan	242	
Stanford Reservoir	221	(181)	147	212	(67)	Dec	193	
Eyebrook Reservoir	239	275	14	-	72	Nov	150	
Pitsford Reservoir	87	98	(70)	167	135	Oct	122	
Hanningfield Reservoir	76	162	44	22	287	Feb	118	
Fairburn Ings	83	243	116	45	100	Dec	117	
Llyn Traffwll	156	122	[29] 153	92	61	Sep	117	
Llyn Alaw	[29] 62	133	[29] 221	159	8	Nov	117	
Staines Reservoirs	112	3	22	127	(244)	Feb	102	
Holme Pierrepont Gravel Pits	134	99	64	102	106	Oct	101	
Clumber Park Lake	111	60	116	66	123	Oct	95	
Belvide Reservoir	31	(2)	59	100	170	Feb	90	
Tophill Low Reservoirs	51	56	85	113	117	Oct	84	
Colwick Country Park	68	41	41	[29] 181	-		83	
Attenborough Gravel Pits	265	18	14	23	(0)		80	
Rostherne Mere	152	24	18	88	66	Jan	70	
Dungeness Gravel Pits	29	33	39	110	134	Dec	69	
Kilconquhar Loch	85	62	58	56	74	Aug	67	
Llynnau Y Fali	92	99	71	29	20	Dec	62	
Great Pool Westwood Park	29	51	77	47	90	Feb	59	
Pugneys Country Park Lakes	65	94	51	35	49	Jan	59	
Blackwater Estuary	32	29	38	80	106	Feb	57	
Cropston Reservoir	156	16	1	47	(0)		55	
Bolton-on-Swale Gravel Pits	29	34	57	66	79	Oct	53	
Farmwood Pool	99	61	41	23	17	Oct	48	
Humber Estuary	(6)	16	23	54	99	Nov	48	▲
Cotswold Water Park (West)	16	[29] 42	33	34	115	Feb	48	
Angler's Country Park Lake	3	39	54	69	[29] 70	Dec	47	
Knight & Bessborough Reservoirs	126	32	32	10	31	Feb	46	
Hule Moss	[29] 14	[29] 41	[29] 73	39	-		42	
Woolston Eyes	40	34	40	48	43	Sep	41	
Tees Estuary	13	25	39	56	71	Oct	41	▲
Thoresby Lake	20	63	19	74	22	Oct	40	
Church Wilne Reservoir	76	2	-	-	-		39	
Brent Reservoir	24	16	46	44	61	Oct	38	
Houghton Green Pool	36	42	38	28	37	Jan	36	
Hollowell Reservoir	7	3	19	60	91	Feb	36	▲
Rufford Lake	51	28	48	22	21	Aug	34	
Hogganfield Loch	15	35	36	44	39	Dec	34	▲
Ravensthorpe Reservoir	11	11	41	58	44	Jan	33	▲
Sutton & Lound Gravel Pits	25	36	-	38	-		33	
Thames Estuary	19	17	31	29	63	Jan	32	▲
Carsington Water	10	10	10	96	(7)	Jun	32	▲
Old Moor Wetlands	25	42	32	31	26	Jul/Aug	31	

Loughs Neagh & Beg 89 28 84 14 53 Feb 54

Important sites not counted in last five years
Capheaton Reservoir

Sites no longer meeting table qualifying levels
Swillington Ings
Worsborough Reservoir
Aqualate Mere
Swithland Reservoir
King George VI Reservoir
Ellesmere Lakes

Other sites surpassing table qualifying levels in 2000–01

King George V Reservoirs	46	Feb
Walthamstow Reservoirs	(41)	Feb
Wigan Flashes 39	Dec	
Linlithgow Loch	36	Sep
Catchpenny Pool	33	Oct
Wintersett & Cold Hiendley Reservoirs	32	Jan
Ellesmere Lakes	31	Oct
Melton Country Park	31	Sep
Carr Vale Flash & Reserve Pond	30	Jul

†   *as site designation does not occur and the 1% criterion is not applied, a qualifying levels of 30 has been chosen to select sites for presentation in this report*

ARGENTINE BLUE-BILL
Oxjura vittata

Escape
Native range: South America

Singles were seen on the Ouse Washes in April
and at Melton Country Park in September.

WATER RAIL
Rallus aquaticus

International threshold: ?
Great Britain threshold: ?[†]
All-Ireland threshold: ?[†]

GB Max: 449 Dec
NI Max: 1 Dec

A highly secretive species, counts represent only a fraction of the total number of birds in the UK. In 2000–01 birds were recorded at 238 sites, lower than in most recent winters. The peak British total, however, was amongst the highest recorded, only exceeded significantly by the 521 in December 1998. It is interesting that, despite the difficulty in detecting the species during counts, the peak count has occurred in December for seven of the last eight years.

Whilst the largely sedentary breeding population is supplemented in winter by birds from continental Europe (Jenkins 2002), this peak is more likely to reflect the increased ease of detection when submergent and bankside vegetation dies back and colder conditions force birds into more open habitats. Counts from key sites are, perhaps not surprisingly, variable and few were of particular note in 2000–01.

	96–97	97–98	98–99	99–00	00–01	Mon	Mean
Sites with mean peak counts of 10 or more birds in Great Britain [†]							
Grouville Marsh	(20)	(20)	(10)	(40)	(30)	Oct	(40)
Somerset Levels	42	29	38	34	43	Dec	37
Rye Harbour & Pett Level	40	2	61	40	31	Oct	35
Stodmarsh & Collards Lagoon	9	14	23	41	25	Oct	22
Leighton Moss	18	25	28	15	-		22
Chew Valley Lake	9	19	42	4	29	Dec	21
Fleet Pond	20	20	15	20	25	Nov/Dec	20
Colwick Country Park	68	0	2	4	-		19

	96–97	97–98	98–99	99–00	00–01	Mon	Mean	
Lower Derwent Valley	26	27	7	8	-		17	
Kenfig NNR	-	[7] 16	[7] 14	[7] 24	[7] 12	Apr	17	▲
Lee Valley Gravel Pits	10	6	10	22	18	Dec	13	
Doxey Marshes SSSI	15	11	10	11	(8)	Oct/Dec	12	
Marston Sewage Treatment Works	-	-	5	18	-		12	
Kilconquhar Loch	11	8	9	14	15	Jan	11	▲
North Norfolk Coast	6	11	16	10	13	Jan	11	
Severn Estuary	9	5	26	5	8	Nov	11	
Rutland Water	10	6	10	20	6	Jan/Feb	10	
Poole Harbour	7	7	7	16	15	Oct	10	▲
Shipley Country Park	0	-	-	-	(20)	Jun	10	▲
Longueville Marsh	(10)	(5)	(10)	(10)	(10)	Dec-Feb	(10)	

Important sites not counted in last five years
Pannel Valley

Sites no longer meeting table qualifying levels
Knocksinnock Lagoons

Other sites surpassing table qualifying levels in 2000–01

Dee Estuary (Eng/Wal)	16	Feb
Southampton Water	13	Nov/Feb
Chichester Harbour	12	Jan
Hornchurch Country Park	10	Dec
Cotswold Water Park (West)	10	Dec

†   *as no British or all-Ireland thresholds have been set, a qualifying level of 10 has been chosen to select sites for presentation in this report*

SPOTTED CRAKE
Porzana porzana

International threshold:	?
Great Britain threshold:	?[†]
All-Ireland threshold:	?[†]

GB Max: 4 Sep
NI Max: 0

During September and October, single birds were recorded at Rye Harbour & Pett Level, Stodmarsh & Collards Lagoon, River Cam: Kingfishers Bridge, North Norfolk Coast, Hornsea Mere and Dee Estuary (Eng/Wal).

MOORHEN
Gallinula chloropus

International threshold:	?
Great Britain threshold:	?[†]
All-Ireland threshold:	?[†]

GB Max: 13,313 Oct
NI Max: 307 Sep

The peak Great Britain count, just over 1,000 below the record count in 1999–2000, was still amongst the highest recorded by WeBS. The survey, however, barely scratches the surface of the Moorhen wintering population which, although no official population estimate exists, may number in the region of 750,000 birds based on the UK breeding population estimate of 240,000 pairs (Gibbons 1993). In Northern Ireland the peak was in the region of recent fluctuations.

Being a highly dispersed species, it is likely that even if a population estimate were available, no single site in Great Britain would attain national importance status (i.e. regularly holding 1% of the national population) as a result of WeBS counts. Based on the approximate figure above, even the top sites in the table below would hold no more than 0.1% of the winter population. Of the key sites, numbers at Martin Mere fell for the fourth consecutive year, whilst numbers at Bewl Water were well above average.

	96-97	97-98	98-99	99-00	00-01	Mon	Mean
Sites with mean peak counts of 100 or more birds in Great Britain †							
Severn Estuary	829	(21)	860	679	735	Nov	776
Martin Mere	739	710	640	570	510	Jan	634
Lower Derwent Valley	816	680	371	419	-		572
Somerset Levels	253	250	4 424	407	310	Oct	329
North Norfolk Coast	179	334	291	441	309	Jan	311
Durham Coast	175	256	269	307	240	Oct	249
Lee Valley Gravel Pits	234	191	215	278	315	Dec	247
Burry Inlet	220	281	198	213	196	Aug	222
Arun Valley	234	190	197	240	202	Aug	213
Thames Estuary	219	144	150	269	268	Oct	210
Ouse Washes	124	201	287	141	29 206	Jan	192
Rutland Water	71	119	160	229	237	Oct	163
Chichester Gravel Pits	167	176	138	(138)	132	Nov	153
Blackwater Estuary	181	165	126	138	96	Nov	141
Chew Valley Lake	125	120	145	130	185	Sep	141
Bewl Water	119	60	170	122	230	Sep	140
Grouville Marsh	(100)	(70)	(80)	(140)	(120)	Jan	(140)
Tring Reservoirs	78	148	207	90	149	Oct	134
Rye Harbour & Pett Level	67	111	222	162	99	Oct	132
Pitsford Reservoir	116	21	(123)	172	175	Sep	121
Sutton & Lound Gravel Pits	120	106	-	136	-		121
R. Idle: Bawtry to Misterton	119	-	-	-	-		119
R. Wye: Bakewell to Haddon	118	160	101	114	101	Jan	119
Marston Sewage Treatment Works	-	-	(110)	118	-		118
Fairburn Ings	104	112	120	113	(115)	Jan	113
Lancaster Canal	106	207	88	85	65	Oct	110
Leighton Moss	170	95	90	65	-		105
Swanbourne Lake	42	(60)	130	140	100	Jan	103
Thanet Coast	135	76	122	83	87	Jan	101
Sites with mean peak counts of 30 or more birds in Northern Ireland †							
Loughs Neagh & Beg	132	137	201	124	183	Sep	155
Upper Lough Erne	164	52	100	67	-		96
Broad Water Canal	83	71	69	-	55	Sep	70

▲

Sites no longer meeting table qualifying levels
Upper Quoile River

Important sites not counted in last five years
Portavo Lake

Other sites surpassing table qualifying levels in 2000–01
Orwell Estuary	160	Jan
Stodmarsh & Collards Lagoon	152	Aug
Dee Estuary (Eng/Wal)	134	Feb
Southampton Water	102	Feb
Belfast Lough	44	Sep

† as no British or all-Irish thresholds have been set, qualifying levels of 100 and 30 have been chosen to select sites, in Great Britain and Northern Ireland respectively, for presentation in this report

COOT
Fulica atra

International threshold: 15,000
Great Britain threshold: 1,100
All-Ireland threshold: 250

GB Max: 109,688 Oct
NI Max: 7,240 Oct

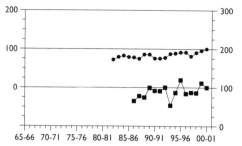

Figure 52. Annual indices for Coot in GB (circles, left axis) and NI (squares, right axis)

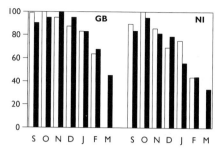

Figure 53. Monthly indices for Coot in GB and NI (white bars 2000–01; black bars 1995–96 to 1999–2000)

The highest counts since 1994–95 at Abberton Reservoir, the UK's premier site for this species, were notable following several years of relatively low numbers. Despite being a widely dispersed species, Abberton and nearby Hanningfield Reservoir may hold in excess of 10% of the birds in the UK at any one time. Other counts of note were at Chew Valley Lake and Little Paxton Gravel Pits, both recording well above average numbers, whilst those at Alton Water dipped considerably.

The peak count in Great Britain was lower than the record total in the previous year, though still amongst the highest recorded by WeBS. This was reflected in the index values

which reached their highest level to date. The peak in October was typical, monthly indices illustrating the early autumn high, tailing off rapidly from mid winter onwards.

In Northern Ireland, counts from Loughs Neagh & Beg make up around 90% of the totals and also strongly influence the index values. Numbers at this site, the second most important in the UK, were typical for recent years and as a consequence peak totals and indices in the province were also around average. Regrettably no data were received for Upper Lough Erne, one of the province's other key sites, during the 2000–01 reporting year.

	96–97	97–98	98–99	99–00	00–01	Mon	Mean
Sites of national importance in Great Britain							
Abberton Reservoir	6,897	4,784	6,493	9,673	11,645	Sep	7,898
Rutland Water	3,935	4,663	3,971	3,759	3,375	Nov	3,941
Hanningfield Reservoir	4,986	3,181	3,337	2,809	4,282	Nov	3,719
Cotswold Water Park (West)	3,110	3,560	3,718	3,980	3,806	Nov	3,635
Lee Valley Gravel Pits	3,023	2,913	2,708	3,559	2,751	Nov	2,991
Cheddar Reservoir	3,100	2,300	2,400	2,500	3,410	Jan	2,742
Hickling Broad	-	-	2,136	4,993	1,021	Sep	2,717
Ouse Washes	[29] 1,661	3,082	2,611	3,803	[29] 2,062	Jan	2,644
Cotswold Water Park (East)	2,268	2,094	3,608	2,944	2,227	Jan	2,628
Chew Valley Lake	2,500	2,260	2,650	1,980	3,500	Sep	2,578
Lower Windrush Valley GP	2,068	2,629	2,619	2,188	2,274	Nov	2,356
Windermere	2,310	2,029	-	-	-		2,170
Fleet/Wey	2,501	1,562	1,777	1,862	2,346	Oct	2,010
Loch Leven	1,546	1,551	2,285	2,340	2,100	Sep	1,964
Pitsford Reservoir	1,222	1,310	2,281	2,415	2,331	Sep	1,912
Fen Drayton Gravel Pits	1,675	1,709	1,948	1,719	1,787	Oct	1,768
Blithfield Reservoir	1,109	1,717	2,305	1,946	1,731	Aug	1,762
Middle Tame Valley Gravel Pits	(2,804)	1,196	(1,348)	1,368	1,674	Jan	1,761
Alton Water	1,142	2,135	1,465	3,090	655	Sep	1,697
Little Paxton Gravel Pits	2,173	485	853	1,235	3,014	Oct	1,552
R. Avon: Fordingbridge to R'wood	1,529	1,749	1,354	1,495	1,439	Nov	1,513

	96–97	97–98	98–99	99–00	00–01	Mon	Mean
Dungeness Gravel Pits	997	1,166	1,350	2,085	1,564	Sep	1,432
Sutton & Lound Gravel Pits	1,716	1,072	-	1,325	-		1,371
Stanford Reservoir	1,270	(1,865)	1,358	157	1,050	Oct	1,140
Fairburn Ings	1,572	959	1,100	1,106	924	Aug	1,132
Baston Langtoft Gravel Pits	1,328	900	1,204	1,249	932	Jan	1,123
North Norfolk Coast	1,110	795	998	1,094	1,553	Aug	1,110 ▲

Sites of all-Ireland importance in Northern Ireland

	96–97	97–98	98–99	99–00	00–01	Mon	Mean
Loughs Neagh & Beg	8,262	5,890	5,568	7,307	6,579	Oct	6,721
Upper Lough Erne	441	412	562	646	-		515
Strangford Lough	378	407	328	703	400	Sep	443

Sites no longer meeting table qualifying levels
Wraysbury Gravel Pits

Important sites not counted in last five years
Ballysaggart Lough

Other sites surpassing table qualifying levels in 2000–01

Hornsea Mere	1,260	Nov	Eyebrook Reservoir	1,310	Oct
Grafham Water	1,203	Dec	Nene Washes	1,235	Feb
Belvide Reservoir	1,246	Aug	Morecambe Bay	(1,253)	Oct
Swale Estuary	1,181	Jan	Breydon Wtr & Berney Marshes	1,476	Dec

---

CRANE
Grus grus

Two were present at Holme on the North Norfolk Marshes in April, and singles were recorded at Spurn Head, Humber Estuary (April) and at Dun's Dish in Angus (August).

OYSTERCATCHER
Haematopus ostralegus

International threshold:	9,000
Great Britain threshold:	3,600
All-Ireland threshold:	500

GB Max: 241,357 Sep
NI Max: 17,814 Nov

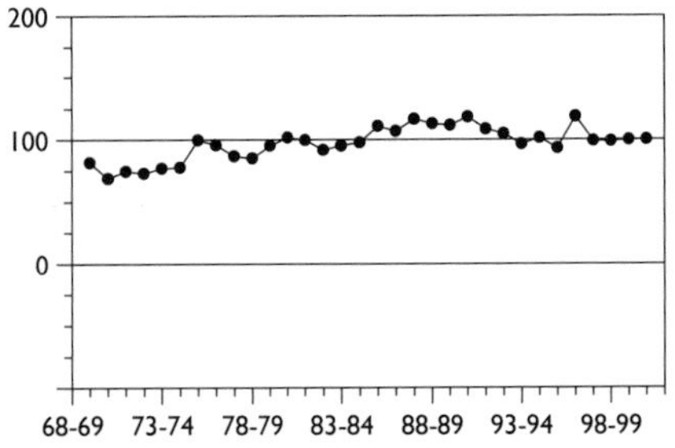

Figure 54. Annual indices for Oystercatcher in the UK

Peak counts and annual indices for Oystercatcher have remained relatively stable, the latter remarkably so, over the last four years. WeBS indices in the UK have fallen by 15% over the last ten years but have increased by 45% over the last 30 years. It has been suggested that rapid declines in numbers on the east coast in the early 1990s may have been due to a reduction in food supply caused by over-fishing and low spatfall of cockles in the Wash (Austin et al. 2000, Atkinson et al. in press). In contrast, numbers have been far more stable on the west coast of Britain. The peak count in Northern Ireland was 18% higher than that recorded in the previous winter.

Lower than average counts were recorded at most sites currently surpassing the threshold for international importance; counts on the Thames Estuary were, by contrast, 10% higher than the most recent five-year peak mean. The Exe Estuary fell below the threshold for national importance and was replaced by the North Norfolk Coast in the table. There were few notable changes in the peak counts at the key sites in Northern Ireland. During autumn passage, particularly large numbers were recorded at Morecambe Bay, the Solway Estuary and the Dee Estuary (Eng/Wal).

	96–97	97–98	98–99	99–00	00–01	Mon	Mean
Sites of international importance in the UK							
Morecambe Bay	57,670	56,511	52,780	50,990	50,831	Nov	53,756
Solway Estuary	(47,729)	34,446	42,038	36,752	31,296	Nov	38,452
Dee Estuary (Eng/Wal)	[30] 28,800	25,142	18,932	12,506	21,326	Feb	21,341
Ribble Estuary	20,846	(28,701)	15,491	19,535	17,784	Jan	20,471
The Wash	(16,363)	17,126	12,068	15,701	13,457	Jan	14,943
Burry Inlet	19,067	9,423	13,344	(17,867)	13,347	Dec	14,610
Thames Estuary	14,681	14,615	(12,162)	12,760	14,937	Nov	14,248
Sites of national importance in Great Britain							
Forth Estuary	6,826	8,045	6,726	8,154	6,186	Nov	7,187
Duddon Estuary	5,630	9,314	6,499	6,890	4,867	Feb	6,640
Inner Moray Firth	5,261	8,334	5,550	4,785	6,049	Jan	5,996
Traeth Lafan	5,780	(3,163)	2,062	(5,781)	6,897	Nov	5,130
Swale Estuary	5,780	3,349	5,042	5,539	5,227	Nov	4,987
Clyde Estuary	5,414	4,781	4,197	4,878	5,060	Jan	4,866
Carmarthen Bay	3,474	3,926	6,423	[30] (4,851)	4,154	Jan	4,566
Medway Estuary	3,162	(5,521)	(4,152)	(4,452)	2,448	Jan	3,947
North Norfolk Coast	3,596	3,383	3,825	3,980	3,755	Jan	3,708 ▲
Sites of all-Ireland importance in Northern Ireland							
Strangford Lough	7,276	6,904	6,661	6,175	7,149	Dec	6,833
Belfast Lough	[30] 6,153	[30] 6,974	[30] 6,653	[30] 6,216	5,647	Jan	6,329
Lough Foyle	(3,352)	(2,865)	3,609	3,087	2,730	Dec	3,195
Dundrum Bay	1,660	1,763	3,328	1,103	1,707	Dec	1,912
Outer Ards	1,523	(1,385)	1,761	1,872	1,621	Nov	1,694
Carlingford Lough	(812)	902	(1,184)	1,289	1,184	Jan	1,140

Important sites not counted in last five years
Dundrum Outer Bay
Carlingford to Newcastle

Sites no longer meeting table qualifying levels
Exe Estuary

Sites surpassing international threshold during passage periods in 2000–01
Morecambe Bay	57,402	Oct
Solway Estuary	48,069	Sep
Dee Estuary (Eng/Wal)	26,713	Sep
Thames Estuary	13,784	Oct
The Wash	13,659	Aug
Forth Estuary	9,982	Sep
Burry Inlet	9,978	Oct

BLACK-WINGED STILT
Himantopus himantopus

Vagrant
Native range: worldwide distribution

The long-staying bird was recorded on the North
Norfolk Coast for the eight consecutive year.

AVOCET
Recurvirostra avosetta

International threshold: **700**
Great Britain threshold: **10***
All-Ireland threshold: **+***

GB Max: 4,564 Jan
NI Max: 0

* 50 is normally used as a minimum threshold

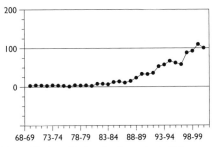

Figure 55. Annual indices for Avocet in the UK

Annual indices indicate that there has been a 207% increase in Avocet numbers in Britain in the last ten years alone. In 2000–01, the British maximum was the highest yet recorded by WeBS yet the annual index declined after reaching a record level in 1999–2000. The increase in the British population has been mirrored in countries across Northwest Europe and has been attributed to improved protection from hunting, a reduction in egg-collecting, improved food supplies due to eutrophication, creation of breeding habitats as an indirect consequence of coastal engineering projects, deliberate habitat management and climate warming (van Impe 1985, Beukema & Cadée 1986, Meininger *et al*. 1992, Cadbury *et al*. 1989).

After another large count in January 2001, the Alde Complex continues to surpass the threshold for international importance and is joined in the table, for the first time, by Poole Harbour. The peak at the latter site was over 75% higher than the most recent five-year peak mean. Notably high counts were also recorded at several east coast resorts surpassing the national importance threshold, including the Blyth Estuary (Suffolk), Breydon Water & Berney Marshes and the Humber Estuary. As usual, there were no records of Avocet in Northern Ireland.

	96–97	97–98	98–99	99–00	00–01	Mon	Mean	
Sites of international importance in the UK								
Alde Complex	437	884	1,336	1,330	1,007	Jan	999	
Poole Harbour	520	585	832	823	1,491	Feb	850	▲
Sites of national importance in Great Britain								
Thames Estuary	450	488	668	766	563	Feb	587	
Exe Estuary	339	369	400	544	366	Feb	404	
Medway Estuary	(368)	(200)	500	(374)	301	Jan	401	
Blyth Estuary (Suffolk)	242	422	-	-	524	Jan	396	
Tamar Complex	301	595	220	(207)	452	Jan	392	
Hamford Water	299	587	276	532	242	Jan	387	
Swale Estuary	(208)	340	306	402	145	Nov	298	
Colne Estuary	150	214	266	417	351	Jan	280	
North Norfolk Coast	(51)	(318)	301	321	72	Mar	253	
Breydon Wtr & Berney Marshes	77	157	94	177	272	Feb	155	
Deben Estuary	100	102	135	172	165	Jan	135	
Minsmere	(0)	70	120	-	120	Mar	103	
The Wash	(83)	196	23	183	6	Feb	102	
Blackwater Estuary	14	24	(38)	44	167	Nov	62	
Humber Estuary	0	28	(49)	82	126	Mar	59	
Pagham Harbour	10	[30] 14	19	27	26	Jan	19	
Abberton Reservoir	0	64	0	0	0	Nov	13	
Horsey Mere	-	(0)	20	0	-		10	

Other sites surpassing table qualifying levels in 2000–01
Chichester Harbour   15   Jan

STONE CURLEW
Burhinus oedicnemus

One was recorded along the North Norfolk Coast at Cley in August. A species not normally recorded by WeBS owing to its nocturnal habits and preference for dry habitats.

LITTLE RINGED PLOVER
Charadrius dubius

International threshold:	?
Great Britain threshold:	?
All-Ireland threshold:	?

GB Max: 246 Apr
NI Max: 0

Following a year when numbers peaked slightly later than normal, the highest count in 2000–01 occurred in April, the earliest recorded by WeBS. The 31 recorded at Old Moor Wetlands in July was the largest number ever recorded by WeBS at a single site.

Sites with 10 or more birds in 2000–01

Old Moor Wetlands	31	Jul	Carr Vale Flash	12	Jun
Severn Estuary	18	Jul	Acre Nook Square	11	Apr
Rutland Water	13	Jul	Dungeness	10	Jul
Humber Estuary	13	Aug	London Wetland Centre	10	May/Jun
Kingsbury Water Park	12	Apr			

RINGED PLOVER
Charadrius hiaticula

International threshold:	500
Great Britain winter threshold:	290
Great Britain passage threshold:	300
All-Ireland threshold:	125

GB Max: 17,840 Aug
NI Max: 750 Oct

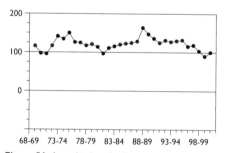

Figure 56. Annual indices for Ringed Plover in the UK

Although the peak count for Britain was similarly low to that recorded in 1999–2000, the annual index increased after declines over the previous three winters. The peak winter count, recorded in January, remained below the 10,000 mark. In the most recent assessment, this species continues to qualify for Amber-listing in the UK based, in part, on the fact that wintering numbers have declined by over 25% over the last 25 years (Gregory *et al.* 2002). However, across the whole of Europe and North Africa, the population has increased markedly over the same timescale (Wetlands International 1999).

Ringed Plovers have apparently redistributed in the UK, from the west coast to the east coast, and this has been related to an increase in mild winters (Austin *et al.* 2000). This may explain why numbers at all sites in Northern Ireland were lower than average in 2000–01. However, the picture in Britain was not so clear with sites in both the west and east supporting lower than average numbers. The peak count at the Thames Estuary, the most important site numerically in the UK, was 25% higher than the most recent five-year peak mean. Numbers were also notably high at the Thanet Coast for the second year running.

Of the 15 sites that surpassed the threshold for international importance during autumn passage, notably high counts were recorded at the Ribble Estuary and the Wash. Given that the peak count nationally is generally recorded in the late summer/early autumn, WeBS continues to highlight the importance of Britain during the passage period.

	96-97	97-98	98-99	99-00	00-01	Mon	Mean
Sites of international importance in the UK							
Thames Estuary	535	792	620	726	895	Nov	714
Langstone Harbour	660	739	383	605	413	Dec	560
Tiree	-	[17] 534	-	[25] 561	-		548
Sites of national importance in Great Britain							
Morecambe Bay	528	515	367	522	473	Nov	481
Hamford Water	482	281	570	365	678	Nov	475
North Norfolk Coast	775	[30] 503	318	373	369	Feb	468
South Ford	-	-	-	570	341	Dec	456
Colne Estuary	(306)	(568)	(462)	(208)	224	Jan	418 ▼
Humber Estuary	249	382	[30] 504	466	409	Nov	403
Stour Estuary	597	(87)	257	[30] 230	[30] 493	Jan	394
Thanet Coast	197	297	386	558	528	Dec	393
Solway Estuary	223	214	906	276	280	Dec	380
South Uist (West Coast)	-	[17] 376	-	-	-		376
Medway Estuary	[30] 442	313	(540)	(351)	126	Jan	354
Forth Estuary	259	317	415	365	316	Jan	334
Swale Estuary	203	301	430	347	292	Dec	315
Sites of all-Ireland importance in Northern Ireland							
Outer Ards	575	350	485	223	313	Nov	389
Strangford Lough	[30] 346	[30] 171	279	216	105	Feb	223
Belfast Lough	133	108	167	192	142	Nov	148
Carlingford Lough	(131)	90	(174)	125	116	Dec	127 ▲

Important sites not counted in last five years

Traighear
East Sanday Coast
Carlingford to Newcastle
Kilkeel to Lee Stone Point

Sites no longer meeting table qualifying levels

Chichester Harbour
Jersey Shore
The Wash

Other sites surpassing table qualifying levels in 2000-01

Loch Fleet Complex	356	Dec

Sites surpassing passage threshold in Great Britain in 2000-01

Ribble Estuary	5,432	May		Pegwell Bay	595	Sep
The Wash	2,164	Aug		Severn Estuary	566	Aug
Humber Estuary	1,818	Aug		Colne Estuary	510	Oct
North Norfolk Coast	1,519	Sep		Mersey Estuary	498	Aug
Hamford Water	1,135	Sep		Tees Estuary	411	May
Thames Estuary	1,097	Sep		Blackwater Estuary	394	Aug
Swale Estuary	934	Aug		Pagham Harbour	368	Aug
Chichester Harbour	852	Aug		Lindisfarne	348	Aug
Solway Estuary	819	Apr		South Ford	348	Oct
Stour Estuary	807	Sep		Alt Estuary	314	Apr
Forth Estuary	621	Sep		Alton Water	307	Oct
Morecambe Bay	605	Aug		Breydon Wtr & Berney Marshes	305	May

KENTISH PLOVER
Charadrius alexandrinus

Scarce

A single was seen at Pagham Harbour in April.

DOTTEREL
Charadrius morinellus

Scarce

One was at Brading Harbour in August, the fourth consecutive year in which this species has been recorded by WeBS.

PACIFIC GOLDEN PLOVER
Pluvialis fulva

Vagrant
Native range: Asia, Australasia and NE Africa

One was recorded on the Humber Estuary in the Brough Haven area in July.

GOLDEN PLOVER
Pluvialis apricaria

International threshold:	18,000
Great Britain threshold:	2,500
All-Ireland threshold:	2,000

GB Max: 144,549 Feb
NI Max: 12,418 Feb

The numbers of Golden Plover recorded by WeBS fluctuate markedly between years. Peaks for both Britain and Northern Ireland were lower than average in 2000–01; 25% lower in Britain than in the previous winter. The species has moved from the Amber to the Green List in the most recent assessment of Birds of Conservation Concern because recent data suggest less than 20% of the East Atlantic Flyway population occurs in the UK during the non-breeding season (Gregory *et al.* 2002). Limited information on breeding and wintering numbers means that there is an considerable guesswork in assessing population trends for this species.

Peak counts at sites also vary between years, primarily because the species uses inland areas outwith the WeBS count boundaries of estuaries, often as a consequence of changing weather patterns. Maxima recorded at the Humber Estuary and the Wash were 22% and 38% lower than average, respectively. Both sites, however, continue to support internationally important numbers during the winter. The Humber Estuary also held large numbers during autumn passage. The count on the Blyth Estuary (Suffolk) was particularly noteworthy.

	96–97	97–98	98–99	99–00	00–01	Mon	Mean
Sites of international importance in the UK							
Humber Estuary	8,741	34,444	(42,848)	42,381	25,133	Nov	30,709
The Wash	6,879	26,461	20,467	42,761	13,740	Nov	22,062
Sites of national importance in Great Britain							
Blackwater Estuary	6,631	8,295	(9,150)	14,902	18,826	Feb	12,164
Breydon Wtr & Berney Marshes	7,550	7,200	10,300	10,600	13,280	Feb	9,786
Swale Estuary	(2,227)	9,535	(7,722)	7,010	6,217	Feb	7,621
Solway Estuary	4,617	7,572	5,374	30 3,984	30 8,065	Nov	5,922
Lower Derwent Valley	3,000	7,950	6,200	3,400	-		5,138
R. Idle: Bawtry to Misterton	5,000	-	-	-	-		5,000
Thames Estuary	3,875	4,925	3,318	4,166	7,881	Feb	4,833
Ribble Estuary	6,530	5,325	4,397	3,546	4,341	Nov	4,828
Somerset Levels	683	8,909	3,366	5,401	5,077	Feb	4,687
Hamford Water	4,611	8,275	3,847	2,245	4,164	Dec	4,628
Blyth Estuary (Suffolk)	830	2,760	-	-	10,000	Feb	4,530 ▲
Colne Estuary	(1,500)	4,350	(3,795)	5,000	4,045	Feb	4,465
Morecambe Bay	4,310	4,745	3,618	3,628	4,121	Dec	4,084
Clifford Hill Gravel Pits	2,000	4,000	3,620	5,500	4,500	Dec	3,924
Carmarthen Bay	10,003	(3,300)	500	9	5,001	Jan	3,878
Lindisfarne	2,604	2,580	(4,990)	4,830	3,598	Nov	3,720
North Norfolk Coast	2,040	4,772	4,165	3,442	3,386	Dec	3,561
Criddling Stubbs Quarry Pools	2,000	5,000	-	-	-		3,500

	96–97	97–98	98–99	99–00	00–01	Mon	Mean
Unspecified SE England site	1,800	2,500	4,500	5,000	1,600	Nov	3,080
Old Moor Wetlands	800	1,800	3,500	4,100	4,700	Nov	2,980 ▲
Crouch-Roach Estuary	(890)	1,218	4,455	1,730	3,889	Jan	2,823
St Mary's Island	(3,000)	6,500	1,500	2,000	1,000	Jan	2,800
Mersey Estuary	4000	2750	[30] 1,938	2440	2227	Jan	2,671
Nene Washes	700	6,109	3,223	2,260	500	Dec	2,558

Sites of all-Ireland importance in Northern Ireland

	96–97	97–98	98–99	99–00	00–01	Mon	Mean
Strangford Lough	[30] 14,375	[30] 12,100	6,872	7,076	4,945	Feb	9,074
Loughs Neagh & Beg	3,902	4,300	8,974	6,675	7,621	Dec	6,294
Lough Foyle	(5,207)	5,456	[29] 7,000	2,600	2,590	Nov	4,571
Outer Ards	5,869	(735)	2,420	2,095	1,411	Feb	2,949

Sites no longer meeting table qualifying levels
Fairburn Ings
Forth Estuary
Dagenham Chase Gravel Pits

Important sites not counted in last five years
New Road Pits
Dundrum Outer Bay

Other sites surpassing table qualifying levels in 2000–01

Stour Estuary	[30] 6,620	Dec
Chichester Harbour	2,941	Jan
Pegwell Bay	4,000	Feb

Sites surpassing international threshold during passage periods in 2000–01

Humber Estuary	38,494	Oct

GREY PLOVER

Pluvialis squatarola

International threshold:	1,500
Great Britain threshold:	430
All-Ireland threshold:	40*

* 50 is normally used as a minimum threshold

GB Max:	51,943 Feb
NI Max:	328 Feb

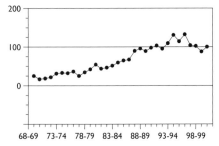

Figure 57. Annual indices for Grey Plover in the UK

The annual index increased for the first time in four years and the peak count for Britain was notably higher than average. Interestingly, although the annual index has risen more than five-fold over the last 30 years, the increase has been only 3% over the last ten years. The reasons for these trends remain unclear given that there was little evidence of maximum densities having been reached in most estuaries by the mid 1990s (Austin & Rehfisch 1998). It has been suggested that the general increase in numbers across Northwest Europe may be, in part, a consequence of a northward shift in the distribution of wintering birds (Wetlands International 1999). However, it is widely accepted that there has probably been a genuine increase in numbers as well.

Of those sites surpassing the threshold for international importance, there were notably low numbers at Lindisfarne (34% lower than the most recent five-year peak mean), Langstone Harbour (33%), the Ribble Estuary (31%), and the Blackwater Estuary (30%). In contrast, the peak count on the Dengie Flats was 80% higher than average and there were proportionately smaller increases at sites elsewhere. During the spring passage period, large counts were made at the Ribble Estuary and the Wash. Another eight sites surpassed the international importance threshold during passage periods.

	96–97	97–98	98–99	99–00	00–01	Mon	Mean
Sites of international importance in the UK							
The Wash	8,952	9,790	5,767	7,432	7,495	Jan	7,887
Ribble Estuary	12,856	[30] 5,408	8,435	3,234	5,139	Feb	7,014
Thames Estuary	9,698	3,708	(5,173)	5,854	6,908	Feb	6,542
Dengie Flats	2,160	4,156	(1,966)	3,252	7,826	Feb	4,349
Blackwater Estuary	(2,383)	(3,549)	(4,874)	4,649	2,920	Feb	4,148
Hamford Water	(7,033)	3,270	3,020	1,672	2,803	Feb	3,560
Stour Estuary	[30] 3,502	(1,705)	2,414	3,739	3,130	Jan	3,196
Swale Estuary	(2,822)	5,313	2,614	1,858	2,992	Feb	3,194
Medway Estuary	1,979	4,612	2,631	(2,631)	3,221	Jan	3,111
Dee Estuary (Eng/Wal)	[30] 6,332	[30] 3,143	1,204	742	823	Feb	2,449
Alt Estuary	1,702	2,316	[30] 2,314	1,877	1,538	Nov	1,949
Chichester Harbour	2,117	1,434	1,849	(2,145)	2,180	Dec	1,945
Lindisfarne	2,118	2,950	1,106	(1,165)	1,230	Nov	1,851
Humber Estuary	539	(3,368)	1,849	1,446	1,320	Feb	1,704
North Norfolk Coast	1,867	2,273	1,270	1,637	1,382	Jan	1,686
Langstone Harbour	(1,480)	2,157	(1,150)	1,454	1,040	Feb	1,550
Sites of national importance in Great Britain							
Mersey Estuary	[30] 753	[30] 3,843	1,623	[30] 630	60	Feb	1,382
Morecambe Bay	1,695	1,243	1,172	1,072	1,288	Jan	1,294
Pagham Harbour	[30] 1,436	2,452	488	[30] 1,139	979	Jan	1,230
Colne Estuary	888	1,462	910	898	1,331	Dec	1,098
Solway Estuary	1,276	990	[30] 903	[30] 678	[30] 520	Feb	873
Beaulieu Estuary	463	782	756	547	600	Jan	630
Forth Estuary	658	724	608	553	508	Dec	610
Eden Estuary	604	491	580	514	646	Dec	567
Orwell Estuary	294	(585)	417	1,034	484	Jan	563
Exe Estuary	513	573	429	422	371	Dec	462
Sites of all-Ireland importance in Northern Ireland							
Strangford Lough	407	189	326	320	268	Feb	302
Carlingford Lough	(93)	93	65	35	17	Jan	61

Sites no longer meeting table qualifying levels
Severn Estuary
Dundrum Bay

Other sites surpassing table qualifying levels in 2000–01

Pegwell Bay	493	Jan
North West Solent	530	Feb
Poole Harbour	646	Feb

Sites surpassing international threshold during passage periods in 2000–01

Ribble Estuary	16,395	May
The Wash	13,893	May
Thames Estuary	3,078	Aug
Alt Estuary	3,044	Apr
Hamford Water	2,583	Sep
Blackwater Estuary	2,516	Aug
Dengie Flats	2,284	May
North Norfolk Coast	1,830	Oct
Chichester Harbour	1,683	Oct
Humber Estuary	1,541	May

SOCIABLE PLOVER
Vanellus gregarius

Vagrant
Native range: Central and southern Asia, and NE Africa

A single was present on the Alde Estuary during
November.

LAPWING
Vanellus vanellus

International threshold:	20,000[**]
Great Britain threshold:	20,000[**†]
All-Ireland threshold:	2,500

GB Max: 349,548 Feb
NI Max: 17,044 Nov

The peak totals of Lapwing in Britain and Northern Ireland were low compared to those recorded in recent years, probably because conditions were very mild for most of the winter. This is perhaps the species most prone to cold weather movements in Europe and, as a consequence, the numbers visiting Britain and Northern Ireland vary markedly between years in response to the severity of winters on the continent. However, there is some evidence to suggest a large-scale decline in breeding numbers across most of Northwest Europe (van Strien *et al*. 2001, Hötker 1991), a decline that may manifest itself in the trends recorded by WeBS in future years, if not already.

The peak at the Somerset Levels was 17% higher than the most recent five-year peak mean; this site remains the most important numerically in Britain. Lower than average numbers were, however, reported from the other three sites currently surpassing the threshold for international importance. Comparatively low numbers were also recorded across most sites regularly supporting more than 5,000 birds in Britain. The most striking exception was the Blackwater Estuary where the 2000–01 peak was over 38% higher than average. All peak counts from the key sites in Northern Ireland were lower than normal, as would be expected at sites further west in the range in a winter with few prolonged periods of cold weather.

	96–97	97–98	98–99	99–00	00–01	Mon	Mean	
Sites of international importance in the UK								
Somerset Levels	16,743	62,886	(55,654)	28,895	50,328	Feb	42,901	
The Wash	9,132	41,538	27,585	86,129	31,165	Feb	39,110	
Humber Estuary	9,352	21,884	(32,999)	32,720	16,870	Jan	22,765	
Breydon Wtr & Berney Marshes	31,000	19,400	27,300	20,500	18,300	Jan	23,300	
Sites with mean peak counts of 5,000 or more birds in Great Britain [†]								
Ouse Washes	[29] (5,756)	[29] 41,250	4,435	29,913	1,289	Feb	19,222	
Morecambe Bay	15,526	26,190	(17,501)	18,796	15,853	Nov	19,091	▼
Ribble Estuary	18,108	24,932	15,360	11,022	12,405	Nov	16,365	
Swale Estuary	(6,271)	(15,430)	(16,241)	18,641	13,585	Feb	16,156	
Blackwater Estuary	4,827	19,377	(11,752)	14,154	20,309	Feb	14,667	
Unspecified SE England site	4,800	18,500	19,000	17,500	5,000	Feb	12,960	
Thames Estuary	8,574	(18,237)	10,373	10,369	14,888	Feb	12,488	
Severn Estuary	10,441	(14,843)	8,029	19,001	9,817	Feb	12,426	
Mersey Estuary	[30] 10,793	[30] 13,599	[30] 14,129	13,620	1,930	Jan	10,814	
Colne Estuary	(1,900)	12,440	8,725	7,500	6,430	Dec	8,774	
Solway Estuary	6,150	12,004	[30] 7,970	8,345	[30] 8,596	Nov	8,613	
Dee Estuary (Eng/Wal)	6,916	8,828	8,828	8,278	6,270	Dec	7,824	
Lower Derwent Valley	11,941	8,487	5,430	3,770	-	-	7,407	
Nene Washes	1,800	8,100	5,500	13,080	7,100	Feb	7,116	
Crouch-Roach Estuary	(2,220)	7,440	5,696	5,962	6,537	Jan	6,409	
Medway Estuary	(3,366)	(11,435)	(4,715)	(6,728)	1,055	Dec	6,406	
North Norfolk Coast	2,339	[30] 9,400	4,682	8,744	5,799	Jan	6,193	
Forth Estuary	6,424	6,892	7,575	3,925	4,974	Dec	5,958	▲
Stour Estuary	[30] 6,228	7,466	3,569	6,192	4,264	Dec	5,543	
Arun Valley	6,005	(7,188)	5,667	4,495	3,259	Feb	5,323	
Hamford Water	3,220	6,968	8,091	4,305	3,170	Dec	5,151	
Alde Complex	3,591	6,048	7,558	4,331	4,026	Nov	5,111	
Sites of all-Ireland importance in Northern Ireland								
Strangford Lough	13,547	[30] 12,961	7,497	5,736	6,214	Jan	9,191	
Loughs Neagh & Beg	7,857	6,777	6,154	10,968	6,281	Nov	7,607	
Outer Ards	6,104	3,059	3,650	3,624	2,373	Nov	3,762	
Lough Foyle	(2,665)	2,315	4,781	2,990	2,277	Dec	3,091	

Sites no longer meeting table qualifying levels
Tees Estuary
Abberton Reservoir

Other sites surpassing table qualifying levels in 2000–01
Tees Estuary   5,562   Jan
Pegwell Bay   5,900   Jan

†   *as few sites exceed the British threshold, a qualifying level of 5,000 has been chosen to select sites for presentation in this report*

KNOT
Calidris canutus

International threshold:	**3,500**
Great Britain threshold:	**2,900**
All-Ireland threshold:	**375**

GB Max: 312,646 Jan
NI Max: 7,125 Jan

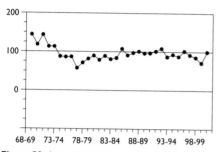

Figure 58. Annual indices for Knot in the UK

redistribution of birds to other sites in the south and southeast of England where numbers have increased in recent winters (Atkinson *et al.* in press). The over-exploitation of shellfish in the Dutch Wadden Sea is having severe impacsts on a number of waterbirds including Eider (Camphuysen *et al.* 2002) and Knot (Piersma & Koolhaas 1997). Given the exchange of birds between the Wadden Sea and southern England, the poor situation there is also likely to influence numbers recorded in Britain.

The annual index rose sharply in 2000–01 and, correspondingly, the maximum count for Britain was much higher than average; the peak count for Northern Ireland was, however, unremarkable. Indices indicate that the number of Knot wintering in the UK has declined by 15% over the past 30 years yet has increased by 4% over the last ten. The long-term decline in the *islandica* population that winters in Britain has been blamed on severe summer weather in the Arctic breeding areas between the early 1970s and mid 1980s (Wetlands International 1999). However, over-fishing of cockles on the Wash may also have been partly responsible for the declines seen in the UK and may have caused a

Peak numbers were above average at 53% of those sites supporting internationally important numbers. Most notably, maximum counts at the North Norfolk Coast and Dengie Flats were 274% and 106% higher than the most recent five-year peak means, respectively. In contrast, the maximum number at the Dee Estuary (Eng/Wal) was 75% lower than the most recent average, mirroring recent declines at sites across the west coast of Britain.

All sites holding internationally important numbers on passage were also internationally important during the winter period. Notable counts during the passage period included those on the Wash, the Ribble Estuary and the North Norfolk Coast.

	96–97	97–98	98–99	99–00	00–01	Mon	Mean
Sites of international importance in the UK							
The Wash	(72,173)	81,950	62,211	60,711	72,939	Jan	69,997
Morecambe Bay	44,134	77,344	71,238	59,530	72,908	Feb	65,031
Thames Estuary	39,121	55,663	(31,090)	21,942	38,307	Jan	38,758
Ribble Estuary	55,752	(36,880)	36,595	22,010	20,331	Jan	34,314
Humber Estuary	22,579	30,283	27,355	25,719	34,888	Nov	28,165
Alt Estuary	25,350	35,881	19,009	20,000	31,219	Nov	26,292
Dee Estuary (Eng/Wal)	30 57,032	14,000	30 17,041	8,683	5,672	Nov	20,486
Dengie Flats	6,600	10,490	14,560	(5,800)	19,400	Nov	12,763
North Norfolk Coast	15,236	9,006	6,136	3,356	29,636	Nov	12,674
Solway Estuary	9,086	5,472	8,986	8,544	30 9,159	Dec	8,249
Strangford Lough	30 12,688	9,456	7,070	3,685	5,863	Jan	7,772
Forth Estuary	11,299	7,866	7,381	6,330	5,798	Dec	7,735
Stour Estuary	30 5,893	(3,565)	4,800	9,677	30 8,036	Dec	7,102

	96–97	97–98	98–99	99–00	00–01	Mon	Mean
Swale Estuary	7,131	5,420	4,020	3,400	4,200	Jan	4,834
Hamford Water	(3,162)	4,234	5,924	3,533	5,431	Jan	4,781
Burry Inlet	8,200	2,080	3,870	(3,562)	4,800	Feb	4,738
Cromarty Firth	(6,829)	1,733	4,229	30 1,685	5,050	Jan	3,905
Inner Moray Firth	(7,773)	3,097	2,021	3,251	3,373	Dec	3,903
Lindisfarne	4,625	3,218	(4,040)	(1,954)	30 3,130	Dec	3,753

Sites of national importance in Great Britain

Blackwater Estuary	3,500	882	(4,077)	2,565	4,470	Dec	3,099	▲
Montrose Basin	3,800	3,800	2,483	1,824	2,800	Feb	2,941	▼

Sites of all-Ireland importance in Northern Ireland

Dundrum Bay	123	0	1,500	1,000	981	Feb	721
Belfast Lough	580	(430)	901	600	120	Feb	550

Sites no longer meeting table qualifying levels
Tees Estuary
Lough Foyle

Important sites not counted in last five years
Dundrum Outer Bay

Other sites surpassing table qualifying levels in 2000–01

Severn Estuary	3,752	Jan
Lough Foyle	490	Jan

Sites surpassing international threshold during passage periods in 2000–01

The Wash	76,675	Sep
Ribble Estuary	37,200	Oct
North Norfolk Coast	29,908	Sep
Humber Estuary	22,844	Oct
Morecambe Bay	18,727	Oct
Alt Estuary	18,053	Oct
Dengie Flats	5,782	Oct
Solway Estuary	4,517	Oct

SANDERLING
Calidris alba

International threshold:	**1,000**
Great Britain winter threshold:	**230**
Great Britain passage threshold:	**300**
All-Ireland threshold:	**35***

* 50 is normally used as a minimum threshold

GB Max:	13,924 May
NI Max:	132 Mar

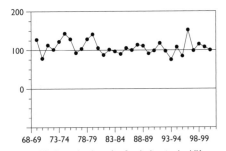

68-69   73-74   78-79   83-84   88-89   93-94   98-99

Figure 59. Annual indices for Sanderling in the UK

As usual, the peak British count occurred during May when birds are on spring migration and concentrated, seemingly, on estuaries in northern England in particular. The British peak was 8% lower than that recorded in the previous year and the Northern Ireland maximum was unremarkable. The annual index, based on winter counts, declined for the second year running but appear stable over the long term. The number of Sanderling wintering in Europe has increased in recent decades, but whether this trend is the result of a genuine increase in population size or the consequence of redistribution of birds remains unclear (Wetlands International 1999).

The Ribble Estuary and Alt Estuary continue to surpass the threshold for international importance yet numbers at these sites were 25% and 13% lower than their respective five-year peak means. A notably high count at the North Norfolk Coast, 78% above average, increased the five-year peak mean for this site considerably, although it remains some way short of the international importance threshold. Several new sites appear in the table as nationally important sites due, in part, to high counts in 2000–01.

	96–97	97–98	98–99	99–00	00–01	Mon	Mean	
Sites of international importance in the UK								
Ribble Estuary	3,085	1,134	1,223	2,501	1,290	Nov	1,847	
Alt Estuary	971	1,352	[30] 1,355	1,320	967	Jan	1,193	
Sites of national importance in Great Britain								
North Norfolk Coast	636	594	720	881	1,179	Jan	802	
Thanet Coast	457	776	603	610	677	Dec	625	
Carmarthen Bay	386	470	797	592	730	Mar	595	
Duddon Estuary	404	547	627	485	606	Nov	534	
South Uist (West Coast)	-	[17] 528	-	-	-		528	
Humber Estuary	635	345	406	496	546	Jan	486	
Tiree	-	[17] 371	-	[25] 589	-		480	
Tees Estuary	[30] 577	470	346	456	373	Feb	444	
The Wash	484	576	348	441	317	Nov	433	
Lade Sands	706	460	240	330	[29] 320	Feb	411	
Jersey Shore	(371)	304	611	443	253	Jan	403	
Thames Estuary	(142)	132	687	(127)	334	Feb	384	
South Ford	-	-	-	540	228	Jan	384	
Dee Estuary (Eng/Wal)	598	429	463	246	100	Nov	367	
Swansea Bay	379	509	379	235	234	Jan	347	▲
North Bay (South Uist)	-	-	-	[29] 302	[29] 302	Feb	302	▲
Durham Coast	372	(380)	154	250	(0)	Nov	289	
Morecambe Bay	137	278	172	235	391	Jan	243	▲
Colne Estuary	278	240	215	176	252	Dec	232	▲
Sites of all-Ireland importance in Northern Ireland								
Dundrum Bay	54	46	72	65	132	Mar	74	
Strangford Lough	[30] 324	[30] 23	0	0	0		69	

Sites no longer meeting table qualifying levels
Solway Estuary

Important sites not counted in last five years
Dundrum Outer Bay

Other sites surpassing table qualifying levels in 2000–01

Pegwell Bay	375	Jan
Poole Harbour	279	Feb
Forth Estuary	262	Jan

Sites surpassing passage threshold in Great Britain in 2000–01

Ribble Estuary	4,370	May	Morecambe Bay	813	May
Alt Estuary	3,760	May	Duddon Estuary	534	Apr
The Wash	2,061	Aug	Dee Estuary	452	Apr
North Norfolk Coast	1,713	May	Thames Estuary	407	Aug
Humber Estuary	1,626	May	Tees Estuary	371	Sep

SEMIPALMATED SANDPIPER
Calidris pusilla

Vagrant
Native range: Americas

Singles were recorded at Rye Harbour & Pett Level in August and on the Forth Estuary in September, typical dates for this transatlantic vagrant.

LITTLE STINT
Calidris minuta

International threshold:	2,100
Great Britain threshold:	?
All-Ireland threshold:	?

GB Max:	139 Sep
NI Max:	6 Sep

2000–01 was the second year running in which unremarkable numbers of this arctic breeding species were recorded. Typically, the peak count occurred in September but was well below the five-year peak mean, as was the total of 62 sites where this species was recorded.

Despite low autumn passage numbers, wintering birds continued to be a feature with peak counts of 18, 23 and six recorded in December, January and February, respectively.

Sites with 10 or more birds in 2000–01

Pegwell Bay	15	Sep
Severn Estuary	14	Sep
Swale Estuary	14	Sep
Loch Gruinart	13	Sep
Chichester Harbour	10	Dec

TEMMINCK'S STINT   Scarce
Calidris temminckii

During May three were at Stodmarsh NNR & Collards Lagoon and singles were recorded at Pagham Harbour, the Humber Estuary and the Tees Estuary. In autumn, one was seen in Chichester Harbour in September.

WHITE-RUMPED SANDPIPER   Vagrant
Calidris fuscicollis   **Native range: Americas**

Single birds were seen on the North Norfolk Coast in August, on the Ouse Washes and at South Ford in September, and on the Hayle Estuary in October.

PECTORAL SANDPIPER   Vagrant
Calidris melanotos   **Native range: America, N Siberia and Australia**

Autumn 2000 produced a more average four records following the 14 recorded in the previous autumn. Singles were seen on the Thames Estuary, the Blackwater Estuary, in Morecambe Bay and at Cors Caron.

CURLEW SANDPIPER

International threshold:	4,500
Great Britain threshold:	?
All-Ireland threshold:	?

Calidris ferruginea

GB Max: 194 Sep
NI Max: 17 Sep

Following record numbers in the previous two years autumn passage in 2000–01 proved to be unremarkable. Of the 63 sites where birds were reported, ten held birds in the spring. Ten or more birds were recorded at only a handful of sites and there were no winter records.

Sites with 10 or more birds in 2000–01

Forth Estuary	38	Aug
Severn Estuary	38	Sep
North Norfolk Coast	24	Aug
Breydon Wtr & Berney Marshes	21	Aug
Swale Estuary	18	Sep
Lough Foyle	15	Sep
Loch Gruinart	13	Sep

PURPLE SANDPIPER
Calidris maritima

International threshold: 500
Great Britain threshold: 210[†]
All-Ireland threshold: 10[*]

[*] 50 is normally used as a minimum threshold

GB Max:	1,325	Feb
NI Max:	93	Nov

Although the national totals for Britain and Northern Ireland were similar to those recorded in previous years, there was, as usual, only very limited coverage of the key sites for this species in 2000–01: of the six sites currently surpassing the threshold for national importance, only two were covered. Numbers at Seahouses to Budle Point were 14% lower than the most recent five-year peak mean, whilst those at the Farne Islands were 43% below the 1998–99 peak, the only other counts received in the previous five years.

At other sites, a count of 334 birds on Egilsay was exceptional whilst the absence of supplementary counts of the roost on the Cambois to Newbiggin section of coast in Northumberland is clearly reflected in the 2000–01 counts. In general, WeBS Core Counts are ineffective for monitoring this species, because coverage of the rocky shores favoured by Purple Sandpipers is relatively poor. Even with greater effort on ths habitat, the practicalities of covering offshore islands and skerries, and even inaccessible mainland sites, will always make surveys of this species an exacting task.

	96–97	97–98	98–99	99–00	00–01	Mon	Mean	
Sites of national importance in Great Britain [†]								
North Ronaldsay	-	[17] 400	-	-	-		400	
South Uist (West Coast)	-	[17] 313	-	(112)	(100)		313	
Farne Islands	-	-	360	-	207	Nov	284	
East Sanday Coast	-	[17] (275)	-	-	-		(275)	
Tiree	-	[17] 262	-	[25] 263	-		263	
Seahouses to Budle Point	144	207	274	310	205	Feb	228	
Sites with mean peak counts of 100 or more birds in Great Britain [†]								
Moray Coast	223	219	178	129	158	Feb	181	
South Westray	-	[17] 159	-	-	-		159	
Tees Estuary	155	166	202	137	118	Nov	156	
Cambois to Newbiggin	[22] 142	[22] 180	[29] 180	[29] 136	19	Jan	131	
Forth Estuary	72	103	142	128	159	Feb	121	▲
Thurso Bay	-	-	-	(120)	- -		(120)	▲
Egilsay	-	7	1	136	334	Jan	120	▲
Durham Coast	153	(161)	(132)	122	21	Feb	118	
North Mainland (Orkney)	-	[17] 117	-	-	-		117	
The Houb (Whalsay)	-	-	-	160	62	Feb	111	▲
Sites of all-Ireland importance in Northern Ireland								
Outer Ards	89	49	147	100	82	Nov	93	
Belfast Lough	38	31	45	19	13	Jan	29	▲
Important sites not counted in last five years								
Fraserburgh to Rosehearty								
SE Stronsay								
SE Deerness								
Other sites surpassing table qualifying levels in 2000–01								
North Bay (South Uist)	[29] 130	Jan						

[†] as few sites exceed the British threshold, a qualifying level of 100 has been chosen to select sites for presentation in this report

DUNLIN
Calidris alpina

GB Max: 402,888 Feb
NI Max: 12,749 Jan

International threshold:	14,000
Great Britain winter threshold:	5,300
Great Britain passage threshold:	2,000
All-Ireland threshold:	1,250

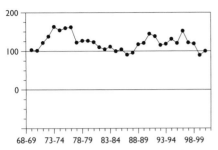

68-69 73-74 78-79 83-84 88-89 93-94 98-99

Figure 60. Annual indices for Dunlin in the UK

the Mersey, Dee (Eng/Wal) and Blackwater Estuaries. Numbers continued to decline at Morecambe Bay and on the Medway Estuary and were well below average on the Severn Estuary.

Five sites exceeded the threshold for international importance during passage. The most notable of these was the Ribble Estuary where numbers were well above average.

Despite an increase from the previous year, the Great Britain maximum was lower than in any other year since 1988–89 while in Northern Ireland the maximum declined for the second consecutive year to its lowest value since 1992–93. As a result UK annual indices remained similar to the low values of the mid-1980s.

Only ten sites in the tables held above average figures, the most notable of these being

	96–97	97–98	98–99	99–00	00–01	Mon	Mean
Sites of international importance in the UK							
Mersey Estuary	55,430	52,015	35,440	42,120	60,330	Jan	49,067
Morecambe Bay	57,617	71,731	38,865	28,411	27,425	Nov	44,810
The Wash	38,741	36,054	32,556	41,503	35,080	Feb	36,787
Ribble Estuary	45,973	30 45,039	32,160	18,040	36,473	Nov	35,537
Thames Estuary	34,145	37,979	(46,450)	26,782	31,442	Jan	35,360
Dee Estuary (Eng/Wal)	30 38,416	30,318	31,619	21,627	41,656	Nov	32,727
Severn Estuary	29,420	(26,851)	37,172	(19,785)	17,417	Feb	28,003
Blackwater Estuary	33,512	22,304	(22,890)	16,792	37,550	Dec	27,540
Langstone Harbour	(14,240)	(15,000)	25,185	24,090	23,700	Feb	24,325
Humber Estuary	10,229	20,695	40,121	21,561	18,502	Nov	22,222
Chichester Harbour	19,567	15,629	16,421	16,680	16,773	Feb	17,014
Medway Estuary	33,313	17,200	11,689	(8,591)	5,118	Dec	16,830
Solway Estuary	20,042	11,982	17,873	30 14,746	15,083	Dec	15,945
Stour Estuary	30 16,676	14,712	13,080	15,168	15,822	Feb	15,092
Sites of national importance in Great Britain							
Swale Estuary	14,243	15,529	7,661	8,587	7,741	Feb	10,752
Forth Estuary	9,118	9,937	10,887	11,276	11,840	Dec	10,612
Dengie Flats	(7,850)	8,100	8,900	10,800	9,700	Feb	9,375
Duddon Estuary	14,416	7,232	9,765	29 10,000	4,258	Jan	9,134
Colne Estuary	8,805	10,510	6,925	8,950	9,100	Dec	8,858
Burry Inlet	14,548	4,539	8,040	(9,271)	5,401	Jan	8,360
Lindisfarne	10,364	6,039	9,880	(8,148)	5,777	Dec	8,042
Hamford Water	9,146	11,970	4,238	3,967	5,625	Jan	6,989
Inner Moray Firth	8,567	5,417	30 6,259	7,059	5,525	Dec	6,565
Poole Harbour	6,347	6,355	6,816	6,693	4,852	Feb	6,213
Orwell Estuary	9,576	30 6,977	30 4,774	30 4,976	30 2,852	Jan	5,829
Cleddau Estuary	8,561	5,318	5,973	(4,381)	2,699	Feb	5,638
Southampton Water	30 5,617	30 7,088	30 6,454	30 4,557	30 4,736	Dec	5,690

	96–97	97–98	98–99	99–00	00–01	Mon	Mean
Sites of all-Ireland importance in Northern Ireland							
Strangford Lough	[30] 16,629	[30] 8,325	6,881	4,103	2,182	Jan	7,624
Lough Foyle	(3,666)	4,106	6,600	3,560	5,800	Jan	5,017
Carlingford Lough	(860)	2,002	2,127	1,861	1,390	Jan	1,845
Outer Ards	2,689	1,890	2,175	1,023	1,312	Feb	1,818
Belfast Lough	1,943	[30] 1,906	[30] 2,055	[30] 1,242	[30] 1,366	Jan	1,702
Bann Estuary	2,910	1,075	865	1,650	1,030	Jan	1,506
Dundrum Bay	1,707	1,893	1,259	352	1,243	Dec	1,291 ▲

Sites no longer meeting table qualifying levels
Portsmouth Harbour

Other sites surpassing table qualifying levels in 2000–01
Dornoch Firth   5,537   Jan

Sites surpassing passage threshold in Great Britain in 2000–01

Ribble Estuary	50,729	May	Mersey Estuary	6,920	May
The Wash	45,349	May	Alt Estuary	5,106	May
Humber Estuary	24,075	Aug	Hamford Water	4,477	Oct
Morecambe Bay	16,031	Oct	Dee Estuary	3,693	Apr
Thames Estuary	15,371	Oct	Swale Estuary	3,192	Apr
Blackwater Estuary	13,638	Oct	Dyfi Estuary	2,835	May
Solway Estuary	9,722	Oct	Breydon Wtr & Berney Marshes	2,482	Apr
Dengie Flats	8,800	Oct	Severn Estuary	2,247	May
Stour Estuary	7,531	Oct	Tay Estuary	2,075	Oct
Lindisfarne	7,440	Oct			

BROAD-BILLED SANDPIPER
Limicola falcinellus

Vagrant
Native range: NE Europe, Asia, E & S Africa and Australia

One was at Dawlish Warren on the Exe Estuary
in May.

BUFF-BREASTED SANDPIPER
Tryngites subruficollis

Vagrant
Native range: NE Siberia and Americas

There were two records for September, singles
at WWT Slimbridge and Goldcliff Saline
Lagoons both on the Severn Estuary.

RUFF
Philomachus pugnax

International threshold: ?
Great Britain threshold: 7[*]
All-Ireland threshold: +[*]

GB Max: 1,142 Sep
NI Max: 5 Nov

[*] *50 is normally used as a minimum threshold*

The Great Britain peak count was the second
highest ever recorded by WeBS and occurred at
a typical time of year.

Although seven sites held 50 or more birds
during the winter (*cf.* seven also in the previous
two years), winter peaks were notably lower.
This was due in part to an absence of records
from Lower Derwent Valley, a site that has held
in excess of 100 birds in recent winters. Also,
peak counts from the Blackwater Estuary,

Rutland Water, The Wash and Abberton
Reservoir were well below their five year
means. The counts from Barleycroft and Fen
Drayton Gravel Pits were particularly notable, as
neither site has held any birds in recent winters.

Nine sites surpassed the minimum
threshold during passage periods but despite the
high September count no sites held exceptional
numbers. Counts at the Ouse Washes returned
to normal after the notable count in 1999–2000.

	96–97	97–98	98–99	99–00	00–01	Mon	Mean	
Sites of national importance in Great Britain								
Ouse Washes	(113)	[29]88	(292)	288	189	Jan	214	
Lower Derwent Valley	81	133	118	111	-	-	111	
North Norfolk Coast	118	[30]81	[29]78	[22]138	103	Nov	104	
Martin Mere	67	90	96	140	116	Jan	102	
Nene Washes	19	60	98	50	38	Nov	53	
Breydon Wtr & Berney Marshes	24	28	11	144	52	Jan	52	
Ribble Estuary	21	25	5	41	63	Nov	31	
Middle Yare Marshes	20	22	15	70	33	Feb	32	
Dungeness Gravel Pits	40	4	15	21	55	Dec	27	▲
Arun Valley	16	(34)	50	7	28	Nov	27	
Blackwater Estuary	19	33	29	41	10	Nov	26	
Barleycroft Gravel Pits	0	0	0	0	126	Jan	25	▲
Swale Estuary	4	27	20	43	29	Nov	25	
Rutland Water	21	17	31	36	9	Jan	23	
Hamford Water	(23)	32	38	7	12	Jan	22	
Somerset Levels	42	21	18	[29]4	15	Feb	20	
Thames Estuary	52	15	1	25	6	Nov	20	
The Wash	(4)	3	69	0	3	Nov	19	
Holland Marshes	-	1	0	45	23	Jan	18	
Abberton Reservoir	18	30	0	37	0	Nov	17	
Cresswell Pond	-	-	-	-	15	Dec	15	▲
Unspecified SE England site	36	9	2	15	9	Feb	14	
Stodmarsh & Collards Lagoon	0	0	7	(37)	25	Dec	14	
Humber Estuary	2	14	[30]30	18	4	Jan	14	
Lakenheath Fen	(13)	(0)	-	-	-	-	(13)	
Sandbach Flashes	-	10	11	13	8	Feb	11	
Fen Drayton Gravel Pits	0	0	0	0	46	Jan	9	▲
Eyebrook Reservoir	0	0	18	-	25	Nov	9	▲
Dee Estuary (Eng/Wal)	12	8	10	2	8	Nov	8	
Tees Estuary	7	2	17	4	10	Feb	8	
Romney Marsh	-	-	0	11	12	Feb	8	▲
Minsmere	(3)	5	7	8	8	Jan	7	▲
Sites with mean peak counts of 7 or more birds in Northern Ireland [†]								
Strangford Lough	0	[30]40	0	0	0		8	

Sites no longer meeting table qualifying levels
Colne Estuary

Other sites surpassing table qualifying levels in 2000–01

North Cave Gravel Pits	18	Dec
Bolton-on-Swale Gravel Pits	15	Nov
Poole Harbour	8	Jan
Meadow Lane Gravel Pits	15	Feb

Sites holding 50 or more birds on passage in 2000

Humber Estuary	187	Sep
North Norfolk Coast	179	Aug
Ouse Washes	109	Oct
Ribble Estuary	100	Oct
Breydon Wtr & Berney Marshes	73	Apr
Dungeness Gravel Pits	62	Sep
Blackwater Estuary	51	Aug
Middle Yare Marshes	51	Sep
Martin Mere	50	Sep

†   *as no all-Ireland threshold has been set, a qualifying level of seven has been chosen to select sites for presentation in this report*

JACK SNIPE
Lymnocryptes minimus

International threshold:	?
Great Britain threshold:	?[†]
All-Ireland threshold:	250

GB Max: 128 Jan
NI Max: 2 Nov-Jan

WeBS does not give a true reflection of this species, owing to its secretive nature and favoured habitats of marsh and wet grassland, habitats poorly covered by WeBS.

Numbers recorded in 2000–01 were similar to those of the five-year peak mean although the summed site maxima of 303 was slightly below those of recent years (*cf*. 336 in 1999–2000 and 338 in 1998–99).

Sites with five or more birds in 2000–01

Chichester Harbour	20	Jan	R. Kennet: Littlecote/Knighton	6	Feb
Waulkmill Glen & Littleton Rsrs	15	Jan	Rye Harbour & Pett Level	5	Oct
Upton Warren LNR	12	Dec	Foryd Bay	5	Nov/Jan
Severn Estuary	12	Feb	Shipton on Cherwell Quarry	5	Several
Stour Estuary	9	Nov	Forth Estuary	5	Dec
Dee Estuary (England/Wales)	9	Feb	Thames Estuary	5	Jan
Inner Moray Firth	7	Oct	Mersey Estuary	5	Feb
Doxey Marshes SSSI	6	Apr/Feb	Somerset Levels	5	Feb
Fenn's & Whixall Mosses	6	Sep			

SNIPE
Gallinago gallinago

International threshold:	20,000[**]
Great Britain threshold:	?[†]
All-Ireland threshold:	?[†]

GB Max: 7,505 Jan
NI Max: 225 Feb

The Great Britain and Northern Ireland maxima were around average for the past five years but occurred slightly later than usual.

Whilst the Somerset Levels remains the most important site for this species, the counts at Maer Lake and Newgale Beach were both notable for being well below the average for the last five years.

This species' favoured habitats of marsh and wet grassland are poorly covered by WeBS and its secretive nature means any trends in numbers should be treated with caution.

	96–97	97–98	98–99	99–00	00–01	Mon	Mean	
Sites with mean peak counts of 200 or more birds in Great Britain [†]								
Somerset Levels	1,041	1,975	2,196	1,578	1,817	Jan	1,721	
Maer Lake	480	550	610	490	280	Feb	482	
Lower Derwent Valley	409	500	300	621	-	-	458	
North Norfolk Coast	55	30 611	135	188	207	Jan	239	
Arun Valley	135	272	237	185	335	Jan	233	
Morecambe Bay	188	260	268	213	218	Nov	229	
Severn Estuary	81	110	193	396	301	Dec	216	▲
Newgale Beach	-	230	400	-	0	Jan	210	
Sites with mean peak counts of 50 or more birds in Northern Ireland [†]								
Larne Lough	47	97	91	93	60	Feb	78	▲

Sites no longer meeting table qualifying levels
Swale Estuary
Exe Estuary

Other sites surpassing table qualifying levels in 2000–01

Cleddau Estuary	215	Dec	Middle Yare Marshes	217	Nov
North Norfolk Coast	207	Jan	Belfast Lough	65	Nov

[†]   *as no British or all-Ireland thresholds have been set, qualifying levels of 200 and 50 have been chosen to select sites for presentation in this report*

LONG-BILLED DOWITCHER
Limnodromus scolopaceus

Vagrant
Native range: NE Siberia and N America

One from 1999–2000 remained on the Swale Estuary in April and singles were recorded in Pegwell Bay in October, Belfast Lough from December to February and on the Alt Estuary at Seaforth from November to February.

WOODCOCK
Scolopax rusticola

International threshold:	**20,000**[**]
Great Britain threshold:	**?**[†]
All-Ireland threshold:	**?**[†]

GB Max:	**37 Dec**
NI Max:	**0**

As a species favouring woodland habitats, it is perhaps no surprise that relatively few are recorded during WeBS counts. The peak was in the lower range of recent years, and only three sites held five or more birds (*cf.* four to seven in last five winters).

Other sites surpassing table qualifying levels in 2000–01

Grouville Marsh	15	Sep
Longueville Marsh	8	Jan/Feb
Hamford Water	6	Jan

BLACK-TAILED GODWIT
Limosa limosa

International threshold:	**700**
Great Britain threshold:	**70**
All-Ireland threshold:	**90**

GB Max:	**21,183 Sep**
NI Max:	**406 Sep**

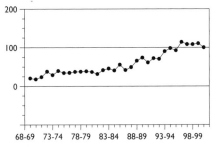

Figure 61. Annual indices for Black-tailed Godwit in the UK

The peak number of Black-tailed Godwit in Britain was the highest yet recorded by WeBS. The annual index has remained relatively stable over the last five years following a 455% increase over the last 30 years. The Northern Ireland peak count was the second highest on record.

Numbers at the top five sites were similar to the most recent five-year peak mean. Notably high counts over the past five years from the Exe Estuary, Humber Estuary, and Breydon Water & Berney Marshes mean that these sites now appear on the list of internationally important sites for this species. In contrast, there were very low counts at a number of sites, most noteworthy being those on the Ouse Washes, Mersey Estuary, Medway Estuary, Orwell Estuary and Alde Complex. Twelve sites exceeded the threshold for international importance during the passage period, including impressive counts at the Wash and the Ribble Estuary.

Buffer effects occur when sites vary in quality and fluctuations in population size are reflected by large changes in bird numbers in low quality sites but only minor changes in high quality sites. Poor sites 'buffer' the good sites, a mechanism that can potentially drive population regulation if there are demographic costs of using poor sites. In accordance with the buffer effect, analyses using WeBS data have shown that rates of increase in Black-tailed Godwit numbers have been greatest on estuaries with low initial numbers and that birds on these sites have lower prey-intake rates, lower survival rates and arrive later in Iceland than birds on sites with stable numbers (Gill *et al.* 2001).

	96–97	97–98	98–99	99–00	00–01	Mon	Mean	
Sites of international importance in the UK								
The Wash	5,738	3,104	1,104	1,844	3,555	Nov	3,069	
Ribble Estuary	2,319	911	(1,216)	2,596	3,271	Nov	2,274	
Stour Estuary	[30] 2,514	1,724	2,105	1,862	[30] 2,846	Feb	2,210	
Blackwater Estuary	(1,088)	(608)	(680)	(697)	2,094	Feb	2,094	
Dee Estuary (Eng/Wal)	2,203	1,642	1,602	2,543	2,366	Feb	2,071	
Poole Harbour	1,771	1,895	1,596	2,051	1,134	Nov	1,689	
Swale Estuary	(1,409)	1,010	1,514	1,495	2,153	Feb	1,543	
Mersey Estuary	1,703	[30] 2,655	1,573	976	810	Dec	1,543	
Ouse Washes	[29] 1,236	[29] 1,362	1,715	[29] 2,900	[29] 268	Feb	1,496	
Humber Estuary	544	924	1,620	1,685	545	Jan	1,064	▲
Exe Estuary	226	1,132	667	1,113	880	Dec	804	▲
Southampton Water	147	982	(685)	522	1,265	Nov	729	▲
Breydon Wtr & Berney Marshes	367	503	493	883	1,376	Jan	724	▲
Sites of national importance in Great Britain								
R. Avon: R'wood to Christchurch	0	0	[29] 248	0	[29] 2,630	Jan	576	▲
Thames Estuary	637	241	(1,180)	368	103	Feb	506	
Nene Washes	80	509	1,520	64	281	Feb	491	
Chichester Harbour	[30] 498	464	[30] 738	(511)	136	Nov	469	
Hamford Water	732	352	270	371	601	Dec	465	
Medway Estuary	[30] 417	653	(551)	(389)	0		405	
Orwell Estuary	458	[30] 352	622	[30] 395	[30] 73	Jan	380	
North West Solent	265	[30] 378	251	(231)	323	Nov	304	
Alde Complex	254	701	168	308	30	Jan	292	
Beaulieu Estuary	(246)	161	197	233	495	Jan	272	
Colne Estuary	85	214	(412)	135	450	Feb	259	
Crouch-Roach Estuary	87	416	236	252	272	Feb	253	
Langstone Harbour	240	327	[30] 202	(304)	97	Nov	234	
Blyth Estuary (Suffolk)	200	215	-	-	271	Feb	229	
Eden Estuary	176	183	233	182	170	Dec	189	
Deben Estuary	354	154	112	209	114	Feb	189	
Portsmouth Harbour	(204)	[30] 358	4	211	70	Jan	169	
Pagham Harbour	98	[30] 124	[30] 300	182	248	Feb	165	
Fen Drayton Gravel Pits	19	0	0	0	780	Feb	160	▲
Newtown Estuary	130	148	198	[30] 218	86	Nov	156	
Morecambe Bay	21	42	354	82	219	Feb	144	
Fal Complex	131	146	135	112	103	Nov	125	
Tamar Complex	(127)	119	100	(44)	130	Nov	119	
Solway Estuary	460	9	31	26	[30] 63	Nov	118	
Severn Estuary	[30] 116	230	166	35	5	Jan	110	
Forth Estuary	33	(87)	225	93	55	Feb	102	
Burry Inlet	114	233	45	99	7	Dec	100	
Abberton Reservoir	159	322	3	0	0	Nov	97	
North Norfolk Coast	(21)	[30] 60	119	98	108	Jan	96	
Dengie Flats	1	17	247	(6)	32	Nov	74	▲
Caerlaverock WWT	98	176	15	11	62	Nov	72	▲
Sites of all-Ireland importance in Northern Ireland								
Belfast Lough	418	178	266	[30] 401	[30] 383	Jan	329	
Strangford Lough	486	[30] 445	191	214	83	Jan	284	

Sites surpassing international threshold during passage periods in 2000–01

The Wash	4,303	Sep	Stour Estuary	1,366	Oct
Ribble Estuary	4,024	Sep	Nene Washes	1,135	Apr
Mersey Estuary	2,850	Sep	Swale Estuary	1,086	Aug
Thames Estuary	1,956	Aug	Poole Harbour	956	Oct
Dee Estuary	1,813	Oct	Orwell Estuary	834	Sep
Breydon Wtr & Berney Marshes	1,387	Aug	Humber Estuary	824	Aug

BAR-TAILED GODWIT
Limosa lapponica

International threshold:	1,000
Great Britain threshold:	530
All-Ireland threshold:	175

GB Max:	48,459 Jan
NI Max:	1,719 Jan

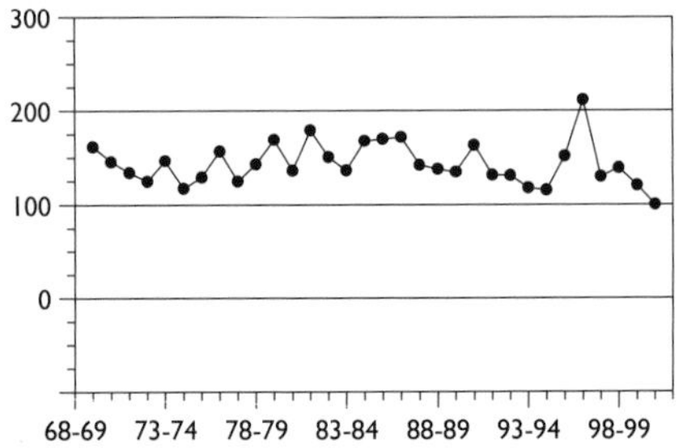

Figure 62. Annual indices for Bar-tailed Godwit in the UK

Although the peak count in Britain has remained relatively stable over the last four years, annual indices indicate that the species has declined by 39% over the last ten years and 31% over the last 30 years, reaching its lowest value to date in 2000–01. Regional analyses of WeBS data indicate that numbers have increased on the east coast and decreased on the west (Austin *et al.* 2000). It has been suggested that increasingly mild winters mean it is no longer necessary for

some waders to winter on the traditionally milder west coast to avoid cold-weather mortality that had been particularly high on the east coast. The peak count in Northern Ireland remained notably low for the second year running.

Over 80% of internationally important sites supported below average numbers. Interestingly, the three sites that held more birds than average were all east coast resorts, the Wash supporting 18% more birds than the five-year peak mean. The numbers of birds recorded at the Dee Estuary (Eng/Wal) were again well below average, the absence of Low Tide Counts in recent winters being largely responsible for the apparent decline.

During passage periods, ten sites exceeded the threshold for international importance. Most notably, the Wash supported 20,443 birds during October, the highest count at any time during 2000–01.

	96–97	97–98	98–99	99–00	00–01	Mon	Mean
Sites of international importance in the UK							
The Wash	16,246	16,435	10,319	13,062	17,223	Jan	14,657
Alt Estuary	9,015	9,424	6,883	8,001	6,146	Nov	7,894
Ribble Estuary	15,885	[30] 10,431	4,093	4,346	4,118	Nov	7,775
Thames Estuary	16,164	5,797	(4,416)	2,584	3,019	Jan	6,891
Dee Estuary (Eng/Wal)	[30] 8,460	[30] 5,464	[30] 3,359	232	990	Dec	3,701
Morecambe Bay	3,658	1,818	5,540	5,374	1,685	Dec	3,615
Lindisfarne	2,770	3,225	(3,086)	(3,993)	4,066	Feb	3,514
Humber Estuary	1,505	(2,970)	[30] 3,787	3,433	2,065	Nov	2,752
North Norfolk Coast	3,360	3,108	2,400	1,842	1,676	Jan	2,477
Solway Estuary	4,273	2,495	2,592	931	1,434	Jan	2,345
Dengie Flats	5,500	1,402	(1,050)	900	1,388	Feb	2,298
Forth Estuary	1,869	2,157	2,076	1,703	1,513	Jan	1,864
Cromarty Firth	(1,225)	1,654	1,779	[30] 1,852	2,193	Jan	1,741
Lough Foyle	(2,120)	1,535	3,820	678	208	Nov	1,672
Strangford Lough	[30] 1,671	2,433	1,299	1,360	1,543	Jan	1,661
Tay Estuary	2,305	1,315	1,160	(1,250)	1,400	Feb	1,545
Inner Moray Firth	2,792	1,301	[30] 1,344	1,015	1,510	Dec	1,592
Dornoch Firth	(2,125)	847	1,216	837	406	Feb	1,086
South Ford	-	-	-	1,052	1,042	Feb	1,047
Chichester Harbour	1,100	820	(1,175)	(462)	925	Feb	1,005
Sites of national importance in Great Britain							
East Sanday Coast	-	[17] (951)	-	-	-		(951)
North Uist (West Coast)	-	[17] 662	-	-	-		662
Hamford Water	1,380	548	381	506	334	Feb	630
Swale Estuary	824	597	366	407	700	Feb	579

Sites surpassing international threshold during passage periods in 2000–01

The Wash	20,443	Oct	North Norfolk Coast	3,483	Oct
Ribble Estuary	7,219	Oct	Forth Estuary	1,151	Sep
Alt Estuary	4,608	Oct	Humber Estuary	1,109	Oct
Thames Estuary	4,456	Sep	Cromarty Firth	1,062	Oct
Lindisfarne	4,127	Sep	Inner Moray Firth	1,025	Oct

WHIMBREL
Numenius phaeopus

International threshold:	6,500
Great Britain threshold:	+*
All-Ireland threshold:	+*

GB Max:	2,343 May
NI Max:	18 May

* 50 is normally used as a minimum threshold

The peak British count and summed site maxima of 2,935 were above the five-year peak mean but not quite as high as the record numbers recorded in 1998–99. As is typical of this species larger flocks were recorded on the west coast in spring and on the east coast in autumn.

For the third consecutive year, peak numbers in Northern Ireland were low. Not since 1997–98, when 331 were recorded, has there been a notable spring passage.

Sites with 50 or more birds in 2000–01

Burry Inlet	366	May	North Norfolk Coast	92	May
Humber Estuary	275	Jul	Blackwater Estuary	79	May
Morecambe Bay	226	May	Breydon Wtr & Berney Marshes	71	May
The Wash	189	Jul	Tay Estuary	60	Aug
Severn Estuary	171	May	Dyfi Estuary	57	May
Swale Estuary	142	May	Crouch-Roach Estuary	55	May
Langstone Harbour	116	May	Exe Estuary	51	Jul
Chichester Harbour	106	May	Taw-Torridge Estuary	50	May

CURLEW
Numenius arquata

International threshold:	3,500
Great Britain threshold:	1,200
All-Ireland threshold:	875

GB Max:	87,521 Sep
NI Max:	6,893 Feb

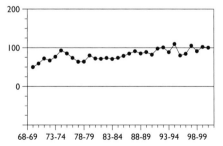

Figure 63. Annual indices for Curlew in the UK

The peak count for Britain was 4% higher than the most recent five-year peak mean and the Northern Ireland maximum was also similar to those recorded in recent years. National indices indicate that the species has increased by 22% over the last ten years and 69% over the last 30 years.

Numbers recorded at individual sites have remained relatively stable over the most recent five years. Wigtown Bay and The Ouse & Lairo Water now surpass the threshold for national importance whereas Hamford Water has fallen below. Passage counts at Morecambe Bay and the Wash were particularly noteworthy. Seven sites surpass the threshold for international importance during passage though, notably, Humber, Thames and the Forth Estuaries do not surpass this threshold outside these periods.

	96–97	97–98	98–99	99–00	00–01	Mon	Mean	
Sites of international importance in the UK								
Morecambe Bay	12,357	14,858	16,778	16,586	13,756	Dec	14,867	
Solway Estuary	4,062	5,716	5,935	7,230	4,417	Nov	5,472	
Dee Estuary (Eng/Wal)	4,583	5,370	4,490	3,373	4,583	Feb	4,480	
The Wash	3,241	3,803	4,306	5,056	4,058	Jan	4,093	
Sites of national importance in Great Britain								
Humber Estuary	1,426	(3,284)	(3,980)	3,532	4,044	Jan	3,253	
Thames Estuary	3,873	2,590	2,343	2,151	2,918	Feb	2,775	
Duddon Estuary	1,801	2,008	2,629	2,576	2,516	Dec	2,306	
Forth Estuary	1,599	2,545	2,082	2,624	2,404	Dec	2,251	
Severn Estuary	2,001	(2,903)	1,784	2,086	1,485	Jan	2,052	
Inner Moray Firth	1,828	2,334	30 1,630	2,456	1,698	Dec	1,989	
Ribble Estuary	1,593	2,507	880	2,631	1,709	Feb	1,864	
Mersey Estuary	1,501	30 2,117	30 1,308	1,507	1,976	Feb	1,682	
Poole Harbour	1,652	1,783	1,508	1,712	1,484	Feb	1,628	
North Norfolk Coast	1,489	30 1,467	1,441	1,863	1,686	Feb	1,589	
Blackwater Estuary	(1,533)	1,426	1,511	1,842	1,502	Feb	1,570	
Clyde Estuary	(1,088)	1,543	1,423	1,497	1,604	Feb	1,517	
Traeth Lafan	1,446	1,044	522	(1,836)	2,240	Jan	1,418	
Swale Estuary	(1,124)	1,435	1,110	1,658	1,368	Jan	1,393	
Chichester Harbour	1,135	1,433	1,452	(1,389)	1,501	Jan	1,382	
Cromarty Firth	1,092	1,542	1,639	30 1,141	1,354	Jan	1,354	
Stour Estuary	(1,041)	(1,492)	1,316	1,174	1,378	Feb	1,340	
Medway Estuary	1,061	1,413	1,554	(1,648)	862	Jan	1,308	
Cleddau Estuary	1,283	1,330	1,448	(1,173)	1,167	Dec	1,307	
Wigtown Bay	(1,127)	1,144	(1,301)	1,417	1,299	Dec	1,290	▲
Lindisfarne	577	1,330	(1,420)	(1,483)	1,636	Feb	1,289	
The Ouse & Lairo Water	560	540	1,200	2,170	1,574	Jan	1,209	▲
Sites of all-Ireland importance in Northern Ireland								
Lough Foyle	(2,187)	1,879	2,686	2,129	2,682	Nov	2,344	
Strangford Lough	30 2,021	2,102	1,560	1,625	2,305	Jan	1,923	
Outer Ards	1,025	758	1,669	2,113	1,270	Nov	1,367	
Sites no longer meeting table qualifying levels								
Hamford Water								

Other sites surpassing table qualifying levels in 2000–01

Newark Bay	2,150	Dec
Alde Complex	1,354	Jan
Belfast Lough	30 955	Nov

Sites surpassing international threshold during passage periods in 2000–01

Morecambe Bay	12,818	Oct	Thames Estuary	4,334	Oct
The Wash	10,803	Aug	Solway Estuary	4,259	Sep
Dee Estuary (Eng/Wal)	5,837	Sep	Forth Estuary	4,057	Sep
Humber Estuary	5,273	Aug			

SPOTTED REDSHANK
Tringa erythropus

International threshold:	1,200
Great Britain threshold:	+*
All-Ireland threshold:	+*

* 50 is normally used as a minimum threshold

GB Max:	268 Sep
NI Max:	1 Dec

Following annual declines since the high numbers of the mid 1990s, numbers in 2000–01 remained almost identical to the previous year. Although the peak count was above average for the last five years the summed site maxima of 432 was well below the five-year peak mean.

Of the 40 sites that held birds during the winter, the only double-figure counts were 11 on the North Norfolk coast in November and 19 on the Severn Estuary in January and February.

Sites with 10 or more birds in 2000–01

Swale Estuary	78	Sep
Blackwater Estuary	46	Oct
The Wash	27	Jul
Dee Estuary (England/Wales)	20	Sep
Humber Estuary	19	Aug
Severn Estuary	19	Jan/Feb
Tees Estuary	12	Sep
North Norfolk Coast	11	Aug/Sep/Nov
Blyth Estuary (Suffolk)	10	Sep

REDSHANK
Tringa totanus

GB Max:	94,213	Sep	
NI Max:	8,827	Oct	

International threshold:	**1,500**
Great Britain winter threshold:	**1,100**
Great Britain passage threshold:	**1,200**
All-Ireland threshold:	**245**

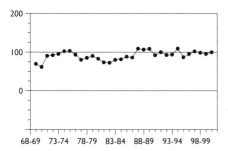

Figure 64. Annual indices for Redshank in the UK

The peak count in Britain in September was 4% lower than the previous year but notably higher than the peaks recorded in the preceding five. The annual index was around average for recent years, though it has risen 8% over the last 10 years and 62% over the last 30 years. The Northern Ireland peak was similar to that recorded in recent winters.

Numbers were slightly higher than average at the top four sites in Britain yet, overall, numbers were lower at 54% of internationally important sites. Differences in the table are a consequence of changing numbers at sites in southern England: Chichester Harbour and the Swale Estuary now qualify as internationally important whereas recent low counts at the Colne Estuary mean that this site has fallen below this threshold. In Northern Ireland, numbers recorded at Lough Foyle and Dundrum Bay were 88% and 21% higher than the most recent five-year peak means. Numbers at the other key sites in the province were unremarkable.

During the passage period, peak counts at 30 sites exceeded the threshold for international importance. Notable counts in 2000–01 included those on the Dee Estuary (Eng/Wal) and the Mersey Estuary, both in September, and at Morecambe Bay in October.

	96–97	97–98	98–99	99–00	00–01	Mon	Mean
Sites of international importance in the UK							
Morecambe Bay	6,350	6,968	7,082	7,262	8,524	Nov	7,237
Dee Estuary (Eng/Wal)	6,226	7,570	4,907	4,792	5,893	Nov	5,878
Mersey Estuary	5,212	30 6,973	30 5,087	4,476	6,045	Dec	5,559
Humber Estuary	1,948	4,758	6,109	5,357	4,990	Nov	4,632
Forth Estuary	3,602	4,768	4,450	3,664	3,950	Dec	4,087
Solway Estuary	2,512	3,196	3,958	4,135	2,693	Nov	3,299
Alde Complex	2,303	5,268	2,825	2,783	2,742	Nov	3,184
Blackwater Estuary	(1,930)	2,523	(2,158)	2,541	4,199	Feb	3,088
The Wash	(3,056)	3,279	3,046	2,722	3,286	Feb	3,083
Strangford Lough	2,832	2,713	4,157	2,827	2,729	Nov	3,052
Thames Estuary	3,469	2,992	2,557	2,695	3,397	Nov	3,022
Inner Moray Firth	2,177	2,373	30 2,494	2,360	2,862	Dec	2,453
Deben Estuary	2,632	2,704	1,729	1,996	2,881	Dec	2,388
Clyde Estuary	(2,092)	1,768	2,538	30 2,956	2,324	Feb	2,336
Stour Estuary	2,853	1,908	2,730	30 2,511	30 2,038	Nov	2,408
Duddon Estuary	1,344	1,856	2,356	2,367	2,816	Dec	2,148

	96–97	97–98	98–99	99–00	00–01	Mon	Mean	
Belfast Lough	[30] 2,068	[30] 2,148	[30] 2,463	[30] 2,108	1,677	Feb	2,093	
Hamford Water	2,322	2,486	2,373	1,796	1,473	Feb	2,090	
Montrose Basin	2,508	2,440	2,093	1,800	1,509	Nov	2,070	
Medway Estuary	[30] 2,058	3,020	(1,599)	(1,896)	900	Jan	1,993	
Ribble Estuary	2,208	1,901	1,253	2,622	1,734	Feb	1,944	
Orwell Estuary	[30] 1,978	[30] 2,256	[30] 1,575	[30] 2,197	[30] 1,637	Jan	1,929	
Ythan Estuary	1,344	1,380	1,976	2,990	-	-	1,923	
North Norfolk Coast	1,356	[30] 3,542	1,639	1,473	1,412	Jan	1,884	
Severn Estuary	2,072	1,790	(2,134)	1,149	1,528	Feb	1,735	
Chichester Harbour	1,442	1,391	1,691	(1,342)	1,702	Jan	1,557	▲
Swale Estuary	1,268	1,364	2,116	1,359	1,476	Nov	1,517	▲

Sites of national importance in Great Britain

	96–97	97–98	98–99	99–00	00–01	Mon	Mean	
Colne Estuary	1,157	1,485	1,640	1,823	1,342	Nov	1,489	▼
Blyth Estuary (Suffolk)	1,426	1,761	-	-	1,265	Feb	1,484	
Alt Estuary	1,790	(1,000)	979	1,627	1,470	Nov	1,467	
Tees Estuary	1,079	1,408	1,386	1,282	1,441	Dec	1,319	
Cromarty Firth	701	1,385	1,404	[30] 1,842	1,157	Jan	1,298	

Sites of all-Ireland importance in Northern Ireland

	96–97	97–98	98–99	99–00	00–01	Mon	Mean
Outer Ards	1,035	(957)	1,428	1,308	1,428	Nov	1,300
Carlingford Lough	1,194	1,043	924	1,334	1,325	Feb	1,164
Lough Foyle	805	720	901	844	1,974	Nov	1,049
Dundrum Bay	831	853	826	801	1,051	Dec	872
Larne Lough	317	362	388	427	379	Nov	375
Bann Estuary	190	420	346	260	422	Dec	328

Sites no longer meeting table qualifying levels
Poole Harbour

Other sites surpassing table qualifying levels in 2000–01
Breydon Wtr & Berney Marshes	[30] 1,456	Nov
Traeth Lafan	1,270	Nov

Sites surpassing passage threshold in Great Britain in 2000–01

Dee Estuary (Eng/Wal)	11,991	Sep	Belfast Lough	2,018	Oct
Mersey Estuary	9,302	Sep	Cromarty Firth	1,979	Oct
Morecambe Bay	8,443	Oct	Deben Estuary	1,919	Oct
The Wash	6,504	Sep	Montrose Basin	1,869	Oct
Humber Estuary	6,414	Sep	Swale Estuary	1,773	Oct
Ribble Estuary	6,224	Sep	Severn Estuary	1,750	Sep
Thames Estuary	5,305	Oct	Tees Estuary	1,675	Sep
Forth Estuary	5,032	Sep	Lindisfarne	1,555	Sep
Strangford Lough	4,418	Oct	Stour Estuary	1,551	Aug
Solway Estuary	3,366	Oct	Colne Estuary	1,528	Oct
Blackwater Estuary	2,913	Oct	North Norfolk Coast	1,330	Aug
Chichester Harbour	2,607	Oct	Dundrum Bay	1,256	Sep
Hamford Water	2,563	Sep	Medway Estuary	1,247	Oct
Moray Firth	2,137	Oct	Breydon Wtr & Berney Marshes	1,245	Sep
Clyde Estuary	2,093	Oct	Eden Estuary	1,231	Oct

MARSH SANDPIPER
Tringa stagnatilis

Vagrant
Native range: Africa, Asia and Australia

Singles were present in Christchurch Harbour in
April and at Stodmarsh NNR & Collards Lagoon
in September.

GREENSHANK
Tringa nebularia

International threshold: ?
Great Britain threshold: +*†
All-Ireland threshold: 9*

*50 is normally used as a minimum threshold

GB Max: 2,133 Aug
NI Max: 148 Oct

Peak numbers in Great Britain occurred slightly earlier than usual but were at the higher end of values for the last decade. In Northern Ireland the peak was the second highest ever recorded by WeBS and was typically later than the Great Britain peak.

    Wintering numbers were around average for the past five years in both Great Britain and Northern Ireland. The peak of 43 at Chichester Harbour is notable as a wintering flock.

    Fourteen sites held 50 or more birds during passage, with The Wash supporting exceptionally high numbers for the second year running.

	96–97	97–98	98–99	99–00	00–01	Mon	Mean
Sites with mean peak counts of 9 or more birds in Great Britain †							
Chichester Harbour	10	36	20	(19)	29 43	Jan	27
Tamar Complex	24	22	19	(25)	29	Dec	24
Kingsbridge Estuary	26	27	18	29	14	Jan	23
Fal Complex	16	14	24	(23)	26	Feb	21
Taw-Torridge Estuary	11	28	(9)	16	19	Feb	19
Cleddau Estuary	12	11	22	(15)	27	Dec	18
Exe Estuary	11	16	27	13	14	Nov	16
Grouville Marsh	(6)	(15)	(2)	13	15	Jan	14
Foryd Bay	11	10	13	10	9	Jan	11
North West Solent	9	15	10	(10)	8	Feb	11
Tyninghame Estuary	10	17	10	7	8	Nov	10
Blackwater Estuary	(1)	(2)	(5)	2	17	Nov	10 ▲
Sites of all-Ireland importance in Northern Ireland							
Strangford Lough	30 37	38	56	48	41	Nov	44
Lough Foyle	(17)	30	28	30	16	Nov	26
Carlingford Lough	8	15	15	14	13	Dec	13
Dundrum Bay	30 10	10	16	12	11	Dec	12
Outer Ards	15	15	16	7	4	Nov	11
Larne Lough	8	10	11	8	9	Nov	9

Sites no longer meeting table qualifying levels
Yealm Estuary

Other sites surpassing table qualifying levels in 2000–01

Queens Valley Reservoir	17	Feb
Rough Firth	9	Nov

Sites holding 50 or more birds on passage in 2000

The Wash	424	Aug	Strangford Lough	75	Oct
Thames Estuary	200	Sep	Exe Estuary	64	Sep
Chichester Harbour	192	Jul	Langstone Harbour	62	Aug
North Norfolk Coast	143	Aug	Morecambe Bay	58	Aug
Blackwater Estuary	118	Sep	Breydon Wtr & Berney Marshes	54	May
Dee Estuary (Eng/Wal)	83	Sep	Pegwell Bay	53	Sep
Humber Estuary	75	Aug	Poole Harbour	50	Sep

†   as no British threshold has been set, a qualifying level of nine has been chosen to select sites for presentation in this report

GREEN SANDPIPER

Tringa ochropus

International threshold: ?
Great Britain threshold: ?
All-Ireland threshold: ?

GB Max: 537 Aug
NI Max: 0

The peak count, derived from 105 sites which held Green Sandpiper, was slightly above average for the last five years and occurred in the typical month for this passage migrant and winter visitor.

During winter birds were recorded at 118 sites with 17 of these sites holding five or more birds. Beddington Sewage Farm, where numbers peaked at 10 in February and 11 in March, was the only site to hold ten or more birds in this period.

Sites with 15 or more birds in 2000–01

Pegwell Bay	44	Jul	Brandon Marsh Nature Reserve	23	Jul
Swale Estuary	42	Aug	Blackwater Estuary	22	Aug
Thames Estuary	40	Sep	Beddington Sewage Farm	20	Aug
Rye Harbour & Pett Level	32	Jul	Southampton Water	18	Aug
North Norfolk Coast	30	Aug	Tophill Low Reservoirs	18	Aug
Humber Estuary	28	Jul			

WOOD SANDPIPER

Scarce

Tringa glareola

GB Max: 36 Aug
NI Max: 0

Despite the peak count being only just above average for the past five years, the summed site maxima of 97 was notably higher (*cf.* 66 and 54 in the previous two years). All records were from May to October, with the spring peak in May only six less than that in autumn.

For the second year running double figures were recorded at Dungeness Gravel Pits.

Sites with three or more birds in 2000–01

Dungeness Gravel Pits	10	Jul	Stodmarsh & Collards Lagoon	4	May
North Norfolk Coast	9	Aug	Swale Estuary	4	May
Breydon Wtr & Berney Marshes	6	Jul	Colne Estuary	3	Sep
Belvide Reservoir	5	Jul	Humber Estuary	3	Aug
Blackwater Estuary	4	Aug	Lindisfarne	3	May
Pegwell Bay	4	Jul			

COMMON SANDPIPER

Actitis hypoleucos

International threshold: ?
Great Britain threshold: ?
All-Ireland threshold: ?

GB Max: 1,116 Jul
NI Max: 5 Jul

For only the second time since 1992–93, the peak count fell below the previous year's value and was the lowest of the last five years. Typically the peak count for this species occurs in August so the July peak was noteworthy. The 2000–01 August total was 857, just half that of the previous year. Despite these low figures, the 453 sites where this species was seen was the highest ever recorded by WeBS.

Sites with 40 or more birds in 2000–01

Pegwell Bay	82	Jul
Morecambe Bay	52	Jul
North Norfolk Coast	47	May
Dungeness Gravel Pits	46	Jul
Abberton Reservoir	45	Aug
Pegwell Bay	40	Aug

TURNSTONE
Arenaria interpres

International threshold: 700
Great Britain threshold: 640
All-Ireland threshold: 225

GB Max: 14,057 Feb
NI Max: 1,606 Nov

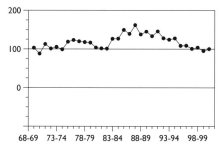

Figure 65. Annual indices for Turnstone in the UK

The peak count for Great Britain rose to its highest level since 1994–95 but was still noticeably lower than the highs of the mid to late 1980s. This situation was reflected in Northern Ireland with below average numbers

recorded for the fourth consecutive year. The UK annual indices remained relatively stable though still in the lower range of values.

Seven sites qualified as being internationally important but four of these held numbers below their five-year peak means. Numbers at Morecambe Bay continued the gradual decline but the Dee Estuary (Eng/Wal) and Belfast Lough reversed the downward trend of recent years. The absence of Low Tide Counts on the Mersey Estuary is apparent in the table, the feeding flock on the estuary mouth roosting on adjacent sites and hence not recorded during Core Counts. The Humber Estuary held numbers in excess of the international 1% threshold for the second year running.

	96–97	97–98	98–99	99–00	00–01	Mon	Mean	
Sites of international importance in the UK								
Morecambe Bay	1,248	1,198	1,402	1,181	1,175	Jan	1,241	
Mersey Estuary	[30] 1,717	[30] 1,188	[30] 1,727	[30] 703	0		1,067	
Outer Ards	1,040	(715)	1,136	1,102	879	Nov	1,039	
Tiree	-	[17] 905	-	[25] 858	-		882	
Dee Estuary (Eng/Wal)	1,193	978	771	453	791	Feb	837	
Thanet Coast	481	784	855	892	827	Dec	768	
East Sanday Coast	-	[17] (734)	-	-	-		(734)	
Sites of national importance in Great Britain								
Forth Estuary	636	700	776	533	716	Nov	672	▼
The Wash	(766)	444	965	641	515	Feb	666	▼
Sites of all-Ireland importance in Northern Ireland								
Belfast Lough	785	510	566	399	524	Dec	557	
Strangford Lough	207	207	194	301	248	Nov	231	
Other sites surpassing table qualifying levels in 2000–01								
Humber Estuary		659	Nov					
Sites surpassing international threshold during passage periods in 2000–01								
Morecambe Bay		958	Sep					
Forth Estuary		748	Sep					
Stour Estuary		732	Aug					

GREY PHALAROPE
Phalaropus fulicarius

Eight birds were recorded at seven sites during the year. At Guernsey Shore two were present in December and elsewhere singles were recorded at Traeth Bach, Eglwys Nunydd Reservoir, North Norfolk Coast, Ouse Washes, River Avon: Ringwood to Christchurch and Widewater, all between September and December.

MEDITERRANEAN GULL
Larus melanocephalus

Scarce

| GB Max: | 100 Jul |
| NI Max: | 1 Dec |

WeBS reflects the continuing increase of this species in Great Britain, with the peak national total, the summed site maxima and the number of sites where this species was recorded all being the highest ever recorded by WeBS. Seventy-five sites produced a summed site maxima of 282 birds (*cf.* 259, 169 and 215 in the preceding three years).

The Northern Ireland record, a single present at Belfast Lough in December, is notable as being only the second ever to be recorded by WeBS.

Sites with five or more birds in 2000–01

Newtown Estuary	49	Apr
Brading Harbour	35	Jul
Tamar Complex	28	Jul
Ryde Pier to Puckpool Point	16	Jan
Thames Estuary	12	Jan
Swansea Bay	11	Aug
Foreland	8	Oct
Medway Estuary	7	Apr
Exe Estuary	6	Oct
Chichester Harbour	5	Apr

LITTLE GULL
Larus minutus

Scarce

| GB Max: | 208 Sep |
| NI Max: | 1 various |

The peak count was above the five-year peak mean and occurred later than in recent years, largely due to the relatively high count at Hornsea Mere, a recognised site for this species in autumn.

During the winter, birds were recorded at 14 sites with a peak of four in Langstone Harbour during December. Unusually for Northern Ireland, individuals were recorded in several months: on the Bann Estuary in May and September (also present on an additional count in April) and at Belfast Lough in October.

Sites with five or more birds in 2000–01

Hornsea Mere	163	Sep	North Norfolk Coast	18	Jun
Monikie Country Park	135	Jun	Staines Reservoirs	10	May
Alt Estuary	67	Apr	Humber Estuary	10	Sep
Eden Estuary	44	Jul	Arlington Reservoir	5	Oct
Benacre Broad	30	Sep	Barcombe Mills Reservoir	5	Oct
Walthamstow Reservoirs	22	Oct			

BONAPARTE'S GULL
Larus philadelphia

Vagrant
Native range: Americas

Birds were recorded at five sites during 2000–01. During May and June what was presumably the same bird was seen at King George V Reservoirs and Queen Elizabeth II Reservoir. Singles were also recorded on the Thames Estuary in September and at Crockfoot Reservoir and the Lower Windrush Valley Gravel Pits in November.

BLACK-HEADED GULL
Larus ridibundus

International threshold:	**20,000**[**]
Great Britain threshold:	**19,000**[†]
All-Ireland threshold:	**?**[†]

GB Max: 267,408 Jan
NI Max: 11,884 Jan

Although Tophill Low Reservoirs and Morecambe Bay remain internationally important, the peak counts for these sites in 2000–01 were over 40% and 17% lower than their respective five-year peak means. The peak count for Great Britain remained higher than average yet represented only 14% of the provisional British population estimate. Counts of over 10,000 birds were recorded at a further six sites. In Northern Ireland, the peak count was lower than average.

The species has moved onto the 'Amber' list published in the 'Population Status of Birds in the UK' in 2002 (Gregory *et al.* 2002). This is, in part, because the breeding population has declined by 40% over the past 25 years.

	96–97	97–98	98–99	99–00	00–01	Mon	Mean	
Sites of international importance in the UK								
Tophill Low Reservoirs	15,000	43,800	17,000	18,000	12,500	Nov	21,260	
Morecambe Bay	18,653	25,294	26,624	17,670	17,605	Sep	21,169	
Sites with mean peak counts of 10,000 or more birds in Great Britain [†]								
The Wash	13,975	5,780	8,191	31,403	9,008	Nov	13,671	
Tyne Estuary	[22] 21,000	[22] 21,000	[22] 15,500	[22] 6,250	[22] 4,000	Feb	13,550	▲
Portsmouth Harbour	(7,845)	12,642	9,388	(15,509)	14,247	Feb	12,947	
Lower Derwent Valley	17,500	19,000	1,100	-	-		12,533	
Poole Harbour	(10,732)	15,844	8,816	10,629	10,162	Oct	11,363	
Chasewater	10,000	12,000	12,000	-	-		11,333	
Southampton Water	[30] 11,269	[30] 9,606	[30] 14,356	[30] 8,129	[30] 9,751	Jan	10,622	
Pitsford Reservoir	8,000	8,000	(15,000)	10,000	[22] 10,000	Oct	10,200	▲
Thames Estuary	7,197	6,308	5,794	12,050	19,308	Nov	10,131	▲
Church Wilne Reservoir	[22] 5,000	15,000	-	-	-		10,000	▲
Sites with mean peak counts of 1,000 or more birds in Northern Ireland [†]								
Outer Ards	4,848	2,332	6,141	8,040	3,290	Feb	4,930	
Belfast Lough	[30] 4,450	[30] 5,953	4,303	[30] 4,028	[30] 7,496	Nov	5,246	
Loughs Neagh & Beg	4,102	2,963	4,409	-	-		3,825	
Strangford Lough	[30] 3,338	3,899	4,693	2,730	3,588	Nov	3,650	
Lough Foyle	2,577	2,455	1,521	3,019	1,214	Dec	2,157	
Larne Lough	1,386	1,839	1,663	2,639	942	Feb	1,694	
Dundrum Bay	1,067	946	1,237	1,068	1,173	Jan	1,098	
Other sites surpassing table qualifying levels in 2000–01								
Forth Estuary		16,451	Jan					
Clyde Estuary		15,356	Jan					
Nene Washes		[22] 15,000	Feb					
Derwent Reservoir		[22] 14,000	Jan					
Pegwell Bay		10,290	Feb					
Rutland Water		10,000	Sep					

[†] *as few sites exceed the British threshold, and as no all-Ireland threshold has been set, qualifying levels of 10,000 and 1,000 have been chosen to select sites in Great Britain and Northern Ireland, respectively, for presentation in this report*

RING-BILLED GULL
Larus delawarensis

Vagrant
Native range: North America

Three returning and long-staying birds were recorded in southwest England, at the Hayle Estuary, Par Sands Pool and on the Taw/Torridge Estuary. A second bird was also present on the Hayle Estuary in February.

Elsewhere, two were on the Avon Estuary in April and singles were seen at Chew Valley Lake, Drift Reservoir, Maer Lake, Swansea Bay, Wellington Gravel Pits and the Thames Estuary.

COMMON GULL
Larus canus

International threshold:	16,000
Great Britain threshold:	9,000[†]
All-Ireland threshold:	?[†]

GB Max: 70,892 Jan
NI Max: 7,250 Oct

After collation of new data, three new sites in northern England now join Tophill Low Reservoirs as internationally important: Hallington Reservoir (Northumberland), Derwent Reservoir (Durham) and Haweswater Reservoir (Cumbria). In addition, Colt Crag Reservoir (Northumberland) now qualifies as nationally important, with Lower Derwent Valley falling below the threshold due to a lack of recent data. The peak total in Great Britain was 28% lower than in the previous year, yet the peak for Northern Ireland was high as a consequence of a much larger count at Lough Foyle.

Given that the supplementary counts from the new sites in northern England were not used to calculate the national totals, and that less than 8% of the provisional British population estimate is recorded by WeBS, it is clear that this survey massively underestimates the numbers of Common Gulls wintering in the UK. Although this species was already 'Amber' listed in the 1996 assessment of the 'Population Status of Birds in the UK', it now qualifies, in part, because the breeding population has declined by 37% over the past 25 years (Gregory *et al.* 2002).

	96–97	97–98	98–99	99–00	00–01	Mon	Mean	
Sites of international importance in the UK								
Hallington Gravel Pits	[22] 65,000	[22] 48,000	[22] 46,000	[22] 32,000	[22] 19,000	Sep	42,000	▲
Derwent Reservoir	[22] 26,000	[22] 48,000	[22] 20,000	[22] 33,000	[22] 41,000	Jan	33,600	
Tophill Low Reservoirs	14,000	22,000	38,000	42,000	24,500	Nov	28,100	
Haweswater Reservoir	[22] 13,639	[22] 19,120	[22] 19,541	[22] 11,000	[22] 26,480	Mar	17,956	▲
Sites of national importance in Great Britain								
Colt Crag Reservoir	[22] 8,700	[22] 21,000	[22] 6,850	[22] 1,140	[22] 16,000	Aug	10,738	▲
Sites with mean peak counts of 3,000 or more birds in Great Britain [†]								
West Water Reservoir	4,500	12,500	(8,000)	(5,400)	-		8,500	
Lower Derwent Valley	6,400	8,000	320	-	-		4,907	
Morecambe Bay	4,187	5,536	5,869	3,397	4,860	Aug	4,770	
Hule Moss	[29] 6,000	[29] 5,400	[29] 1,100	[29] 5,500	-		4,500	
Rutland Water	6,000	8,000	2,000	500	4,000	Nov/Jan	4,100	
Pitsford Reservoir	2,500	4,000	5,500	6,000	[22] 2,000	Oct	4,000	
The Wash	(1,321)	(887)	1,693	4,324	3,681	Aug	3,233	
Cromarty Firth	-	-	-	[30] 3,842	-		3,842	
Eccup Reservoir	5,000	2,500	4,000	4,000	3,500	Dec	3,800	
Thames Estuary	3,455	(830)	(3,114)	3,685	3,496	Aug	3,545	
Alt Estuary	[30] 2,228	1,340	[30] 5,423	4,800	3,850	Jan	3,528	
North Norfolk Coast	227	177	[22] 8,400	2,237	5,271	Dec	3,262	
Tees Estuary	5,014	2,204	1,089	3,617	3,258	Oct	3,036	
Sites with mean peak counts of 1,000 or more birds in Northern Ireland [†]								
Lough Foyle	2,291	2,045	2,802	3,759	6,095	Oct	3,398	

Other sites surpassing table qualifying levels in 2000–01

Wigtown Bay	4,503	Dec
Burry Inlet	5,085	Aug
Longnewton Reservoir	4,300	Jan
Blyth Estuary (Suffolk)	2,750	Jan
Ribble Estuary	3,077	Jan
Belfast Lough	1,416	Jan

†   as few sites exceed the British threshold, and as no all-Ireland threshold has been set, qualifying levels of 3,000 and 1,000 have been chosen to select sites, in Great Britain and Northern Ireland respectively, for presentation in this report

---

LESSER BLACK-BACKED GULL
Larus fuscus

International threshold:	4,500
Great Britain threshold:	500
All-Ireland threshold:	?

GB Max: 45,768 Jul
NI Max: 89 Sep

Morecambe Bay supports by far the largest numbers of Lesser Black-backed Gulls in the UK as recorded by WeBS, supporting some 8% of the provisional national population estimate. The Severn Estuary and Alde Complex remain internationally important and recently collated data also identifies Llys-y-fran Reservoir in Dyfed as an internationally important site.

Although representing complete counts under definitions used for WeBS Core Counts, several numbers in the table (as with counts of other gulls) clearly represent the importance of these sites; roost counts are required at some to determine their true status and simply treating these obviously low counts as undercounts would greatly elevate their five-year peak means.

The peak count for Great Britain was lower than the previous five years. The absence of this species during counts made at Loughs Neagh and Beg means that the Northern Ireland total remained lower than average for the second year running.

The Severn Estuary supports large numbers of birds throughout the year, peaking in late autumn in most years. Large numbers of post-breeding adults and juveniles congregate in the upper reaches during the late summer. Many of these birds originate from the city of Gloucester colony which was established in 1967 and now contains a remarkable 2,100 pairs (Durham 2002).

	96–97	97–98	98–99	99–00	00–01	Mon	Mean	
Sites of international importance in the UK								
Morecambe Bay	30,880	51,829	43,590	41,945	40,590	Jul	41,767	
Llys-y-fran Reservoir	8,500	400	0	[22] 12,000	[22] 11,000	Jan	6,380	▲
Severn Estuary	7,017	6,085	7,102	7,224	669	Nov	5,619	
Alde Complex	542	9,633	1,529	15,000	36	Nov	5,348	
Sites of national importance in Great Britain								
Chasewater	3,500	3,000	3,400	-	-		3,300	
Wellington Gravel Pits	77	1,400	3,350	2,500	2,400	Dec	1,945	
Great Pool Westwood Park	1,750	1,500	2,000	2,000	2,000	Dec	1,850	
Alt Estuary	2,480	1,957	2,230	769	1,122	Aug	1,712	
Hule Moss	[29] 160	[29] 240	[29] 5,200	[29] 1,010	-		1,653	▲
Rutland Water	(150)	3,000	1,000	1,500	600	Sep	1,525	
Lower Windrush Valley GP	589	1,714	865	1,339	2,424	Feb	1,386	
The Wash	(1,338)	239	1,506	2,206	1,139	Nov	1,286	
Chew Valley Lake	0	0	6,000	0	0		1,200	
Longnewton Reservoir	34	780	2,600	1,800	340	Oct	1,111	
Hayle Estuary	735	1,095	690	1,750	852	Feb	1,024	
Llangorse Lake	820	860	1,280	1,060	1,050	Oct	1,014	
Portworthy Mica Dam	2,250	1,000	500	465	750	Aug	993	
R. Avon: Fordingbridge to R'wood	61	386	(10)	2,508	961	Nov	979	▲
Cleddau Estuary	2,073	477	414	(1,246)	625	Nov	967	
NE Glamorgan Moorland Pools	1,352	1,418	330	-	732	Nov	958	

	96–97	97–98	98–99	99–00	00–01	Mon	Mean	
Pitsford Reservoir	550	1,200	(1,000)	700	[22] 1,000	Sep	890	
Rodbourne Sewage Works	-	-	562	(1,100)	-		831	
Colliford Reservoir	296	600	43	3,040	52	Oct	806	
R. Nith: K'bank to Nunholm	(126)	(700)	(680)	(485)	(455)	Jul	(700)	▲
Crowdy Reservoir	400	650	410	1,000	1,000	Oct	692	
Caistron Quarry	[22] 965	[22] 930	[22] 790	[22] 395	[22] 206	Oct	657	
Solway Estuary	517	1,143	262	725	436	Jun	617	
King's Mill Reservoir	600	(84)	-	-	-		600	▲
Heaton Park Reservoir	-	2,000	170	201	21	Jan	598	
Otmoor	-	-	-	-	581	Nov	581	▲
Aqualate Mere	206	150	[29] 1,500	[29] (800)	14	Oct	534	▲
Sprotborough Flash	1,000	1,500	10	20	50	Sep	516	▲
Poole Harbour	482	353	264	888	565	Oct	510	▲

Sites with mean peak counts of 500 or more birds in Northern Ireland [†]

Loughs Neagh & Beg	1,064	972	1,129	0	0		633	

Sites no longer meeting table qualifying levels
Blackmoorfoot Reservoir
Camel Estuary

Other sites surpassing table qualifying levels in 2000–01

Thames Estuary	700	Oct	Nene Washes	[22] 625	Nov	
Blyth Estuary (Suffolk)	886	Dec	Port Meadow	620	Nov	
Walthamstow Reservoirs	524	Nov	Chillington Hall Pool	(500)	Dec	

†   as no all-Ireland threshold has been set, a qualifying level of 500 has been chosen to select sites for presentation in this report

---

HERRING GULL
Larus argentatus

International threshold:	13,000
Great Britain threshold:	4,500 [†]
All-Ireland threshold:	?

GB Max: 78,827 Jan
NI Max: 8,055 Feb

Morecambe Bay continues to be the only site currently qualifying as internationally important for Herring Gull in the UK as identified by WeBS, with numbers in 2000–01 similar to those recorded in the previous four years. The late summer peak coincides with movements of post-breeding adults and fledglings from nearby colonies. The national total continues to increase annually, up 12% from the previous year, although such a comparison makes no allowance for variations in coverage. In contrast, the breeding population has declined by over 60% in the last thirty years (Gregory *et al.* 2002).

The maximum count for Northern Ireland remained high for the second consecutive year. Numbers recorded at Belfast Lough were particularly high in 2000–01, as with Common Gull over 50% above the five-year peak mean.

	96–97	97–98	98–99	99–00	00–01	Mon	Mean	
Sites of international importance in the UK								
Morecambe Bay	17,260	18,165	19,168	20,553	20,470	Jul	19,123	
Sites of national importance in Great Britain								
The Wash	5,147	12,649	4,430	5,589	10,003	Jan	7,564	
Alt Estuary	5,300	5,500	[30] 9,070	6,800	3,967	Jan	6,127	
North Norfolk Coast	2,845	802	4,923	4,196	15,291	Jan	5,611	
Sites with mean peak counts of 2,500 or more birds in Great Britain [†]								
Alde Complex	312	8,569	4,253	7,186	1,196	Jan	4,303	
Ribble Estuary	430	[30] 2,559	1,250	7,287	9,032	Jan	4,112	
Solway Estuary	4,269	2,884	4,759	2,962	2,255	Jun	3,426	
Guernsey Shore	3,073	-	(1,409)	(1,850)	3,525	Oct	3,299	
Gaddon Loch	-	-	3,414	3,500	1,956	Jan	2,957	
Forth Estuary	3,747	1,893	2,311	3,289	3,154	Jan	2,879	
Chasewater	1,700	2,800	3,000	-	-		2,500	▲
R. Devon: Tullibody Bridge	(1)	(60)	2,500	-	-		2,500	▲

	96–97	97–98	98–99	99–00	00–01	Mon	Mean	
Sites with mean peak counts of 1,000 or more birds in Northern Ireland [†]								
Belfast Lough	[30] 9,381	2,598	5,291	3,637	6,749	Feb	5,531	
Outer Ards	362	1,312	2,179	3,003	898	Feb	1,551	▲
Other sites surpassing table qualifying levels in 2000–01								
Burry Inlet	4,428	Jul						
Pegwell Bay	3,890	Jan						
Carmarthen Bay	(2,600)	Mar						

†   as few sites exceed the British threshold, and as no all-Ireland threshold has been set, qualifying levels of 2,500 and 1,000 have been chosen to select sites in Great Britain and Northern Ireland, respectively, for presentation in this report

YELLOW-LEGGED GULL   Scarce
Larus argentatus cachinnans/michahellis

GB Max: 111 Aug
NI Max: 0

As in previous years, the majority of birds recorded by WeBS were not racially identified. During the three years in which these subspecies have been reported on by WeBS,

2000–01 produced the lowest peak count. Records followed the now established pattern of peaking in late summer before declining during autumn and winter.

Sites with five or more birds in 2000–01

Southampton Water	92	Aug
Alde Complex	33	Dec
Thames Estuary	32	Sep
Poole Harbour	16	Jan
Purfleet Chalk Pit	11	Oct
Great Pool Westwood Park	5	Dec
Poole Harbour	5	Sep
Rutland Water	5	Sep

Of those that were racially identified, only two records related to Caspian Gull (*Larus argentatus cachinnans*). Singles were at Ditchford Gravel Pits in November and on the Thames Estuary in December. Western Yellow-legged Gulls (*Larus argentatus michahellis*) were recorded at six sites with nine on the Thames Estuary in November and three at College Lake Reservoir in October being the only records of more than one bird. It is likely that the majority of unspecified Yellow-legged Gulls relate to *michahellis* birds.

ICELAND GULL   Scarce
Larus glaucoides

Relatively low numbers were recorded by WeBS during 2000–01, with birds being recorded at 17 sites. Almost half of the records occurred in April or May. All were singles with the exception of two at Gaddon Loch, at Longnewton Reservoir during January and on the North Norfolk Coast in April.

GLAUCOUS GULL   Scarce
Larus hyperboreus

Birds were reported from 21 sites in Great Britain with a peak of seven in November. In Northern Ireland one at Belfast Lough in January and February was the only record. Other than four at Burra Firth in November, three on the North Norfolk Coast in April and two on the Thames Estuary in January, all records were of singles, mostly in the period January to March. One seen on The Wash in July was notable for its out of season occurrence.

GREAT BLACK-BACKED GULL
Larus marinus

International threshold: 4,800
Great Britain threshold: 400
All-Ireland threshold: ? [t]

GB Max: 10,500 Nov
NI Max: 526 Nov

The peak count in Great Britain was very similar to that recorded in the previous two years. Peak counts from the Tees Estuary, Loch of Strathbeg, Pegwell Bay and Chasewater were over twice as high as their respective five-year peak means. However, numbers fluctuate markedly between years at many of the key sites.

In Northern Ireland, peak counts were similar to those recorded in the previous five years. Belfast Lough remains the key site for this species in the province.

	96–97	97–98	98–99	99–00	00–01	Mon	Mean	
Sites of national importance in Great Britain								
Tophill Low Reservoirs	835	1,040	2,600	2,200	1,880	Dec	1,711	
The Wash	(1,087)	630	745	3,025	1,303	Sep	1,426	
Portsmouth Harbour	(216)	(420)	1,329	872	1,028	Dec	1,076	
Lower Derwent Valley	1,750	1,105	271	-	-		1,042	
Creswell to Chevington Burn	685	2,000	1,700	612	190	Oct	1,037	
Tees Estuary	1,068	1,152	482	463	1,558	Oct	945	
Loch of Strathbeg	(1,200)	670	(153)	134	[29] 1,280	Nov	821	
Pegwell Bay	750	1,000	[29] 186	364	1,050	Jan	670	
Morecambe Bay	621	668	907	451	697	Nov	669	
Thames Estuary	789	(505)	444	451	774	Jan	615	
Dungeness Gravel Pits	1,600	90	18	(0)	(0)		569	
Lossie Estuary	1,053	847	251	414	127	Dec	538	
North Norfolk Coast	85	426	[22] 800	548	567	Sep	485	▲
Fleet/Wey	234	307	1,195	312	213	Oct/Feb	452	
Don Mouth to Ythan Mouth	0	86	397	511	1,225	Aug	444	▲
Chasewater	300	500	460	-	-		420	
Sites with mean peak counts of 500 or more birds in Northern Ireland [t]								
Belfast Lough	550	349	1,035	227	398	Feb	512	
Sites no longer meeting table qualifying levels								
Dee Estuary (Eng/Wal)								
Other sites surpassing table qualifying levels in 2000–01								
Rutland Water		500	Jan					
Forth Estuary		533	Sep					
Angler's Country Park Lake		[29] 450	Dec					

† as no all-Ireland threshold has been set, a qualifying level of 500 has been chosen to select sites for presentation in this report

---

KITTIWAKE
Rissa tridactyla

International threshold: ?
Great Britain threshold: ?
All-Ireland threshold: ?

GB Max: 2,903 Aug
NI Max: 27 Jun

Coverage of key sites in eastern Scotland and northeast England in late summer and early autumn has the greatest influence on the numbers recorded by WeBS. The peak in 2000–01 rose sharply (double that of 1999–2000) though remained low in comparison with preceding years. Counts at a number of key sites were well below normal, although the influence

of weather conditions and the coincidence of priority count dates with relatively short-lived local peaks also has a large effect on numbers recorded at an individual site. With the exception of Arran, all sites supporting 200 or more birds in 2000–01 were on the east coast of Scotland.

Sites with 200 or more birds in 2000–01

Dee Estuary (Scotland)	774	Aug
Don Mouth to Ythan Mouth	595	Aug
Lossie Estuary	463	Aug
Deveron Estuary	290	Aug
Forth Estuary	254	Aug
Inner Moray Firth	250	Oct
Arran	225	Sep
Loch of Strathbeg	200	Aug

SANDWICH TERN
Sterna sandvicensis

International threshold:	1,500
Great Britain threshold:	?[†]
All-Ireland threshold:	?[†]

GB Max:	8,871	Aug
NI Max:	421	Sep

A large peak count on the North Norfolk Coast in June 2000 means that this site joins the Forth Estuary as the only internationally important sites in the UK identified by WeBS. The peak count for Great Britain was notably high for the second year running and occurred during the late summer when UK-bred birds are joined by those moving southwards from colonies in northern Europe. An extraordinary count of 1,329 birds was made at the Humber Estuary during August and demonstrates the potential importance of this site as a staging post for the species. The peak in Northern Ireland was similar to that recorded in previous years.

The numbers of breeding birds in Britain and Ireland fell by 20% during the 1990s but have remained stable since then (Ratcliffe *et al.* 2000). This decline was confined to the North Sea and has been related to events at individual colonies rather than at all colonies in the area.

	96–97	97–98	98–99	99–00	00–01	Mon	Mean	
Sites of international importance in the UK								
Forth Estuary	1,394	1,499	918	3,868	3,424	Aug	2,221	
North Norfolk Coast	472	311	1,165	2,907	5,015	Jun	1,974	▲
Sites with mean peak counts of 200 or more birds in Great Britain [†]								
Dee Estuary (Eng/Wal)	2,090	636	1,256	629	672	Aug	1,057	
Duddon Estuary	808	753	764	1,204	994	Jul	905	
Tees Estuary	489	227	1,386	1,238	897	Jul	847	
Loch of Strathbeg	(750)	(1,000)	(1,000)	(24)	0		688	
The Wash	186	586	674	420	310	Jul	435	
Humber Estuary	32	240	62	154	1,329	Aug	363	▲
Pegwell Bay	140	45	750	432	320	Jul	337	
Blyth Estuary (Northumberland)	57	[29] 700	[29] 93	[29] 600	[29] 202	Jul	330	▲
Cemlyn Bay & Lagoon	1,380	0	0	0	0		276	
Lindisfarne	143	(160)	(355)	350	220	Aug	267	
Ythan Estuary	380	488	0	0	-		217	
Tay Estuary	401	25	225	300	132	Sep	217	
Don Mouth to Ythan Mouth	-	212	88	72	434	Aug	202	▲
Sites with mean peak counts of 200 or more birds in Northern Ireland [†]								
Dundrum Bay	212	592	353	234	166	Jun	311	
Belfast Lough	244	188	194	239	195	Sep	212	▲
Sites no longer meeting table qualifying levels								
Exe Estuary								
Other sites surpassing table qualifying levels in 2000–01								
St Andrews Bay			312	Aug				
Loch Ryan			200	Jul				
Tyne Estuary			255	Jul				

†   *as no British or all-Ireland thresholds have been set, a qualifying level of 200 has been chosen to select sites for presentation in this report*

ROSEATE TERN

Scarce

Sterna dougallii

Three were noted on the Tees Estuary in July, two were on the Thames Estuary in June and singles were on the Exe Estuary in May and on the Tyne Estuary in June and August.

COMMON TERN

Sterna hirundo

International threshold:	6,000
Great Britain threshold:	?[†]
All-Ireland threshold:	?[†]

GB Max: 7,560 Aug
NI Max: 13 Sep

The Great Britain peak total was higher than that recorded during the three preceding years and occurred during the late summer when there is a southwards post-breeding movement of adults and juveniles from colonies in the UK and elsewhere in northern Europe. The highest counts were recorded at the Humber, Alt and Tees Estuaries. That made at the Humber Estuary in August 2000 was notable, being almost four times higher than the five-year peak mean for the site.

Common Terns spend very little time at staging sites during the late summer and the actual peak numbers at sites are therefore probably only rarely recorded by WeBS. This may explain why the counts on the Humber Estuary, a site that may be an important temporary staging area, are so variable. As usual, very few birds were recorded in Northern Ireland.

	96–97	97–98	98–99	99–00	00–01	Mon	Mean	
Sites with mean peak counts of 200 or more birds in Great Britain [†]								
Alt Estuary	596	1,038	1,004	1,156	1,292	Aug	1,017	
Tees Estuary	453	841	620	1,038	876	Jul	766	
Humber Estuary	7	23	(23)	21	2,165	Aug	554	▲
North Norfolk Coast	344	176	620	599	611	Jun	470	
Dee Estuary (Eng/Wal)	641	225	567	348	246	Jun	405	
The Wash	310	215	300	370	262	Aug	291	
Tay Estuary	320	230	150	600	40	Aug	268	
Forth Estuary	390	(343)	92	200	310	Aug	267	
Thames Estuary	187	64	487	229	284	Aug	250	▲
Sites no longer meeting table qualifying levels								
Loch of Strathbeg								
Ythan Estuary								
R. Thames: Roding to Beam								
Other sites surpassing table qualifying levels in 2000–01								
Eden Estuary	310	Aug						
Southampton Water	238	Aug						
St Andrews Bay	260	Aug						
Chichester Harbour	209	Jul						

[†]   as no British or all-Ireland thresholds have been set, a qualifying level of 200 has been chosen to select sites for presentation in this report

ARCTIC TERN

Sterna paradisaea

International threshold:	?
Great Britain threshold:	?[†]
All-Ireland threshold:	?[†]

GB Max: 981 May
NI Max: 0

Arctic Terns stage very briefly during their autumn migration and therefore actual peak numbers probably only rarely coincide with WeBS Core Count dates. Considering that 40,000 pairs breed in the UK, it is perhaps surprising that so few are recorded by the survey during passage periods. In 2000–01, the Great Britain peak total occurred in May when birds from breeding colonies will have been counted at some sites. Compared to peak counts in recent years, the maximum in 2000–01 was quite high.

There were few notable counts with most key sites located in northern and eastern Scotland.

	96–97	97–98	98–99	99–00	00–01	Mon	Mean	
Sites with mean peak counts of 50 or more birds in Great Britain [†]								
Tay Estuary	40	1,000	55	150	80	Aug	265	
Eden Estuary	90	190	115	361	220	Aug	195	
Loch of Brow	-	-	-	200	150	Jun	175	▲
Loch of Clumlie	-	-	-	250	45	Jun	148	▲
St Andrews Bay	121	22	10	283	170	Aug	121	▲
Morecambe Bay	105	124	144	74	103	Jun	110	
Lunda Wick	-	-	-	5	190	Jul	98	▲
Loch of Spiggie	-	-	-	100	70	Jun	85	▲
North Ronaldsay Lochs	(210)	138	50	4	0		80	
Balranald RSPB Reserve	-	80	-	-	-		80	
Ythan Estuary	100	204	0	0	-		76	
The Houb (Whalsay)	-	-	-	100	50	Jul	75	▲
Forth Estuary	22	139	23	94	76	Jun	71	
Don Mouth to Ythan Mouth	0	66	6	207	34	Aug	63	

Sites no longer meeting table qualifying levels
Loch of Strathbeg
Loch Indaal

Other sites surpassing table qualifying levels in 2000–01
Montrose Basin   100   Aug
Dee Estuary (Scotland)   70   Jul
Loch Indaal   61   Jun

†   as no British or all-Ireland thresholds have been set, a qualifying level of 50 has been chosen to select sites for presentation in this report

---

FORSTER'S TERN
Sterna forsteri

Vagrant
Native range: North America

The bird recorded throughout 1999–2000 was seen again on the Blackwater Estuary at Old Hall Marshes in August.

LITTLE TERN
Sterna albifrons

International threshold:	340
Great Britain threshold:	? [†]
All-Ireland threshold:	? [†]

GB Max: 656 Jun
NI Max: 0

As with Arctic Tern, the peak count in Great Britain was recorded during June and therefore many counts will have included birds from breeding colonies. Both national and site totals were similar to those of the preceding four years. Large numbers of birds were recorded during late summer at several sites in southwest England and may relate to birds on passage. The potential importance of these sites for staging birds should not be ignored.

Recent analyses have shown that the breeding population of Little Terns in Britain and Ireland declined by 39% between 1975 and 1998 (Ratcliffe *et al.* 2000). This, in part, is why the species is 'Amber' listed in the 'Population Status of Birds in the UK' (Gregory *et al.* 2002). This decline has occurred throughout the species' range. Nest predation and flooding of nest sites during spring tides have been identified as potential causes.

	96–97	97–98	98–99	99–00	00–01	Mon	Mean
Sites with mean peak counts of 50 or more birds in Great Britain [†]							
Thames Estuary	467	6	(422)	297	161	Aug	271
North Norfolk Coast	15	171	209	300	241	Jun	187
Dee Estuary (Eng/Wal)	145	160	150	200	111	Jun	153
The Wash	330	30	114	148	56	Jun	136
Fleet/Wey	50	203	154	125	102	Jun	127
Blackwater Estuary	42	29	(120)	80	101	Jul	74
Hamford Water	6	10	142	102	8	Sep	54
Swale Estuary	73	33	57	63	40	Jul	53 ▲

Sites no longer meeting table qualifying levels
Langstone Harbour
Pagham Harbour
Tees Estuary

Other sites surpassing table qualifying levels in 2000–01

Tees Estuary	64	Jul

†   *as no British or all-Ireland thresholds have been set, a qualifying level of 50 has been chosen to select sites for presentation in this report*

BLACK TERN
Chlidonias niger

International threshold:	**2,000**
Great Britain threshold:	**?**
All-Ireland threshold:	**?**

GB Max:	**389 May**
NI Max:	**0**

Timing of spring passage movements coincided well with Core Count priority dates, the British peak in May being the highest yet recorded by WeBS (the previous high of 340 occurring during autumn passage in 1998). Correspondingly, the number of sites at which birds were noted (60 in total) was also the highest to date, the majority being in the midland counties of England. Interestingly, only two of the sites which held five or more birds in September 1998 feature in the 19 sites which surpassed this figure in 2000–01. Autumn numbers were lower than in recent years, though a single bird was recorded as late as November (on the Ribble Estuary).

Sites with 5 or more birds in 2000–01

Hanningfield Reservoir	72	May	Barton Broad	11	May
The Wash	41	May	Croxall Pits	11	May
Severn Estuary	29	May	Humber Estuary	9	Sep
Clifford Hill Gravel Pits	29	May	Fleet/Wey	6	May
Thrapston Gravel Pits	26	May	Blithfield Reservoir	6	May
Middle Tame Valley Gravel Pits	22	May	Dee Estuary (Eng/Wal)	6	Aug
North Norfolk Coast	21	May	Pugneys Country Park Lakes	6	May
Staines Reservoirs	16	May	Earls Barton Gravel Pits	5	May
King George VI Reservoir	14	May	Brandon Marsh Nature Reserve	5	May
Stewartby Lake	11	May			

WHITE-WINGED BLACK TERN
Chlidonias leucopterus

Vagrant
Native range: E Europe. S Asia and Africa

One was at Llangorse Lake in September.

KINGFISHER
Alcedo atthis

International threshold: 2,000
Great Britain threshold: ?
All-Ireland threshold: ?

GB Max: 390 Sep
NI Max: 1 Jul-Nov

The majority of Kingfishers recorded by WeBS are located along rivers or on flooded gravel quarries. The Great Britain peak total was lower than the highest ever WeBS total recorded in the previous year but was similar to the maxima from the preceding winters. Peak counts at most sites are made during the autumn or early winter.

	96–97	97–98	98–99	99–00	00–01	Mon	Mean	
Sites with mean peak counts of 5 or more birds in Great Britain [†]								
Lee Valley Gravel Pits	26	14	12	8	6	Aug/Dec	13	
Somerset Levels	10	5	12	14	10	Dec	10	
Colne Valley Gravel Pits	10	7	9	9	(11)	Nov	9	
Middle Tame Valley Gravel Pits	(4)	7	8	11	8	Aug	9	
R. Teith: Daldorn to Deanston	-	-	-	-	8	Jan	8	▲
Southampton Water	5	5	7	7	8	Sep	6	
Eversley Cross & Yateley GP	6	9	5	3	6	Oct/Dec	6	
Old Moor Wetlands	6	4	3	6	8	Aug	5	
Ditchford Gravel Pits	2	2	7	8	8	Oct	5	▲
Thames Estuary	12	3	2	3	6	Nov	5	▲
R. Wye: Putson	4	6	4	(6)	5	Aug	5	▲

Sites no longer meeting table qualifying levels
Wraysbury Gravel Pits
R. Irwell
Tamar Complex
Colwick Country Park
Cleddau Estuary
Stodmarsh & Collards Lagoon
Holme Pierrepont Gravel Pits
Hoveringham Gravel Pits

Other sites surpassing table qualifying levels in 2000–01

Thorpe Water Park	9	Sep	Morecambe Bay	5	Feb
Wraysbury Gravel Pits	8	Feb	Brandon Marsh Nature Reserve	5	Aug
Deben Estuary	7	Sep	Pitsford Reservoir	5	Sep
Blackwater Estuary	6	Sep	Cotswold Water Park (East)	5	Nov
Arun Valley	6	Aug	Walthamstow Reservoirs	5	Oct
Rutland Water	6	several	Fleet Pond	5	Feb
R. Avon: Fordingbridge to R'wood	6	Nov	Hamford Water	5	Sep
Chichester Gravel Pits	5	Oct/Nov	Meadow Lane Gravel Pits	5	Oct

†   *as no British or all-Ireland thresholds have been set, a qualifying level of 50 has been chosen to select sites for presentation in this report*

PRINCIPAL SITES

Table 4 below lists the principal sites for non-breeding waterfowl in the UK as monitored by WeBS. All sites supporting more than 10,000 waterbirds are listed, as are all sites supporting internationally important numbers of one or more waterbird species. Naturalised species (e.g. Canada Goose and Ruddy Duck) or non-native species presumed to have escaped from captive collections have been excluded from the calculations, as have gulls and terns since recording of these species is optional (see *Analysis* for further details).

A total of 178 sites are listed. Of these 156 supported one or more species in internationally important numbers and 83 held five-year peak mean waterbird totals of 10,000 or more birds. There are relatively few changes in the top 20 sites in the list, although there several sites have changed position. Whilst the Wash remains the top site in terms of waterbird numbers, Morecambe Bay is now second on the list following lower than average counts on the Ribble Estuary. Sustained high counts on the North Norfolk Coast are reflected in the sites leap to fifth position. Low counts at Hamford Water and on the Medway Estuary saw both sites fall out of the top 20, being replaced by the Alt Estuary and Montrose Basin.

Amongst sites supporting 10,000 waterbirds or more, numbers in 2000-01 were stable (within ±10% of previous five-year peak mean waterbird total) at 57% of sites, up (rise of 10%

or more) at 17%, and down (a fall of 10% or more) at 27%. This was the fourth successive year in which more sites have shown a drop in numbers than have increased.

Fourteen sites showed major changes in numbers (a rise or fall of more than 30% in the present year compared with the five-year peak mean). High counts of Dunlin, Golden Plover, Lapwing and Wigeon accounted for the increased numbers on the Blackwater Estuary (+34%), the last two species also being the major influence on counts at the Somerset Levels (+31%). High numbers of Wigeon and Pink-footed Geese were chiefly responsible for the increase on Lindisfarne (+31%), the latter also accounting for significant changes at Dupplin Lochs (-49%), Slains Lochs (+41%), Loch of Skene (+62%) and at Wigtown Bay (-37%). Low counts were recorded for a wide number of species on the Medway Estuary (-52%). At the Ouse Washes (-35%) counts of Wigeon and Pintail were well down on previous years, whilst at Traeth Lafan (+42) counts for a number of wader species (notably Curlew, Oystercatcher and Redshank) continued the encouraging increases of recent years. At Loch of Harray (+37%), high Wigeon numbers were the major influence on the totals, whilst at Pitsford Reservoir (-33%) low numbers of the same species, coupled with below average counts of Lapwing and Golden Plover, saw the peak species total continue to fall.

Table 4. Total number of waterbirds at principal sites in the UK, 1996-97 to 2000-01 (includes only Core Count data and roost counts of Pink-footed and Greylag Geese), and species occurring in internationally important numbers at each (based on all survey data). Species codes are listed at the end of the table.

Site	96-97	97-98	98-99	99-00	00-01	Average	Int. imp. species
The Wash	279,907	345,431	289,879	374,095	286,586	315,180	PG SU OC GP GV L. KN DN BW BA CU RK
Morecambe Bay	251,813	312,950	265,610	232,806	246,807	261,997	PG SU PT OC KN DN BA CU RK TT BH LB HG
Ribble Estuary	299,134	281,427	259,593	236,382	222,068	259,721	BS WS PG SU WN T. PT OC GV KN SS DN BW BA RK
Thames Estuary	171,098	185,175	158,088	125,737	158,792	159,778	DB GA OC RP GV KN DN BA RK
North Norfolk Coast	119,201	170,687	143,217	178,106	168,919	156,026	PG DB WN PT GV KN BA RK TE
Humber Estuary	81,633	159,866	192,589	172,515	163,066	153,934	SU GP GV L. KN DN BW BA RK
Solway Estuary	157,399	146,086	152,251	141,460	128,292	145,098	WS PG YS SU PT OC KN DN BA CU RK
Dee Estuary (Eng/Wal)	151,210	128,426	108,017	92,284	135,113	123,010	SU T. PT OC KN DN BW CU RK TT
Mersey Estuary	116,030	117,312	93,910	106,045	109,878	108,635	SU T. PT DN BW RK
Loughs Neagh & Beg	101,708	82,232	103,350	97,308	101,668	97,253	CA WS PO TU SP GN

Site	96-97	97-98	98-99	99-00	00-01	Average	Int. imp. species
Blackwater Estuary	85,774	83,810	77,413	84,468	122,116	90,716	DB SU GV DN BW RK
Somerset Levels	38,384	111,426	96,853	76,110	114,210	87,397	WN GA T. SV L.
Forth Estuary	87,507	85,466	89,580	76,059	92,546	86,232	SZ PG SU KN BA RK TE
Swale Estuary	100,443	88,974	80,032	76,437	80,289	85,235	WN SV GV KN BW RK
Severn Estuary	80,323	69,979	75,554	70,196	62,064	71,623	BS PT DN RK LB
Strangford Lough	90,390	73,205	69,731	61,268	63,016	71,522	QN SU KN BA RK
Breydon Water & Berney Marshes	58,537	54,951	67,207	65,904	70,632	63,446	BS PG L. BW
Ouse Washes	57,074	72,264	44,898	85,390	38,755	59,676	BS WS WN GA PT SV PO BW
Alt Estuary	54,760	69,639	47,151	54,753	59,337	57,128	GV KN SS BA
Montrose Basin	38,829	62,009	58,464	41,157	49,600	50,012	PG RK
Hamford Water	70,066	56,295	48,096	32,704	42,671	49,966	DB GV KN RK
Medway Estuary	64,538	60,097	45,564	51,216	23,521	48,987	SU PT GV DN RK
Burry Inlet	64,395	35,232	52,062	52,700	37,917	48,461	PT SV OC KN
Stour Estuary	45,019	47,693	45,099	53,725	48,724	48,052	GV KN DN BW RK
Inner Moray Firth	53,880	45,468	44,975	45,982	48,137	47,688	JI KN BA RK
Chichester Harbour	49,303	45,866	45,130	47,115	47,369	46,957	DB GV DN BA RK
Lindisfarne	42,568	38,657	48,771	40,522	60,666	46,237	PG QS GV KN BA
Loch of Strathbeg	40,121	47,285	48,440	37,293	52,053	45,038	WS PG YS
Dengie Flats	39,339	39,374	36,539	33,361	48,668	39,456	GV KN BA
Langstone Harbour	32,840	36,702	42,071	43,949	41,082	39,329	DB RP GV DN
Lough Foyle	37,810	37,485	45,242	38,049	37,208	39,159	WS QN BA
Lower Derwent Valley	41,304	42,104	32,830	29,107	-	36,336	T.
Colne Estuary	27,953	42,271	33,808	35,396	36,323	35,150	DB
Loch Leven	38,737	32,810	35,652	30,881	31,869	33,990	PG GA SV
Dornoch Firth	29,415	36,850	31,244	31,943	37,722	33,435	JI WN BA
Abberton Reservoir	34,800	42,264	24,514	33,805	25,923	32,261	GA T. SV PO
Cromarty Firth	34,423	31,638	31,215	24,089	39,001	32,073	PG JI KN BA
Duddon Estuary	37,113	34,086	32,600	32,110	23,637	31,909	PT RK
Alde Complex	27,340	35,365	36,750	29,349	26,534	31,068	AV RK LB
Dupplin Lochs	40,665	29,998	42,504	22,826	15,550	30,309	PG
Nene Washes	15,166	37,826	33,798	28,414	32,167	29,474	BS PT SV
West Water Reservoir	25,879	39,173	21,969	28,438	26,500	28,392	PG
Poole Harbour	32,846	28,477	26,246	23,886	25,672	27,425	AV BW
Martin Mere	16,865	22,014	29,295	37,658	25,367	26,240	BS WS PG T.
Tay Estuary	32,633	19,569	28,775	17,310	22,259	24,109	PG JI BA RK
Rutland Water	22,890	28,297	23,249	24,105	19,157	23,540	GA SV
Walland Marsh	18,103	29,770	30,709	28,988	9,714	23,457	BS
Crouch-Roach Estuary	19,483	24,419	22,171	25,156	24,733	23,192	DB
Clyde Estuary	23,035	21,728	20,084	23,022	23,752	22,324	RK
Exe Estuary	19,924	23,846	23,416	20,947	21,169	21,860	BW
Tees Estuary	24,257	20,148	22,146	19,585	22,796	21,786	
Carsebreck & Rhynd Lochs	16,089	19,455	23,808	20,208	23,456	20,603	PG
Belfast Lough	18,389	21,669	20,868	20,176	20,943	20,409	GG RK
Cleddau Estuary	21,631	19,914	20,366	19,009	15,551	19,294	
Southampton Water	18,813	22,783	17,248	14,146	17,895	18,177	BW
Deben Estuary	18,554	16,854	14,628	18,126	18,879	17,408	RK
Slains Lochs	17,630	12,226	16,405	15,535	24,292	17,218	PG
Orwell Estuary	23,937	13,813	17,134	15,316	15,617	17,163	
Pagham Harbour	20,358	19,262	13,937	14,576	16,064	16,839	PT
Hule Moss	20,411	21,067	12,107	15,403	14,830	16,764	PG
Ythan Estuary	12,952	18,789	15,622	18,461	-	16,456	PG RK
Beaulieu Estuary	16,109	19,077	17,434	12,289	16,975	16,377	
Arun Valley	14,969	17,798	16,262	14,313	17,416	16,152	
Blyth Estuary (Suffolk)	13,472	15,501	-	-	18,876	15,950	
Loch of Skene	14,722	15,026	13,497	9,065	25,167	15,495	PG JI
Taw-Torridge Estuary	14,922	17,159	13,256	19,235	12,082	15,331	

Site	96-97	97-98	98-99	99-00	00-01	Average	Int. imp. species
Carmarthen Bay	23,365	13,190	12,832	12,559	14,670	15,323	
Wigtown Bay	15,894	17,980	17,123	15,643	9,584	15,245	PG
Outer Ards	21,863	11,126	16,786	14,720	11,647	15,228	TT
Dungeness Gravel Pits	11,156	20,799	13,394	14,897	14,720	14,993	
Fleet/Wey	15,700	15,137	16,501	12,496	14,155	14,798	
Dinnet Lochs	27,095	25,656	4,996	10,772	4,773	14,658	JI
Eden Estuary	13,519	15,856	13,923	12,707	15,345	14,270	
Traeth Lafan	15,310	8,906	5,152	18,392	18,852	13,322	
Loch of Harray	8,139	13,238	11,996	11,710	17,058	12,428	
Cotswold Water Park (W)	9,089	13,051	16,096	12,245	11,602	12,417	
North West Solent	13,518	11,899	12,843	10,717	10,841	11,964	
Rye Harbour & Pett Level	10,631	11,663	13,450	10,956	9,852	11,310	
Pitsford Reservoir	13,167	13,520	13,288	8,905	7,462	11,268	
Hanningfield Reservoir	13,138	13,860	8,568	8,707	11,078	11,070	
Dyfi Estuary	12,370	8,492	9,136	14,100	10,837	10,987	
Middle Tame Valley GP	11,700	10,963	8,919	9,591	9,417	10,118	
Middle Yare Marshes	10,636	9,784	9,823	9,319	10,577	10,028	
Fen Drayton Gravel Pits	5,602	10,318	10,499	9,755	12,624	9,760	GA
Loch of Lintrathen	4,735	13,369	8,526	14,616	4,537	9,157	PG JI
Thanet Coast	6,256	7,092	11,541	11,032	9,667	9,118	TT
Carlingford Lough	7,460	8,729	9,172	10,036	8,432	8,766	QN
Loch Spynie	6,491	5,690	9,802	5,370	16,001	8,671	PG JI
Upper Lough Erne	9,243	8,225	7,149	8,297	-	8,229	WS
Lee Valley Gravel Pits	7,661	7,277	6,800	8,728	8,129	7,719	GA
Loch Eye	5,926	7,292	12,220	7,475	4,302	7,443	PG JI
Cameron Reservoir	5,475	13,068	6,596	4,532	6,455	7,225	PG
Tophill Low Reservoirs	4,068	8,636	5,657	9,529	7,509	7,080	BH CM
Loch Fleet Complex	7,249	4,935	7,327	5,225	7,253	6,398	JI
Wraysbury Gravel Pits	5,787	7,341	6,710	5,617	4,205	5,932	GA
R. Avon: F'bridge to R'wood	6,034	6,680	5,356	5,834	5,706	5,922	GA
Fala Flow	5,000	7,500	2,100	7,550	4,910	5,412	PG
Thrapston Gravel Pits	6,965	5,130	3,400	5,626	5,142	5,253	GA
Gladhouse Reservoir	8,063	7,350	2,022	6,720	1,610	5,153	PG
South Ford	-	-	-	5,283	4,884	5,084	BA
Loch Tullybelton	4,658	8,000	8,600	0	4,050	5,062	PG
Drummond Pond	8,645	5,476	5,192	2,902	2,894	5,022	PG JI
Tay-Isla Valley	5,007	1,384	8,640	4,775	4,553	4,872	PG JI
R. Clyde: Carstairs to Thankerton	-	627	2,076	7,795	8,046	4,636	WS PG
Holburn Moss	3,533	5,010	4,930	2,460	6,182	4,423	PG
Larne Lough	4,230	3,742	4,270	4,466	4,685	4,279	QN
Horsey Mere		4,022	3,806	5,022	3,620	4,118	PG
Upper Cowgill Reservoir	6,060	9,400	1,000	2,900	300	3,932	PG
Heigham Holmes	3,915	5,582	2,126	6,276	1,330	3,846	PG
Kilconquhar Loch	4,322	4,249	2,985	2,907	3,654	3,623	JI
Loch Long	159	318	8,000	6,356	2,834	3,533	PG
Minsmere Levels	2,882	5,496	3,472	360	4,399	3,322	RH
Threipmuir & Harlaw Rsrs	2,433	1,051	4,209	6,781	2,066	3,308	JI
St Benet's Levels	4,003	4,119	2,707	795	2,973	2,919	BS
Loch Ken	1,780	2,611	1,977	3,444	3,855	2,733	NW JI
Strathearn (West sites)	2,730	-	-	-	-	2,730	PG
R. Earn: Lawhill Oxbows	-	-	-	-	2,649	2,649	JI
Loch Mahaick	2,779	6,792	1,458	875	1,012	2,583	PG
Loch Mullion	0	3,000	2,000	5,500	660	2,232	PG
Loch of the Clans	1,942	2,300	-	-	-	2,121	JI
Stranraer Lochs	-	1,781	3,852	537	1,328	1,875	NW JI
Derwent Reservoir	1,655	2,013	1,820	1,101	1,392	1,596	CM

Site	96-97	97-98	98-99	99-00	00-01	Average	Int. imp. species
R. Eamont & Eden: Honeypot to Edenhall	756	2,080	1,985	1,548	1,458	1,565	JI
Loch Garten	589	735	-	1,650	2,700	1,419	JI
Lower Teviot Valley	1,861	1,297	96	3	3,491	1,350	JI
Killimster Loch	2,518		102			1,310	JI
Melbost Sands & Tong Saltings	-	1,027	1,174	1,134	1,543	1,220	JH
Birgham Haugh	1,150	-	-	-	-	1,150	JI
Black Cart Water	237	508	837	660	804	609	WS
Haweswater Reservoir	505	301	331	401	571	422	CM
Loch Ordais and Port Mhor Bragar	421	232	205	335	721	383	JH
Ravenstruther	-	-	-	-	347	347	WS
Killough Harbour	319	-	-	-	-	319	QN
Hallington Reservoir	185	160	316	510	354	305	CM
R. Foyle: Grange	387	150	-	-	-	269	WS JI
Loch Sheil: West	193	272	358	252	258	267	JH
Llys-y-fran Reservoir	481	193	148	160	335	263	LB
South Walls	-	97	390	-	-	244	YN
Loch Broom	-	-	74	66	367	169	JH
Rhunahaorine	-	-	165	-	-	165	NW JH
Loch Urrahag	100	232	182	73	203	158	JH
Clachan/Whitehouse	-	-	139	-	-	139	JH
Machrihanish	41	172	266	28	148	131	NW JH
Loch Kishorn	-	-	70	67	200	112	JH
Aberlady Bay							PG
Bay of Sandoyne to Holme Sound							ND
Benbecula							JH
Bute							JI
Caithness Lochs							JI
Coll							NW JH YN
Colonsay/Oransay							JH YN
East Sanday Coast							TT
Entrance to Deer/Shapinsay Sounds							ND
Findhorn Bay							JI
Holkham Bay							PG
Islay							NW YN JH
Keills Peninsula & Isle of Danna							NW YN
Loch Eye & Cromarty Firth							PG JI
Moine Mhor							JH
Monach Isles							YN
Moray Firth							SZ
Munlochy Bay							JI
North Sutherland							YN
North Uist							JH YN
Orkney Islands							JI
Scapa Flow							ND SZ
Scolt Head							PG
Snettisham							PG
Sound of Harris							YN
South Uist							JH
SW Lancashire							PG
Tankerness							ND
Tiree							NW JH YN RP TT
Upper Tay							JI
Martin Mere/Ribble Estuary							BS WS PG
Ythan Estuary/Slains Lochs							PG

Species codes

AV	Avocet	ND	Great Northern Diver
BA	Bar-tailed Godwit	NW	Greenland White-fronted Goose
BS	Bewick's Swan	OC	Oystercatcher
BW	Black-tailed Godwit	PG	Pink-footed Goose
CA	Cormorant	PO	Pochard
CO	Coot	PT	Pintail
CU	Curlew	QS	Light-bellied Brent Goose (Svalbard population)
DB	Dark-bellied Brent Goose	QN	Light-bellied Brent Goose (Greenland poplulation)
DN	Dunlin	RK	Redshank
E.	Eider	RM	Red-breasted Merganser
EW	European White-fronted Goose	RP	Ringed Plover
GA	Gadwall	SP	Scaup
GD	Goosander	SS	Sanderling
GN	Goldeneye	SU	Shelduck
GP	Golden Plover	SV	Shoveler
GV	Grey Plover	SZ	Slavonian Grebe
HG	Herring Gull	T.	Teal
JI	Greylag Goose (Icelandic population)	TE	Sandwich Tern
JH	Greylag Goose (Northwest Scotland population)	TT	Turnstone
KN	Knot	TU	Tufted Duck
L.	Lapwing	WM	Whimbrel
LB	Lesser Black-backed Gull	WN	Wigeon
LN	Long-tailed Duck	WS	Whooper Swan
MA	Mallard	YN	Barnacle Goose (Greenland population)
MS	Mute Swan	YS	Barnacle Goose (Svalbard population)

WeBS Low Tide Counts

AIMS

Despite involving only a relatively small number of sites, estuaries collectively represent the most important habitat for non-breeding waterbirds in the UK. The influence of the tide means that the birds have to be much more mobile, both within and between sites. WeBS Core Counts on estuaries have, in general, been based around high tide roosts. Although important in themselves, roost sites are usually secondary in importance to the manner in which waterbirds make use of a site for feeding. Therefore, information gathered about these sites at high tide will only provide part of the picture. The WeBS Low Tide Counts scheme, which was initiated in the winter of 1992–93, aims to monitor, assess and regularly update information on the relative importance of intertidal feeding areas of UK estuaries for wintering waterbirds and thus to complement the information gathered by WeBS Core Counts on estuaries.

WeBS Low Tide Counts provide the crucial information needed to assess the potential effects on waterbird populations of a variety of human activities which affect the extent or value of intertidal habitats, such as proposals for dock developments, recreational activities, tidal power barrages, marinas and housing schemes. The data gathered contribute greatly to the conservation of waterbirds by providing supporting information for the establishment and management of the UK network of Ramsar sites and Special Protection Areas (SPAs), other site designations and whole estuary conservation plans. In addition, WeBS Low Tide Counts enhance our knowledge of the low water distribution of waterbirds and provide the data that highlight regional variations in habitat use. In particular, WeBS Low Tide Counts should help us to understand, predict and possibly plan for compensation for the effects of sea-level rise on the UK's internationally important estuarine waterbird populations.

METHODS

The scheme provides information on the numbers of waterbirds feeding on subdivisions of the intertidal habitat within estuaries. Given the extra work that Low Tide Counts entail, often to the same counters that carry out the Core Counts, WeBS aims to cover most individual estuaries about once every six years, although on some sites more frequent counts are made. Co-ordinated counts of feeding and roosting waterbirds are made by volunteers each month between November and February on pre-established subdivisions of the intertidal habitat in the period two hours either side of low tide.

DATA PRESENTATION

Tabulated Statistics

Table 5 presents three statistics for 18 of the more numerous waterbird species present on eight estuaries covered during the 2000–01 winter: the peak number of a species over the whole site counted in any one month; an estimate of the mean number present over the winter for the whole site (obtained by summing the mean counts of each species for each count section) and the mean density over the site (in birds per hectare), which is the mean number divided by the total area surveyed (in hectares). The area value used for these calculations is the sum of the inter-tidal and non-tidal components of each count section but omits the sub-tidal areas (i.e. those parts of the count section which are under water on a mean low tide).

Dot Density Maps

WeBS Low Tide Count data are presented as dot density maps, with subdivision of count sections into basic habitat elements, as was introduced in the report for 1998–99. The reason for such a subdivision is to overcome the situations encountered in the past in which, for example, flocks of Great Crested Grebes are plotted on mudflats or flocks of Dunlin are plotted on open water. Both of these cases obviously look wrong but more importantly can give an unrealistic density value by using a nonsensical area for the calculations. To deal with this issue, each section for which a count has been made has been divided into up to three different habitat components:

Inter-tidal: Counted areas which lie between mean high water and mean low water.
Sub-tidal: Counted areas which lie below mean low water. In more 'open-coast'-type situations, a subtidal zone reaching 500m out from the intertidal sections has been created arbitrarily, to indicate the approximate extent of visibility offshore from land-based counts.
Non-tidal: Counted areas which lie above mean high water (usually saltmarsh although some grazing marshes are also counted).

The mean count for the sector is then divided amongst a varying number of the different components, dependent on the species involved. For example, Dunlin dots are plotted exclusively on inter-tidal sections whereas Wigeon dots are spread across inter-tidal, sub-tidal and non-tidal areas (in proportion with the relative areas of these three components).

Currently, throughout all WeBS Low Tide Count analyses, mean low tide and mean high tide are taken from the most recent Ordnance Survey Pathfinder maps. It is recognised, unfortunately, that these maps represent the current real shape of the mudflats, water channels and saltmarshes to varying degrees of accuracy. However, in the interests of uniformity across the UK, the Ordnance Survey outlines are adhered to throughout the analyses.

The maps display the average number of birds in each count section as dots spread randomly across habitat components of count sections, thus providing an indication of both numbers and density. **It is important to note that individual dots do not represent the precise position of individual birds; dots have been arbitrarily assigned to habitat components and are then randomly placed within those areas. No information about the distribution of birds at a finer scale than the count sector level should be inferred from the dot density maps.** For all maps in the present report, one dot is equivalent to one bird. The size of individual dots has no relevance other than for clarity. Additionally, any count sections that were not counted during the 2000–01 winter are marked with an asterisk. The dot density maps enable a clearer depiction of actual bird density, instead of the arbitrary grouping into bands of densities that was presented in previous years. It is hoped that dot density distributions and habitat components will lead to an easier and fuller appreciation of low tide estuarine waterbird distribution. More detailed information concerning analysis and presentation of WeBS Low Tide Counts can be obtained from the National Organiser (WeBS Low Tide Counts) at the BTO.

ESTUARY ACCOUNTS

WeBS Low Tide Counts were carried out at 12 sites during the 2000–01 winter, namely Belfast Lough, Breydon Water, Dornoch Firth, (partial), Lindisfarne, Loch Fleet, Morecambe Bay (partial, mid-tide counts only), Orwell Estuary, Severn Estuary (partial), Solway Firth, Southampton Water, Stour Estuary and Strangford Lough (data unfortunately not submitted in time for incorporation into this report). Accounts are not presented for the sites for which only partial coverage was obtained, but all of the datasets can be accessed via the WeBS National Organiser (Low Tide Counts) if required.

Data for each of the estuaries cover the period November to February inclusive. In each case, a list of species present in nationally and internationally important numbers, based on Core Counts (five year peak means as presented within this report) and a description of the estuary are given. This is followed by an outline of the key results. Distribution maps are presented for two species for which that site is of particular importance or interest. Background information for the estuary accounts has been provided by local organisers and other counters, in addition to information obtained from key references such as *An inventory of UK estuaries* (JNCC 1993–1997) and *Coasts and seas of the United Kingdom* (JNCC 1995–1998).

ACKNOWLEDGEMENTS

Many thanks go to all of the following counters who took part in WeBS Low Tide Counts during the winter of 2000–01; apologies to anyone who inadvertently may have been missed.

Christopher Baines, R & M Biddle, Sally Brakes, Mike Carrier, Alex Carroll, MJ Case, Paul Charlton, Dominic Coath, Chris Cockburn, Peter Combridge, Steve Cooper, Mike Creighton, Curly Curtis, John & Janet Dedman, Frances Donnan, Pete Durnell, Ian Enlander, Dave Fairlamb, John Foskew, Jack Garstang, Geoff Gibbs, Chris & Maureen Gibson, John Glazebrook, Frances Godfrey, Paul Green, Larry Griffith, Dave Groundwater, A Harbott, Clive Hartley, Ian Hawkins, Tony Heath, Richard Hesketh, Neale Hider, Mike Hodgson, Norman Holton, Philip Johnston, Geoff Kelso, Simon King, Keith Kirk, Brian Knight, Bill Last, Russell Leavett, Richard Levett, Ralph Loughlin, Kerry Mackie, Paddy Mackie, Tony Mainwood, E Marsh, Tony Martin, Frank Mawby, Niall McCutcheon, Ken McGregor, Ivor McPherson, Richard Mearns, Peter & Sue Morrison, Gary Mortimer, Ken Moss, John Norton, Tom Oliver, James Orr, Hugh & Veronica Owen, Jess Pain, Mark Painter, Alice Parfitt, Ian Paterson, Terry Paton, David Patterson, Rod Plowman, J Poland, Peter Raby, Neil Ravenscroft, Ian Robinson, Jim Rowe, L Sanderson, P Sands-Robinson, Jan Schubert, James Scott, David Shackleton, Jack Sheldon, Rod Ship, Pearson Silburn, Brian Smith, Len Stewart, Tony Stones, Fraser Symonds, John Thirlwell, David Thompson, Lynne Tinkler, Jack Torney, John Turner, Rick Vonk, Nick Wall, J Walshe, Richard Waring, Rodney West, Jo Whatmough, Craig Whyte, Caroline Wilson, Jim Wilson, David Wimpress, Mick Wright, Wally Wright.

Species	Belfast Lough			Breydon Water			Lindisfarne		
	Peak No.	Mean No.	Mean Dns.	Peak No.	Mean No.	Mean Dns.	Peak No.	Mean No.	Mean Dns.
Brent Goose	40	16	0.03	2	1	+	1,941	1,941	0.68
Shelduck	319	211	0.42	488	335	0.83	1,219	1,219	0.43
Wigeon	132	110	0.22	9,490	5,502	13.55	1,100	1,100	0.38
Teal	170	141	0.28	691	250	0.62	56	56	0.02
Mallard	388	268	0.54	516	233	0.57	304	304	0.11
Pintail	0	0	0	221	120	0.30	41	41	0.01
Oystercatcher	5,354	4,863	9.78	67	54	0.13	856	856	0.30
Ringed Plover	113	69	0.14	21	11	0.03	37	37	0.01
Golden Plover	700	309	0.62	2,700	2,232	5.50	726	726	0.25
Grey Plover	1	0	+	47	24	0.06	486	486	0.17
Lapwing	1,509	1,212	2.44	6,540	3,142	7.74	1,041	1,041	0.36
Knot	43	27	0.05	310	157	0.39	3,130	3,130	1.09
Dunlin	1,366	925	1.86	2,895	2,365	5.83	3,866	3,866	1.35
Black-tailed Godwit	383	315	0.63	810	669	1.65	0	0	0
Bar-tailed Godwit	169	83	0.17	0	0	0	1,339	1,339	0.47
Curlew	955	649	1.31	788	684	1.68	1,431	1,431	0.50
Redshank	1,575	1,279	2.57	1,456	1,059	2.61	766	766	0.27
Turnstone	208	166	0.33	5	2	+	55	55	0.02

Species	Loch Fleet			Orwell Estuary			Solway Firth		
	Peak No.	Mean No.	Mean Dns.	Peak No.	Mean No.	Mean Dns.	Peak No.	Mean No.	Mean Dns.
Brent Goose	0	0	0	1,228	821	0.66	0	0	0
Shelduck	105	67	0.12	637	467	0.37	1,791	1,627	0.08
Wigeon	1,005	761	1.31	1,936	1,515	1.21	2,268	1,585	0.08
Teal	509	376	0.65	661	389	0.31	793	540	0.03
Mallard	629	353	0.61	800	469	0.38	1,385	1,031	0.05
Pintail	0	0	0	179	78	0.06	2,818	1,372	0.07
Oystercatcher	1,290	1,089	1.88	1,570	1,220	0.98	26,449	22,810	1.13
Ringed Plover	49	25	0.04	198	115	0.09	133	73	+
Golden Plover	0	0	0	620	220	0.18	8,065	3,880	0.19
Grey Plover	1	0	+	289	238	0.19	520	313	0.02
Lapwing	108	42	0.07	1,487	833	0.67	8,596	5,701	0.28
Knot	600	188	0.32	1,824	804	0.64	9,159	5,276	0.26
Dunlin	293	179	0.31	2,852	2,236	1.79	12,628	9,960	0.49
Black-tailed Godwit	0	0	0	73	58	0.05	63	38	+
Bar-tailed Godwit	187	106	0.18	1	0	+	556	258	0.01
Curlew	268	202	0.35	718	639	0.51	4,200	3,217	0.16
Redshank	168	111	0.19	1,637	1,510	1.21	2,578	2,328	0.11
Turnstone	1	0	+	170	149	0.12	64	55	+

Table 5i. Peak and mean counts, and mean density (birds per hectare), of 18 waterbird species present on estuaries covered by the 2000–01 WeBS Low Tide Counts. "+" indicates non-zero densities of less than 0.01 birds per hectare.

Species	Southampton Water			Stour Estuary		
	Peak No.	Mean No.	Mean Dns.	Peak No.	Mean No.	Mean Dns.
Brent Goose	1,742	900	0.60	1,717	1,194	0.73
Shelduck	163	97	0.06	2,164	1,621	0.99
Wigeon	2,207	1,728	1.15	4,218	3,478	2.12
Teal	2,096	1,365	0.91	2,413	1,203	0.73
Mallard	240	157	0.10	496	328	0.20
Pintail	63	52	0.03	686	511	0.31
Oystercatcher	1,445	1,367	0.91	1,040	966	0.59
Ringed Plover	207	129	0.09	493	257	0.16
Golden Plover	517	316	0.21	6,620	2,708	1.65
Grey Plover	246	171	0.11	2,123	1,787	1.09
Lapwing	1,034	956	0.64	3,813	2,004	1.22
Knot	2	1	+	8,036	4,694	2.86
Dunlin	4,736	3,781	2.53	14,111	11,610	7.08
Black-tailed Godwit	21	13	0.01	2,846	1,635	1.00
Bar-tailed Godwit	2	2	+	88	52	0.03
Curlew	575	462	0.31	915	873	0.53
Redshank	457	414	0.28	2,038	1,773	1.08
Turnstone	293	242	0.16	350	330	0.20

Table 5ii. Peak and mean counts, and mean density (birds per hectare), of 18 waterbird species present on estuaries covered by the 2000–01 WeBS Low Tide Counts. "+" indicates non-zero densities of less than 0.01 birds per hectare.

BELFAST LOUGH
Co. Antrim / Co. Down

Internationally important: Great Crested Grebe, Redshank

Nationally important: Mute Swan, Shelduck, Scaup, Eider, Goldeneye, Red-breasted Merganser, Oystercatcher, Ringed Plover, Knot, Dunlin, Black-tailed Godwit, Turnstone

Site description

Belfast Lough is a large sea lough in the north-east of Ireland, with the city of Belfast at its head. The outer parts of the lough's shore are generally rocky with some sandy bays, but more extensive areas of intertidal mud are located toward Belfast. Industrial land claim has, however, reduced the area of the mudflats over the last 150 years, and Belfast has become the main port in Northern Ireland for heavy cargo. More recently, some of the area, including the RSPB Belfast Lough reserve, has been given a degree of protection, but there is a continuing threat to the remaining intertidal mudflats from potential future harbour expansion. The wash from the shipping activities, including high-speed passenger ferries, may also cause increased erosion of intertidal habitats. Additionally, a proposed new water-taxi service which would operate outside the main shipping lanes could cause increased disturbance. There has been a loss of disturbance-free high-tide roosts within the inner lough, along with problems of refuse disposal and pollution, as would be expected at a highly urbanised and industrialised site. Recreational activities only occur over relatively small, localised parts of the lough. However, extensive areas of Belfast Lough are licensed for shellfish aquaculture, the impact of which is currently unclear.

Bird Distribution

The greatest concentrations of Oystercatchers and Ringed Plovers were to be found within the southwestern section of the lough, with the latter also favouring the flats off Carrickfergus and Bangor. Golden Plover were only present on the RSPB Belfast Lough reserve. Lapwing also favoured the various pools in the southwestern end of the lough. By far the highest densities of Dunlin were found close to Belfast city (Figure 66). Knot were present in very low numbers this winter on the inner estuary. Both Black-tailed and Bar-tailed Godwits were also confined to the extreme southwestern end of the lough. Curlew, which declined over the winter, were to be found scattered throughout much of the inner two-thirds of the lough. Redshank were the most widespread of all the waders, distributed throughout, but concentrated within the western half of the lough. The numbers of Redshank increased during the course of the winter. Turnstone were also widespread but in low numbers compared to core count maxima. Other waders occasionally recorded during the course of the winter included Grey Plover, Purple Sandpiper, Ruff and Snipe.

Small numbers of Light-bellied Brent Geese were recorded during the second half of the winter. Shelduck were confined to the extreme southwestern end of the lough. Most of the small numbers of Wigeon, Teal and Shoveler were to be found at the RSPB Belfast Lough reserve, whilst Pochard and Tufted Duck were only found in Victoria Park, also the favoured area for most of the Mute Swans and Greylag Geese. Mallard were more generally distributed within the lough. Scaup numbers peaked at an impressive 323 in January, exceeding numbers recorded during recent winters. Goldeneye were scattered along much of the coastline within the southwestern part of the estuary and also occurred on the RSPB Belfast Lough reserve. Eider numbers rapidly increased to a staggering 2,219 in January, considerably higher than previous low tide counts at the site. Figure 66 shows that the greatest concentrations of Eider occurred along the coastline between Green Island and Whitehouse Lake (on the northern shore), with smaller numbers favouring the area between Swineley and Ballymacormick Point (on the southern shore). Red-breasted Mergansers were widely distributed but peak numbers were much lower than during other recent low tide counts, reflecting recent UK declines. Up to 12 Long-tailed Ducks frequented the northern shoreline, whilst the occasional Smew and Goosander were also noted. A relatively low peak count of 970 Great Crested Grebes was made in February, their distribution within the lough being similar to previous winters with the greatest concentrations between Carrickfergus and Whitehouse Lake. The Core Counts also recorded a decrease, with numbers down by 20% compared to the 1999–2000 peak count. Cormorants preferred the flats between Swineley Point and Bangor, with a scatter along the northern shoreline and a similar pattern was seen for Shags. Of the five regular species of gull recorded, Black-headed was the most abundant, followed by Herring Gull. Red-throated Diver, Little Grebe, Grey Heron, Moorhen and Coot were also recorded, mostly in small numbers.

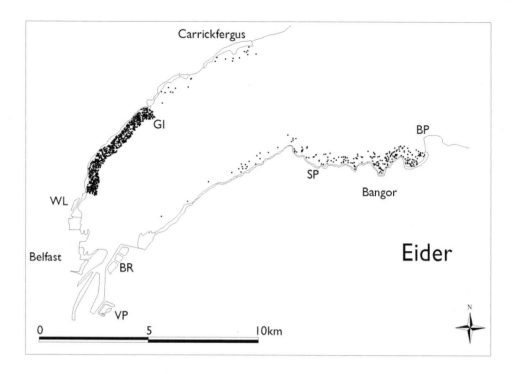

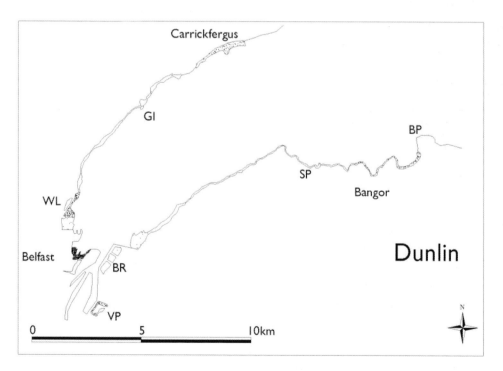

Figure 66. WeBS Low Tide Counts of Eider and Dunlin at Belfast Lough, winter 2000–01. (BR=RSPB Belfast Lough reserve, VP=Victoria Park, GI=Green Island, WL=Whitehouse Lake, SP=Swineley Point, BP=Ballymacormick Point).

BREYDON WATER
Norfolk

Internationally important: Bewick's Swan, Pink-footed Goose, Lapwing, Black-tailed Godwit

Nationally important: European White-fronted Goose, Wigeon, Gadwall, Teal, Shoveler, Avocet, Golden Plover, Ruff

Site description

Breydon Water is a bar-built estuary separated from the North Sea by the spit of land on which Great Yarmouth sits and forms the lower reaches of the Yare and Waveney rivers which drain much of central East Anglia. With the renowned flatness of the land around the Norfolk Broads, the rivers are tidal for many miles inland but only the estuary proper (from the confluence of the rivers) is considered here. At high tide, Breydon Water forms a large lake but as the tide recedes, all the water that remains is a narrow channel, well-marked by buoys for the numerous leisure cruisers which travel through between the northern and southern Broads. There are some fairly small areas of saltmarsh, principally at the eastern end. To the north of the estuary stretches the huge expanse of the Halvergate Levels, Breydon Marshes and Berney Marshes, a massive area of grazing marshes although much 'improved' by increased drainage in recent years. Breydon is surrounded by linear sea-defences. The main high tide roosts occur at the RSPB reserve at Berney Marshes and in the eastern saltmarsh. The main conservation issues in the area involve boating, shooting and grazing marsh management although, being a major port, the river channel leading out from Breydon through Great Yarmouth to the sea is very industrialised.

Bird distribution

Lapwing were fairly widely distributed within the estuary, both to the north and south of the River Yare. However, the greatest numbers occurred at the southern end of Breydon Water on the Burgh Flats. Whilst large numbers of Lapwings were recorded at low tide, the peak of 6,540 in January was much lower than recorded by the core counts (23,300), the latter also including the surrounding non-tidal marshes which support large flocks of this species. Similarly, the counts of up to 2,700 Golden Plovers were also far fewer than for the core counts. The greatest concentrations were to be found at the eastern end of the estuary. Black-tailed Godwits favoured the mudflats in the southeast corner and also those north of the river adjacent to Acle Marshes (Figure 67). The numbers recorded by both core and low tide counts at this site have increased dramatically

over recent years, and currently exceed the threshold for international importance. Another species wintering at the site in increasing numbers is Avocet, numbers of which peaked in January. The birds were found exclusively on the flats north of the Yare, adjacent to the Acle Marshes windmill. Dunlin, Curlew and Redshank were generally scattered throughout the estuary, but avoided or were present in very low numbers on the flats in the southwest corner around the Berney Arms. The greatest concentrations of Curlew were present to the north of the Yare, especially on the flats off the Acle Marshes windmill, with the greatest concentrations of Redshank to be found south of the river in the southeast corner of the estuary. Small numbers of Ringed Plover and Knot favoured the northeast corner of the estuary and the few Oystercatcher the northern mudflats off Stone Corner. Snipe, Sanderling, and Turnstone were also occasionally recorded.

Wigeon numbers built up to 9,500 by January and was concentrated on the mudflats to the north of the Yare, particularly on the western flats. Teal were found mostly at the western end, especially on Burgh Flats (Figure 67). Mallard occurred mostly in the southwestern corner or at the eastern end of the estuary towards Great Yarmouth. Pintail were virtually confined to the eastern half of Breydon, mostly on the flats north of the Yare; peak numbers at low tide were considerably higher than during the two previous winters, which was contra to the national trend of a continued decline. Shoveler and Gadwall were thinly scattered throughout the estuary. Virtually all of the Shelduck were confined to the eastern half of the estuary. Greylag and Canada Geese favoured the areas off the Berney Arms in the southwest corner. White-fronted, Dark-bellied Brent and Egyptian Geese were recorded occasionally, along with small numbers of Mute Swan. Up to 60 Cormorants frequented the southwestern corner and the River Yare channel. Grey Heron, Black-headed, Common, Lesser Black-backed, Herring and Great Black-backed Gulls and a single Kingfisher were also recorded. However, no Bewick's Swans, Pink-footed Geese or Ruff were recorded on the estuary; the important wintering populations of these species occur on the adjacent non-tidal habitats.

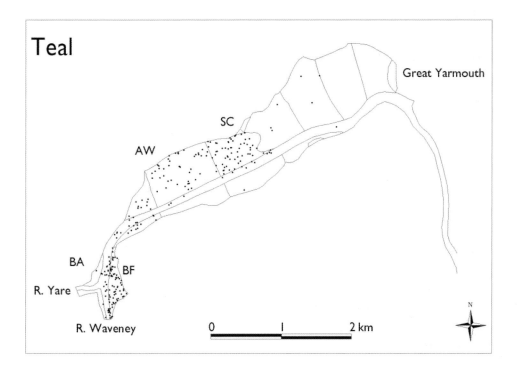

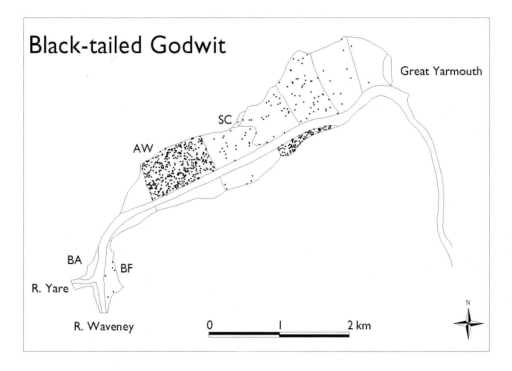

Figure 67. WeBS Low Tide Counts of Teal and Black-tailed Godwit at Breydon Water, winter 2000–01. (BF=Burgh Flats, SC=Stone Corner, BA=Berney Arms, AW=Acle Marshes windmill).

LINDISFARNE
Northumberland

Internationally important: Pink-footed Goose, Light-bellied Brent Goose, Grey Plover, Knot, Bar-tailed Godwit

Nationally important: Cormorant, Shelduck, Wigeon, Eider, Common Scoter, Golden Plover, Dunlin, Curlew

Site description

Lindisfarne, along with Budle Bay, forms one of the largest intertidal areas in north-east England. It is also unusual in being one of only two barrier beach systems in the UK. The majority of the site is sandy, but with increasing amounts of silt in parts of Budle Bay and Fenham Flats. Several freshwater creeks traverse the flats at low tide. There is a fringe of saltmarsh between Goswick to Fenham, around the causeway to Holy Island, and along the southwestern shore of Budle Bay. Extensive sand dunes occur on several parts of the site, with dune slacks, dune heath and dune pasture also represented. The eastern shorelines of Holy Island are mainly rocky, with a few patches of shingle. There is a small harbour on Holy Island but no other industry present, with most activities recreational in nature. Wildfowling occurs in some parts of the site but others are designated as refuges.

Bird distribution

It should be noted that only a single count was made during the winter, in December 2000, as part of an ongoing Northumberland Atlas project (hence the regular 1km grid squares used as count sections). Lindisfarne is the only regular British wintering site for the Svalbard population of Light-bellied Brent Goose, which were distributed over the flats from Crag End to Ross Point (Figure 68). Some of the densest concentrations occurred on parts of the Fenham Flats, whilst Budle Bay was mostly avoided. Small numbers of Pink-footed and Barnacle Geese along with more than 170 Greylag Geese were mostly confined to the western side of Budle Bay. Both Mute Swans and Whooper Swans were present, with the former favouring South Low Channel around the Causeway, and the latter Fenham Flats. Shelduck favoured Fenham Flats and the western end of Budle Bay and tended to avoid the sandier parts of the estuary such as Goswick Sands. Budle Bay was the most important area for Wigeon, with small numbers also using the part of Fenham Flats in the vicinity of Tealhole Point. Mallard were widely distributed both within Budle Bay and on the eastern end of Holy Island itself as well as on Fenham Flats. Small numbers of Teal frequented the southeastern corners of Budle Bay and Holy Island, whilst Pintail preferred the inner part of Fenham Flats. A few Goldeneye and Red-breasted Merganser were recorded from South Low creek and the harbour off the southern end of Holy Island, whilst the few Tufted Duck were confined to The Lough on the east side of the island. Eiders were mostly concentrated around Holy Island, off Emmanuel Head and in the harbour off the southern end; the December count was of over 1,800 Eiders, somewhat higher than the equivalent core count. Cormorant and Shag were mostly to be found on or adjacent to Holy Island, along with Moorhen and Coot. Other species noted were Red-throated and Great Northern Divers, Slavonian and Red-necked Grebes, Grey Heron, Gadwall and Long-tailed Duck.

Oystercatchers were generally scattered throughout the area, but the greatest concentrations were to be found along the northern and southern shorelines of Holy Island, on Oyster Scap in the harbour and along the sandy shore north of Guile Point. Ringed Plover were found almost exclusively on Holy Island Sands, adjacent to the island. Favoured areas for Golden Plover included Fenham Flats and some of Holy Island Sands, as well as in Budle Bay and Ross Black Sands on the north side of the mouth of the bay. Grey Plover, however, showed a much wider scatter on Holy Island Sands and Fenham Flats as well as the southern end of Budle Bay. Lapwing were concentrated into three main areas: the southern end of Budle Bay and Holy Island, and the outer part of Fenham Flats. Knot were widely scattered over Holy Island Sands and Fenham Flats, but very few fed in Budle Bay. Dunlin showed a generally similar distribution to the previous species, but with large concentrations in the southern part of Budle Bay and along Ross Back Sands to the north of the mouth (Figure 68). Bar-tailed Godwits were distributed over most of the flats, with the densest concentrations off Goswick links and fewest in Budle Bay. Curlew exhibited a similar distribution but with the greatest numbers at the southern end of Holy Island and in the south east part of Fenham Flats. Curlew were also present in Budle Bay in reasonable numbers. Redshank were widely distributed, but favoured Holy Island Sands adjacent to the island itself, and also Goswick Sands. A few Turnstone were present around the parts of the causeway and on some of the more stony shorelines of Holy Island. Other species of wader present either occasionally or in very low numbers included Sanderling, Snipe and Jack Snipe.

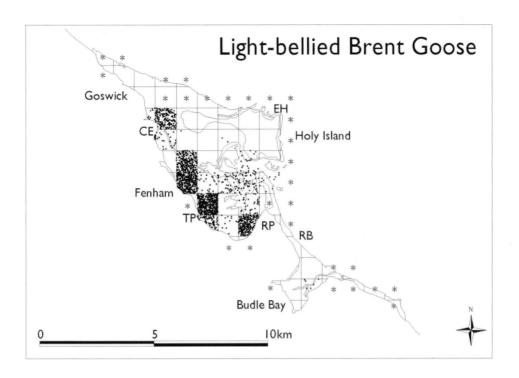

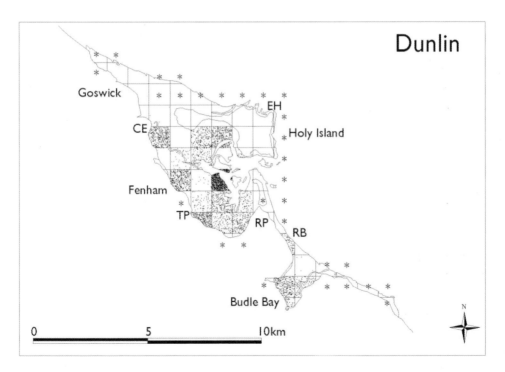

Figure 68. WeBS Low Tide Counts of Light-bellied Brent Goose and Dunlin at Lindisfarne, winter 2000–01. (CE=Crag End, RP=Ross Point, TP=Tealhole Point, EH=Emmanuel Head, RB=Ross Black Sands, * = not counted).

LOCH FLEET
Sutherland/Highland Region

Internationally important: Greylag Goose

Nationally important: None

Site description

Loch Fleet is an enclosed estuary with the mouth now reduced to a narrow tidal channel as a result of the slowly advancing shingle spits, to the north and south. During low tide, extensive areas of mud and sandflat are exposed. Shingle has developed along the southern edge of the estuary, and also in the western part of the loch. Narrow bands of saltmarsh are present along several parts of the shoreline, with the largest area at the head of the bay. At Cambusmore, the saltmarsh is much drier and grades into grassland. An area of dune slack on the seaward side of the Coul Links dune system also contains some saltmarsh. Loch Fleet supports a rich marine fauna, whilst the surrounding dunes and links are important for their plant assemblages, including lichen-rich and moss-rich heaths. The inner part of the loch was separated from the main intertidal area by the construction of an embankment in 1816 called the Mound. This area rapidly developed extensive alder and willow woodland over what was formerly an intertidal part of the estuary. Brackish conditions still prevail in some places due to leakage of saltwater from Loch Fleet. The estuary is in a very rural position, with no industry and very few settlements.

Bird distribution

Although internationally important for roosting Greylag Geese, only small numbers were intermittently recorded during the low tide counts, and these were scattered on the north-western sandflats. Shelduck gradually built up during the winter peaking at 105 birds in February and were generally distributed to the north of the main estuary channel, with the greatest numbers on the flats off Creag Bheag (Figure 69). More than 1,000 Wigeon were present in December, with numbers rapidly decreasing towards the end of the winter. Wigeon were very widely distributed within the estuary with the greatest densities in the eastern half. However, the species appeared to shun the sandy flats between Cambusmore Lodge and Cambusavie Farm along the western fringes. Teal showed a similarly wide distribution, but with the western area of the estuary holding the most birds, and the Cambusavie Flats the least.

Mallard numbers steadily climbed during the first part of the winter to peak at over 600 in January, before declining rapidly again the following month. Mallard were present in most parts of the estuary, but favoured the eastern half, and the area off Skelbo in particular. Small numbers of Eider, Goldeneye and Red-breasted Merganser frequented the main channels, mostly towards the estuary mouth.

Oystercatcher numbers reached 1,290 during December, and although widely distributed within the estuary, favoured the sandy flats towards and around the mouth, particularly those on the northern side. There was also a small concentration around the shingle off Skelbo. The small numbers of Ringed Plover were virtually confined to the large sandflat in the centre of the estuary towards the mouth. Lapwing were rather sporadic in their presence on Loch Fleet, frequenting the stony beach adjacent to Skelbo Castle. The largest count was of 108 birds in February. Up to 600 Knot (Figure 69) and 300 Dunlin fed on an area of sandflat in the main channel adjacent to the mouth and on the shingle adjacent to Skelbo Castle. The largest count of Curlew was made in January, when 268 were present, very evenly distributed all over the estuary. Conversely, Bar-tailed Godwits were rather confined to the flats off Skelbo and just west of the estuary mouth. Redshank were distributed throughout much of the eastern half of the estuary, peaking at 168 individuals in December, but declining to only 15 birds by February. Only singles of Grey Plover and Turnstone were noted all winter. A few Cormorant and Grey Heron were also present.

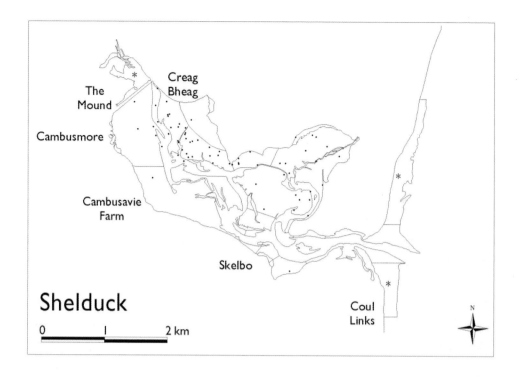

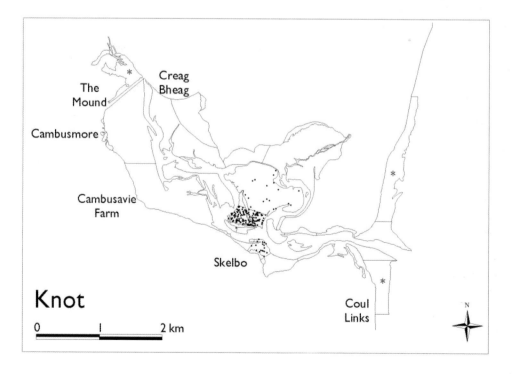

Figure 69. WeBS Low Tide Counts of Shelduck and Knot at Loch Fleet, winter 2000–01 (* = not counted).

ORWELL ESTUARY
Suffolk

Internationally important: Redshank

Nationally important: Dark-bellied Brent Goose, Shelduck, Gadwall, Grey Plover, Dunlin, Black-tailed Godwit

Site description

The Orwell Estuary extends from Ipswich to the Port of Felixstowe where it meets the Stour Estuary. Much of the intertidal substrate is fairly muddy but it becomes sandier towards the mouth. There is a patchy distribution of saltmarsh, whilst freshwater marshes and fields around the estuary provide an important habitat component. In the past, the main conservation concerns were about dockland expansion schemes and marina developments. Dockland expansion at Felixstowe, since around 1964, has claimed all of the outer reaches of the Orwell's northern shore. As a result of the latest development and as legal mitigation for the loss of an important intertidal habitat, the Felixstowe Dock and Railway Company had to lease an area of land and provide the finances to establish a nature reserve at Trimley Marshes. The reserve, established in 1989, is managed by the Suffolk Wildlife Trust. Although the reserve does not replace the lost estuarine habitat it does provide a roost and safe refuge site for several thousand waterbirds during the winter period. Other problems confronting the Orwell include pollution and heavy disturbance from sailing and other leisure activities.

Bird distribution

As in previous years, Dark-bellied Brent Geese were concentrated around the southern end of the estuary, particularly Jill's Hole and Trimley Marshes. A single Black Brant was also noted in January. Large numbers of re-established Greylag and feral Canada Geese, along with occasional White-fronted Geese and feral Snow Goose, were also recorded, mostly from Loompit Lake and Trimley Marshes. Virtually all of the Mute Swans were to be found on the upper part of the Orwell, particularly in the vicinity of Ipswich. Shelduck were generally distributed throughout the estuary but, as usual, the greatest densities were in the northern part of the Orwell. The peak low tide count for Shelduck was the lowest at the site for seven years. Nationally however, the Core Count totals showed a slight increase, although still well below the population levels of the last decade. Wigeon were distributed widely within the estuary, with Trimley Marshes and Jill's Hole being the most favoured areas whilst the northern end of the estuary beyond the Orwell Bridge was avoided (Figure 70). Most of the Gadwall, Pochard, Tufted Duck, Coot and Moorhen were found on Loompit Lake and Trimley Marshes. Mallard were present throughout much of the estuary, with the greatest concentrations on Loompit Lake, Trimley Marshes and in the vicinity of Ipswich at the northern end of the estuary. Teal, Shoveler and Ruddy Duck were only recorded in the southern half of the estuary, especially Trimley Marshes. Although Pintail were found across the Orwell, Cathouse Point, Stratton Hall and Trimley Marshes were the favoured areas. Both Goldeneye and Red-breasted Merganser were widely distributed. Small numbers of Cormorant, Grey Heron, Great Crested Grebe and Little Grebe were found throughout. A Garganey in November was unusual and there were also records of Slavonian Grebe, Common Scoter, Goosander, Water Rail and Kingfisher.

Oystercatcher and Grey Plover favoured the northern shoreline of the estuary, with the greatest concentrations of the former between Mulberry Middle and Nacton. The favoured areas for Golden Plover were the flats off Redgate Hard and Stratton Hall although numbers varied greatly between months. Lapwing displayed a similar distribution, but with the flats off Chelmondiston also favoured. Ringed Plover were found throughout, with a small concentration around the Orwell Bridge. Dunlin were found throughout the greater part of the estuary, with the northern shore holding the greatest numbers, and particularly the mudflats between Nacton and the Orwell Bridge. Curlew showed a very similar distribution to Dunlin, but also fed on the mudflats between Jill's Hole and the mouth (Figure 70). Redshank were widely distributed throughout much of the estuary, with the greatest concentrations between the Orwell Bridge and Nacton on the eastern side, and from Redgate Hard to Cathouse Point on the western side. Numbers of Black-tailed Godwit were at their lowest level for the last seven winters and this was also reflected in the Core Count totals. Most of the birds were encountered in the northern half of the Orwell, with a distinct preference shown for the flats adjacent to Cathouse Point. Knot were virtually confined to the mudflats in the northern half of the Orwell. Turnstone were widely distributed along much of the estuary, with the greatest concentrations between the Orwell Bridge and Mulberry Middle. Other waders recorded either singly or in very small numbers included Avocet, Sanderling, Snipe, Bar-tailed Godwit, Greenshank and Common Sandpiper. Six species of gull were recorded, with Black-headed by far the most abundant whilst a single Mediterranean Gull was present in December.

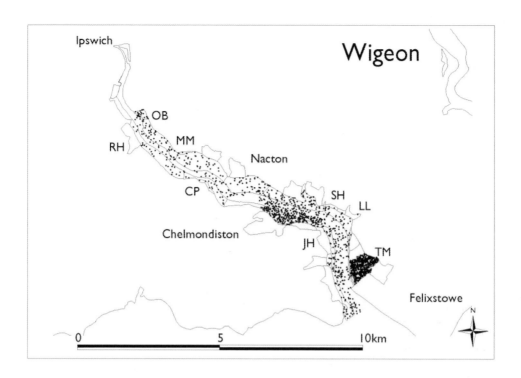

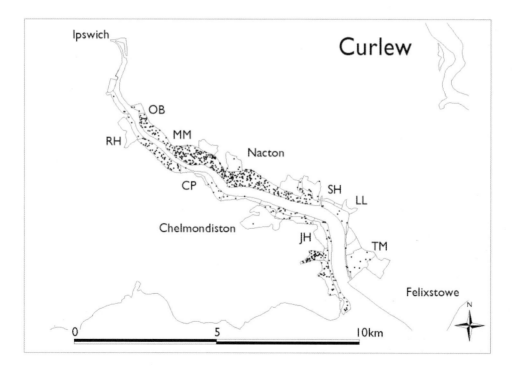

Figure 70. WeBS Low Tide Counts of Wigeon and Curlew at the Orwell Estuary, winter 2000–01. (TM=Trimley Marshes, JH=Jill's Hole, LL=Loompit Lake, OB=Orwell Bridge, CP=Cathouse Point, SH=Stratton House, MM=Mulberry Middle, RH=Redgate Hard).

SOLWAY FIRTH
Dumfries & Galloway / Cumbria

Internationally important: Whooper Swan, Pink-footed Goose, Barnacle Goose, Shelduck, Pintail, Oystercatcher, Knot, Dunlin, Bar-tailed Godwit, Curlew, Redshank

Nationally important: Great Crested Grebe, Cormorant, Scaup, Common Scoter, Red-breasted Merganser, Ringed Plover, Golden Plover, Grey Plover, Black-tailed Godwit

Site description

The Solway Firth, as considered by WeBS, comprises the coastline between Mersehead Sands on the Scottish coast to Workington in Cumbria. Much of this extensive area was covered during winter 2000–01, the main exceptions being the south shore south of Grune Point and some of the more extensive central intertidal banks south of Caerlaverock. The principal inputs to the estuary are from the rivers Esk, Eden, Nith and Annan. The majority of the site is sandy in character with several isolated rocky scars, principally at the mouth of Moricambe Bay. Huge areas of saltmarsh are found along the south side of Moricambe, between Glasson and Burgh and along the Caerlaverock shoreline. However, Rockcliffe Marsh, the most extensive of the saltmarshes, was not covered by the survey. Most of the estuary is surrounded by low-lying farmland and there is little industry in the area. The main issues concerning waterbird conservation on the Solway concern exploitation of natural resources, especially commercial shellfish harvesting. In addition, the issue of siting wind-powered turbines for electricity generation is one which will need careful consideration in the future.

Bird distribution

The greatest concentrations of Knot were on the flats off Carsethorn and Seafield and also adjacent to the mouth of the Annan (Figure 71), whilst other important areas were the mudflats south of Caerlaverock and the area between Grune Point and Bowness-on-Solway. Dunlin displayed a similar distribution, but with greater concentrations at the eastern end of the Solway, particularly off Powfoot. Oystercatcher were widely distributed, but avoided the extreme eastern mudflats. Both Lapwing and Golden Plover favoured Moricambe Bay and the eastern end of the Solway from Powfoot to Torduff Point on the northern side, with Lapwing also concentrated off Bowness-on-Solway on the southern side. Grey Plover mostly preferred the area between Grune Point and Bowness-on-Solway with a few off Carsethorn Point. Moricambe Bay was the main area for the small numbers of Ringed Plover. Curlew were widely distributed throughout the Solway, with the greatest densities in Moricambe Bay and at the

eastern end of the estuary. The numbers of Bar-tailed Godwit were again low compared to core counts, mostly due to the lack of coverage of the outermost parts of the English shore; the species was mostly recorded at low tide on the flats at Grune Point. Up to 63 Black-tailed Godwits frequented Moricambe Bay and the flats off Torduff Point. This compares to a maximum count of only four birds during the equivalent Core Counts. Redshank were concentrated within the inner part of the estuary, including Moricambe Bay, with smaller concentrations between Southerness Point and Overton. Small numbers of Purple Sandpiper and Turnstone occurred off Southerness Point, with a few of the latter also to be found off Carsethorn and Powfoot. Small numbers of Snipe and the odd Greenshank were also recorded over the winter.

Pink-footed and Greylag Geese typically use estuaries as nocturnal roosts but those present during the Solway low tide counts favoured Moricambe Bay. Barnacle Geese peaked at more than 7,000 in November, concentrated along the flats of the River Nith, on Mersehead Sands and around Glasson, but well below the 23,000 birds observed during dedicated goose counts at the site. Shelduck were concentrated within Moricambe Bay, with lesser numbers off Overton and from Powfoot eastwards. Both Teal and Wigeon (Figure 71) favoured the flats off Skinburness in Moricambe Bay, with smaller numbers in the inner part of the estuary, and at the mouth of the Nith. The majority of the Mallard on the Solway were to be found within Moricambe Bay and the inner part of the estuary whilst most Pintail were found in the middle sections of the estuary, with smaller numbers at the mouth of the Nith and off Skinburness and Powfoot. The flock of over 1,800 Scaup was typically concentrated between Carsethorn and Southerness Point, and was substantially higher than the peak Core Count of 832 birds. Most of the Great Crested Grebes were also in the outer estuary. Small numbers of Whooper Swan and Goldeneye frequented the inner part of the estuary, as did most of the Cormorants. Also recorded were Red and Black-throated Divers, Grey Heron, Mute Swan, Greenland White-fronted Goose, Canada Goose, Gadwall, Shoveler, Tufted Duck, Red-breasted Merganser, Goosander, Moorhen and Kingfisher. Black-headed was the most abundant of the five species of gull recorded.

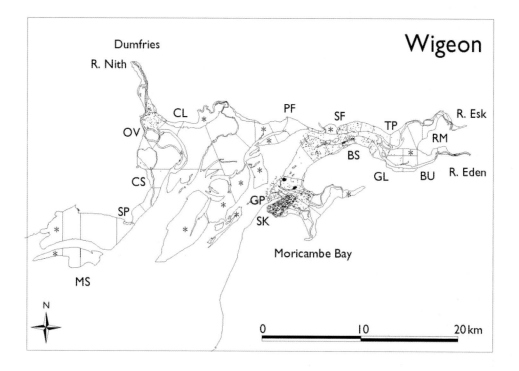

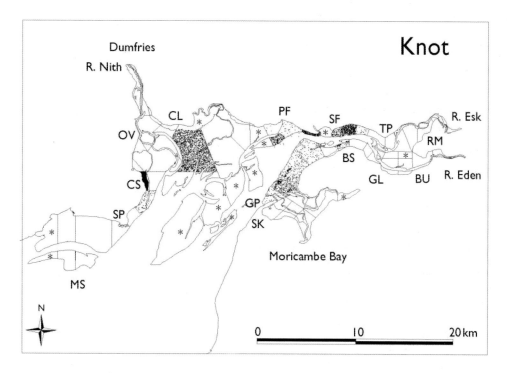

Figure 71. WeBS Low Tide Counts of Wigeon and Knot at the Solway Firth, winter 2000–01. (MS=Mersehead Sands, SP=Southerness Point, CS=Carsethorn, OV=Overton, CL=Caerlaverock, PF=Powfoot, SF=Seafield, TP=Torduff Point, RM=Rockcliffe Marsh, BU=Burgh by Sands, GL=Glasson, BS=Bowness-on-Solway, GP=Grune Point, SK=Skinburness, * = not counted)

SOUTHAMPTON WATER
Hampshire

Internationally important: Black-tailed Godwit

Nationally important: Great Crested Grebe, Cormorant, Dark-bellied Brent Goose, Wigeon, Teal, Dunlin

Site description

Southampton Water is part of the Solent complex and lies between the city of Southampton and the New Forest. The three principal rivers entering Southampton Water are the Test, Itchen and Hamble. There are extensive areas of mud on both shores of the estuary, with a large area of Spartina saltmarsh along the western shore. Southampton Water is one of the most heavily developed estuaries in Britain and, as well as being adjacent to a large city, also has important docks, an oil refinery and a power station along its shores. The area is also extremely heavily used by sailing enthusiasts. One of the most significant current development issues is at Dibden Bay, which is actually no longer a bay since dredgings were pumped onto the land here. This area now supports an extensive area of coastal wet grassland. Development plans, for port expansion, would result in the loss of this grassland and the remaining intertidal mud.

Bird distribution

The distribution of Brent Geese within the estuary was similar to recent winters, with the favoured feeding areas towards the mouth of the estuary. The densest feeding concentrations occurred between Titchfield Haven and the confluence of the Hamble (Figure 72). Canada Geese were recorded in fluctuating numbers, particularly around Eling Marsh, along with the odd Egyptian Goose. Shelduck were mainly present on the flats between Hythe and Calshot, and also in the vicinity of Eling Marsh. Wigeon numbers built up during the winter; the greatest concentrations of birds were off Eling and Bury Marshes and off Hythe and Fawley. The distribution of Teal was broadly similar to that of Wigeon, with the greatest numbers around Eling and Bury Marshes, and around Cadland Creek and Fawley, with lesser numbers on the River Hamble. Mallard were widely distributed throughout the estuary, with the greatest concentrations within the Rivers Itchen and Hamble. Conversely, most of the Pintail were to be found as usual at Cadland Creek. Up to 33 Red-breasted Mergansers frequented the estuary, along with small numbers of Gadwall, Shoveler, Tufted Duck, Goldeneye and Common Scoter. As in previous years, virtually all the records of Moorhen were from the River Itchen and most of the Coot were found near Fawley Power Station. A couple of Water Rail were also noted. The majority of the Mute Swans were on the River Itchen, while Great Crested Grebes were widely distributed within the estuary. Most of the Little Grebes were to be found off Fawley and along the Itchen. Occasional Red-throated and Great Northern Divers were also recorded.

Oystercatcher were widely distributed, with the greatest concentrations off Fawley and around Dibden Bay. Curlew were also widely distributed, but appeared to prefer the flats along the western shoreline, and along the River Hamble. Golden Plover were confined to mudflats around the River Hamble and the flats just to the south, whilst Grey Plover preferred the flats off Weston Shore, Hamble Spit and the area between Cadland Creek and Fawley on the western shoreline. Lapwing numbers remained generally constant at around 1,000 individuals, and were to be found principally around Eling and Bury Marshes, between Cadland Creek and Fawley and along the lower reaches of the Hamble (Figure 72). The peak numbers of Dunlin recorded at low tide were relatively low for a second year running; the birds were widely distributed over much of the estuary. Small numbers of Black-tailed Godwit congregated mostly on Eling and Bury Marshes although, as usual, it should be noted that the key area for this species (non-tidal grasslands at Titchfield Haven) were not covered by the low tide counts. Redshank and Turnstone were widely scattered, with the former favouring Eling and Bury Marshes, the intertidal flats between Fawley and Calshot and along the Itchen and Hamble Rivers and the latter the south-eastern part of the estuary. The distribution of Ringed Plover was very similar to that of Turnstone, with a definite southeastern bias. Very small numbers of Knot, Snipe, Bar-tailed Godwit and Greenshank were also present, whilst single over-wintering Whimbrel and Common Sandpiper were of interest. Cormorants were especially concentrated between Hythe and Cadland Creek, and Little Egrets peaked at 18 individuals in November, exceeding the numbers of Grey Heron present. Seven species of gull occurred, including up to 12 Mediterranean Gulls in December and up to five Yellow-legged Gulls in November.

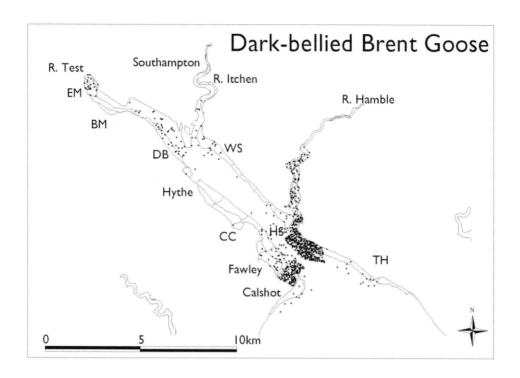

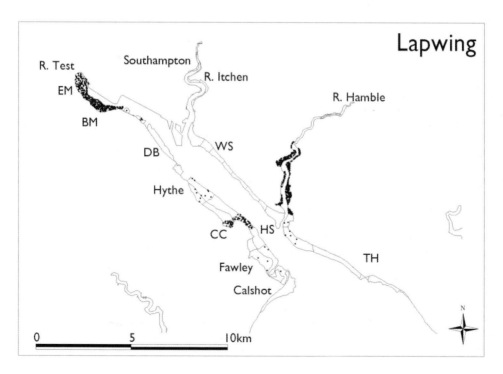

Figure 72. WeBS Low Tide Counts of Dark-bellied Brent Goose and Lapwing at Southampton Water, winter 2000–01. (DB=Dibden Bay, TH=Titchfield Haven, EM=Eling Marsh, BM=Bury Marsh, CC=Cadland Creek, WS=Weston Shore, HS=Hamble Spit)

STOUR ESTUARY
Suffolk/Essex

Internationally important: Pintail, Grey Plover, Knot, Dunlin, Black-tailed Godwit, Redshank

Nationally important: Great Crested Grebe, Cormorant, Mute Swan, Dark-bellied Brent Goose, Shelduck, Wigeon, Goldeneye, Ringed Plover, Curlew

Site description

The Stour Estuary is a long, relatively straight estuary which forms the eastern end of the border between Suffolk and Essex. The estuary's mouth joins that of the Orwell as the two rivers enter the North Sea between Felixstowe and Harwich. The outer parts of the site are sandy, but shores become progressively muddier further upstream. There are five shallow bays; Seafield, Holbrook and Erwarton along the north shore and Copperas and Jacques on the south side. The estuary is backed by wooded cliffs and agricultural land. Since much of this land is private, there is very little disturbance to most of the estuary. Some sailing and shooting occurs. Most of the industrial activity occurs around Harwich, where there is a proposed port development at Bathside Bay.

Bird distribution

Great Crested Grebes peaked at 222 birds during December, the majority of the birds gathering in the middle of the estuary. As in previous years, Cormorants were distributed along most of the estuary but in lower numbers than during Core Counts. Mute Swans were principally concentrated off Manningtree, with smaller numbers around Harwich. Dark-bellied Brent Geese were distributed widely within the estuary with the greatest concentrations found within the eastern part of Seafield Bay and on the flats to the north of Copperas (Figure 73). Canada Geese preferred the upper reaches, from Seafield Bay westwards. Shelduck were widely distributed within the Stour, with the lowest numbers towards the mouth and the largest numbers in Copperas Bay and Jacques Bay. The peak low tide count of over 4,000 Wigeon was the highest at the site in recent winters. The greatest numbers occurred in the western half of the estuary, particularly the flats off Stutton Mill and within the vicinity of Jacques Bay. The majority of the Teal were to be found either at the eastern side of Copperas Bay and off Manningtree at the western end. Pintail favoured Copperas Bay and the western end of the estuary, particularly the flats off Manningtree, whilst most of the Mallard were on the southern shore of the Stour from Jacques Bay eastwards. The creeks and channels around Manningtree were the most important area for Goldeneye, with none recorded towards the eastern end of the estuary at all. Conversely, Red-breasted Mergansers were fairly evenly scattered along the length of the estuary. Other wildfowl recorded were small numbers of Greylag Goose, Gadwall, Shoveler, Pochard, Velvet Scoter and up to nine Smew, whilst an escaped Chiloe Wigeon added a taste of the exotic. Single Light-bellied Brent Goose and Greenland White-fronted Goose were also noted. Black-throated Diver, Little Grebe, Shag, Water Rail, Moorhen, Coot and Kingfisher were also recorded. Up to three Little Egrets were present all winter, along with a few Grey Herons.

Oystercatchers were found throughout much of the estuary with the greatest concentrations present in Seafield Bay and, to a lesser extent, both Holbrook and Erwarton Bays. Peak numbers of Ringed Plover, both at low tide and during core counts, were at a relatively high level during this winter, with most of the birds using Erwarton Bay and the flats off Harwich towards the mouth of the estuary. A short-lived influx of Golden Plover took place on the estuary during December, when over 6,000 birds were present, mostly at Seafield, Jacques and Erwarton bays. Grey Plover were distributed across much of the Stour, but concentrated mainly on the mudflats at Mistley, along with both Holbrook and Copperas Bays. Lapwing numbers fluctuated during the winter and the western half of the Stour held the most birds, although mudflats to the west of Erwarton Ness and Harwich were also important. Figure 73 shows that Dunlin were found virtually throughout the estuary, whilst Knot were more scattered, with the densest concentrations of the latter at the western end of the Stour. A similar distribution was shown by Black-tailed Godwit, the peak count of over 2,800 being well in excess of the peak core count for the winter. Conversely, the small numbers of Bar-tailed Godwit present were distributed within the eastern half of the estuary. Curlew and Redshank were scattered throughout most of the Stour, with the latter species recording a fall in numbers compared to the previous winter. Turnstone frequented the northern shoreline of the eastern half of the estuary. Other wader species occasionally present included Avocet, Sanderling, Ruff, Snipe, Spotted Redshank and Greenshank. Of the five species of gull present, Black-headed was the commonest.

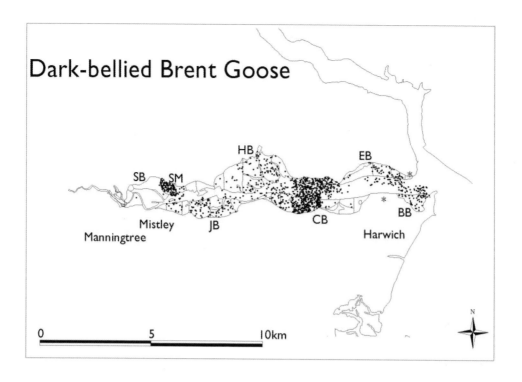

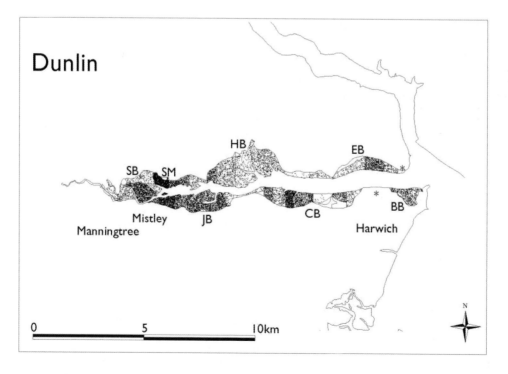

Figure 73. WeBS Low Tide Counts of Dark-bellied Brent Goose and Dunlin at the Stour Estuary, winter 2000–01. (SB=Seafield Bay, HB=Holbrook Bay, EB=Erwarton Bay, CB=Copperas Bay, JB=Jacques Bay, BB=Bathside Bay, SM=Stutton Mill, * = not counted).

References

Atkinson, P.W., Clark, N.A., Bell, M.C., Dare, P.J., Clark, J.A. and Ireland, P.L. (in press). Changes in commercially fished shellfish stocks and shorebird populations in the Wash, England. *Biological Conservation*.

Austin, G.E., Peachel, I. & Rehfisch, M.M. 2000. Regional trends in coastal wintering waders. *Bird Study* 47: 352–371.

Austin, G. & Rehfisch, M.M. 1998. *Had some Estuaries Reached Carrying Capacity for Grey Plovers* Pluvialis squatarola L. *by the Mid-1980s? A Re-analysis of Long-Tern Population Trends with the Benefit of Hindsight*. BTO report to the Wetland Bird Survey partners.

Beukema, J.J. & Cadée, G.C. 1986. Zoobenthois responds to eutrophication of the Dutch Wadden Sea. *Ophelia* 26: 55–64.

Bibby, C.J., Burgess, N.D., Hill, D.A. & Mustoe, S. 2000. *Bird Census Techniques. Second Edition*. Academic Press, London.

BOURC 1999. British Ornithologists' Union Records Committee: 25th Report (October 1998). *Ibis* 141: 175-180.

Cadbury, C.J., Hill, D., Partridge, J. & Sorensen, J. 1989. The history of the Avocet population and its management in England since recolonisation. *RSPB Conservation Review* 3: 9–13.

Camphuysen, C.J., Berrevoets, C.M., Cremers, H.J.W.M., Dekinger, A., Dekker, R., Ens, B.J., Have, T.M. van der, Kats, R.K.H., Kuiken, T., Leopold, M.F., Meer, J. van der & Piersma, T. 2002. Mass mortality of common eiders (*Somateria mollissima*) in the Dutch Wadden Sea, winter 1999/2000: starvation in a commercially exploited wetland of international importance. *Biological Conservation* 106: 303–317.

Carp, E. 1972. *Proceedings of the international conference n the conservation of wetlands and waterfowl. Ramsar, Iran, 30 January - 3 February 1971*. IWRB, Slimbridge.

Cayford, J.T. & Waters, R.J. 1996. Population estimates for waders *Charadrii* wintering in Great Britain, 1987/88-1991/92. *Biological Conservation* 77: 7-17

Central Science Laboratory. 2002. *UK Ruddy Duck control trial final report*. Report to Department for Environment, Food and Rural Affairs, 36 pp.

Chandler, R.J. 1986. Black-necked Grebe *Podiceps nigricollis*. In: Lack, P. (Ed.) *The Atlas of Wintering Birds in Britain and Ireland*. T. & A.D. Poyser, London: 48–49.

Colhoun, K. 2001. *The Irish Wetland Bird Survey 1998-99; results from the fifth winter of the Irish Wetland Bird Survey*. BWI/NPW/WWT, Dublin.

Cranswick, P.A. in press. Status and distribution of common scoter *Melanitta nigra* and velvet scoter *M. fusca* in the United Kingdom. In: *Western Palearctic Scoter Flyway Review; Proceedings of the Seaduck Specialist Group meeting at Fuglesø, Jutland 2000*. NERI technical report: 59–65.

Cranswick, P.A., Kirby, J.S., Salmon, D.G., Atkinson-Willes, G.L., Pollitt, M.S. & Owen, M. 1997 A history of wildfowl counts by The Wildfowl & Wetlands Trust. *Wildfowl* 47: 217-230.

Cranswick, P.A., Waters, R.J., Musgrove, A.J. & Pollitt, M.S. 1997. *The Wetland Bird Survey 1995–96: Wildfowl and Waders Counts*. BTO/WWT/RSPB/JNCC, Slimbridge.

Danielsen, F., Skov, H. & Durnick, J. 1993. Estimates of the wintering population of Red-throated Diver *Gavia stellata* and Black-throated Diver *Gavia arctica* in northwest Europe. *Proceedings of the 7th Nordic Congress of Ornithology, 1990*. pp. 18-24.

Dhondt, A.A. 1987. Cycles of lemmings and Brent Geese *Branta b. bernicla*: a comment on the hypothesis of Roselaar and Summers. *Bird Study* 34: 151–154.

Durham, M. 2002. Surveying the Gloucester gull colony. *The Seabird Group Newsletter* 92: 3–4.

Fox, A.D. & Francis, I. 2002. *Report of the 2000/2001 National Census of Greenland White-fronted Geese in Britain*. Greenland White-fronted Goose Study report. Kalø, Denmark. 8 pp.

Fox, A.D., Hilmarsson, J.O., Einarsson, O., Walsh, A.J., Boyd, H. & Kristiansen, J.N. 2002. Staging site fidelity of Greenland White-fronted Geese *Anser albifrons flavirostris* in Iceland. *Bird Study* 49: 42–49.

Geary, S. & Lock, L. 2001. *Winter nearshore seabird survey of South Cornwall Coast Important Bird Area (1999/2000)*. RSPB unpublished report.

Gibbons, D.W. 1993. Moorhen. In: Gibbons, D.W., Reid, J.B. & Chapman, R. (Eds.) *The New Atlas of Breeding Birds in Britain and Ireland: 1988–91*. T. & A.D. Poyser, London: 152–153.

Gilbert, G., Gibbons, D.W. & Evans, J. 1998. *Bird Monitoring Methods*. RSPB, Sandy.

Gill, J.A., Norris, K., Potts, P.M., Gunnarsson, T.G., Atkinson, P.W. & Sutherland, W.J. 2001. The buffer effect and large-scale population regulation in migratory birds. *Nature* 412: 436–438.

Gregory, R.D., Wilkinson, N.I., Noble, D.G., Robinson, J.A., Brown, A.F., Hughes, J., Procter, D., Gibbons, D.W. & Galbraith, C.A. 2002. The population status of birds in the United Kingdom, Channel Islands and Isle of Man: an analysis of conservation concern 2002–2007. *British Birds* 95: 410–448.

Griffin, L.R. & Coath, D.C. 2001. *WWT Svalbard Barnacle Goose Project Report 2000–2001*. WWT Internal Report, Slimbridge, 25 pp.

Hearn, R.D. 2001. *An assessment of breeding success in the Dark-bellied Brent Goose* Branta b. bernicla *in the UK in 2000*. WWT report, Slimbridge, 7 pp.

Hearn, R.D. 2002. *The 2000 National Census of Pink-footed Geese and Icelandic Greylag Geese in Britain & Ireland*. WWT report, Slimbridge. 16 pp.

Heubeck, M. & Richardson, M.G. 1980. Bird mortality following the *Esso Bernicla* oil spill, Shetland, December 1978. *Scottish Birds* 11: 97–108

Heubeck, M. 2000. *SOTEAG ornithological monitoring programme: 1999 summary report*. SOTEAG, Aberdeen.

Holmes, J.S., Marchant, J., Bucknell, N., Stroud, D.A. & Parkin, D.T. 1998. The British List: new categories and their relevance to conservation. *British Birds* 92: 2-11.

Holmes, J.S. & Stroud, D.A. 1995. Naturalised birds: feral, exotic, introduced or alien? *British Birds* 88: 602-603.

Hötker, H. Waders breeding on wet grasslands in the countries of the European Community – a brief summary of current knowledge on population sizes and population trends. In: Hötker, H. (Ed.) Waders Breeding on Wet Grasslands. *Wader Study Group Bulletin* 61, Supplement April 1991: 50–55.

Jenkins, R.K.B. 2002. Water Rail. In: Wernham, C., Toms, M., Marchant, J., Clark, J., Siriwardena, G. & Baillie, S. (eds.) *The Migration Atlas: Movements of the birds of Britain and Ireland*. T. & A.D. Poyser, London: 261–262.

JNCC (1993–1997) *An inventory of UK estuaries. Volumes 1–7*. Joint Nature Conservation Committee, Peterborough.

JNCC (1995–1998). *Coastal Directories Series – Coasts and seas of the United Kingdom*. Joint Nature Conservation Committee, Peterborough.

Kershaw, M., & Cranswick, P.A. (in press) Numbers of wintering waterbirds in Great Britain, 1994/1995–1998/1999: I. Wildfowl and selected waterbirds. *Biological Conservation*.

Kershaw, M. & Hughes, B. 2002. *The winter status and distribution of Ruddy Ducks* Oxyura jamaicensis *in the UK, 1966/67–1999/2000*. WWT Wetlands Advisory Service report to the Central Science Laboratory. 31 pp.

Kirby, J.S. 1995. Winter population estimates for selected waterfowl species in Britain. *Biological Conservation* 73: 189-198

Kirby, J.S., Salmon, D.G. & Atkinson-Willes, G.L. & Cranswick, P.A. 1995. Index numbers for waterbird populations, III. Long-term trends in the abundance of wintering wildfowl in Great Britain, 1966/67 to 1991/2. *Journal of Applied Ecology* 32: 536-551.

Marchant, J. 2001. Waterways bird surveys – latest results, and a new challenge. *BTO News* 236: 8-10.

Meininger, P.L., Berrevoets, C.M. & Strucker, R.C. 1992. *Coastal breeding birds in the delta area including an overview of 13 years of monitoring 1979–1991*. Rapport DGW 92.024, Rijkswaterstaat, Middelburg, The Netherlands.

Mitchell, C.R., Patterson, D.J., Price, D.J. & Kerr, S. 1997. *Aerial counts of Barnacle Geese on proposed SPA sites in north and west Scotland*. WWT Report to SNH, Contract No. SNH/RASD/043/017/N2K, 19 pp.

Moss, D. L. 2002. Little Grebe *Tachybaptus ruficollis*. In: Wernham, C.V., Toms, M.P., Marchant, J.H., Clark, J.A., Siriwardena, G.M. & Baillie, S.R. (Eds.) *The Migration Atlas: movements of the birds of Britain and Ireland*. T. & A.D. Poyser, London: 112–113.

Musgrove, A.J. 2002.The non-breeding status of the Little Egret in Britain. *British Birds* 95: 62–80.

Musgrove, A.J., Pollitt, M.S., Hall, C., Hearn, R.D., Holoway, SJ, Marshall, P.E., Robinson, J.A. & Cranswick, P.A. 2001. *The Wetland Bird Survey 1999–2000: Wildfowl and Waders Counts*. BTO/WWT/RSPB/ JNCC, Slimbridge.

Nightingale, B. & McGeehan, A. 2000. Recent reports. *British Birds* 93: 574–576.

Ogilvie, M. A. 2001. *Breeding success of Barnacle and Greenland White-fronted Geese on Islay and of Greenland White-fronted Geese on Kintyre in 2000*. Private report, 5 pp.

Oliver, F., Robinson, P. & Howard, C. 2001. *Common Scoter* Melanitta nigra *in Liverpool Bay*. CCW Contract Science Report no 470.

Piersma, T. & Koolhaas, A. 1997. *Shorebirds, shellfish(eries) and sediments around Griend, Western Wadden Sea, 1988–1996. Single large-scale exploitative events lead to long-term changes in the intertidal birds-benthos community*. NIOZ-Rapport 1997–7. Netherlands Instituut voor Onderzoek der Zee, The Netherlands.

Pirot, J.-Y., Laursen, K., Madsen, J. & Monval, J.-Y. 1989. Population estimates of swans, geese, ducks and Eurasian Coot Fulica atra in the Western Palearctic and Sahelian Africa. In: *Boyd, H. & Pirot, J.-Y. (Eds). Flyways and Reserve Networks for Water Birds*. IWRB Special Pulication 9, IWRB, Slimbridge: 12-23.

Prŷs-Jones, R. P., Underhill, L.G. & Waters, R.J. 1994. Index numbers for waterbird populations. II Coastal wintering waders in the United Kingdom, 1970/71 - 1990/91. *Journal of Applied Ecology* 31: 481-492.

Ramsar Convention Bureau 1988. *Convention on Wetlands of International Importance especially as Waterfowl Habitat*. Proceedings of the third meeting of the Conference of the Contracting Parties, Regina, Canada, 1987. Ramsar, Switzerland.

Ratcliffe, N, Pickerell, G & Brindley, E. 2000. Population trends of Little and Sandwich Terns *Sterna albifrons* and *S. sandvicensis* in Britain and Ireland from 1969 to 1998. *Atlantic Seabirds* 2: 211–226.

Rees, E.C., White, G.T. & Bruce, J.H. 2000. *Whooper Swans wintering in the Black Cart Floodplain: winter 1999 - 2000*. WWT Wetland Advisory Service report to Scottish Enterprise.

Rehfisch, M.M., Austin, G.E., Armitage, M.J.S., Atkinson, P.W., Holloway, S.J., Musgrove, A.J. & Pollitt, M.S. (in press) Numbers of wintering waterbirds in Great Britain and the Isle of Man (1994/1995–1998/1999):II. Coastal waders (Charadrii). *Biological Conservation*.

Rehfisch, M.M., Austin, G.E., Holloway, S.J., Allan, J.R. & O'Connell, M. 2002. An approach to the assessment of change in the numbers of Canada *Branta canadensis* and Greylag Geese *Anser anser* in Southern Britain. *Bird Study* 49: 50–59.

Rogers, M.J. and the Rarities Committee. 1998. Report on rare birds in Great Britain 1997. *British Birds* 91: 455-517.

Rogers, M.J and the Rarities Committee. 2001. Report on rare birds in Great Britain in 2000. *British Birds* 94: 452–504.

Rose, P.M. & Scott, D.A. 1997. *Waterfowl Population Estimates - Second Edition*. Wetlands International Publ. 44, Wageningen, The Netherlands.

Rose, P.M. & Stroud, D.A. 1994. Estimating international waterfowl populations: current activity and future directions. *Wader Study Group Bulletin* 73: 19-26.

Simpson, J. & MacIver, A. 2001. *Population and Distribution of Bean Geese in the Slamannan area 2000/01*. Report to the Bean Goose Working Group. 15 pp.

Smit, C.J. & Piersma, T. 1989. Numbers, midwinter distribution and migration of wader populations using the East Atlantic flyway. In: Boyd, H. & Pirot, J.-Y. (Eds.) *Flyways and reserve networks for waterbirds*. IWRB Special Publication 9, Slimbridge: 24-64.

Stenning, J. 1998. *Moray Firth monitoring: winter 1997-98*. RSPB report to Talisman Energy, 4 pp.

Stewart, B., Hughes, B., Bullock, I. & Haycock, R. 1997. *Common scoter* Melanitta nigra *monitoring in Carmarthen Bay following the Sea Empress oil spill*. WWT Wetlands Advisory Service report to the Sea Empress Environmental Evaluation Committee, Contract No. FC 73-02-53, Slimbridge.

Stroud, D.A., Chambers, D., Cook, S., Buxton, N., Fraser, B., Clement, P., Lewis, P., McLean, I., Baker, H. & Whitehead, S. 2001. *The UK SPA network: its scope and content*. JNCC, Peterborough.

Stroud, D.A., Mudge, G.P. & Pienkowski, M.W. 1990. *Protecting internationally important bird sites: a review of the EEC Special Protection Area network in Great Britain*. NCC, Peterborough, 230 pp.

Underhill, L.G. & Prŷs-Jones, R. 1994 Index numbers for waterbird populations. I. Review and methodology. *Journal of Applied Ecology* 31: 463-480.

Underhill, L.G. 1989. *Indices for waterbird populations*. BTO Research Report 52.

van Impe, J. 1985. Estuarine pollution as a probable cause of increase of estuarine birds. *Marine Pollution Bulletin* 16: 271–276.

van Strien, A.J., Pannekoek, J. & Gibbons, D.W. 2001. Indexing European bird population trends using results of national monitoring schemes: a trial of a new method. *Bird Study* 48: 200–213.

Vinicombe, K., Marchant, J. & Know, A. 1993. Review of status and categorization of feral birds on the British List. *British Birds* 75: 1-11

Waltho, C.M. 2001. *Firth of Clyde Eider News: No 1. August 2001*. Private report.

Waltho, C.M. 2002. *Firth of Clyde Eider News, No 2 January 2002*. Private report.

Way, L.S., Grice, P., MacKay, A., Galbraith, C.A., Stroud, D.A. & Pienkowski, M.W. 1993. *Ireland's internationally important bird sites: a review of sites for the EC Special Protection Area network*. JNCC, Peterborough, 231 pp.

Wetlands International 1999. *Report on the Conservation Status of Migratory Waterbirds in the Agreement Area*. Report to the Secretariat of the Agreement on the Conservation of African-Eurasian Migratory Waterbirds, 417 pp.

Wetlands International. 2002. *Waterbird Population Estimates – Third Edition*. Wetlands International Global Series No. 12. Wageningen, The Netherlands.

Williams, E.J. 1999. *Wintering seafowl in Scapa Flow*. Report to Elf, Orkney Islands Harbour Authority, RSPB and SNH, 45 pp.

Woolmer, A., Smith, L. & Hayward, P.J. *Carmarthen Bay Infauna/Scoter Project: Final report March 2001*. University of Wales, Swansea report to CCW, Contract No. FC 73-02-123. 43 pp.

Glossary

The terms listed below are generally restricted to those that have been adopted specifically for use within WeBS or more widely for monitoring.

Autumn For waders, autumn comprises July to October inclusive. Due to differences in seasonality between species (see *Monthly Fluctuations*), a strict definition of autumn is not used for wildfowl.

British Trust for Ornithology (BTO) The BTO is a well respected organisation, combining the skills of professional scientists and volunteer birdwatchers to carry out research on birds in all habitats and throughout the year. Data collected by the various surveys form the basis of extensive and unique databases which enable the BTO to objectively advise conservation bodies, government agencies, planners and scientists on a diverse range of issues involving birds.

Complex site A *WeBS site* that consists of two or more *sectors*.

Core Counts The basic WeBS counts that monitor all wetlands throughout the UK once per month on priority dates. Used to determine population estimates and trends and identify important sites.

Local Organiser Person responsible for co-ordinating counters and counts at a local level, normally a county or large estuary, and the usual point of contact with WeBS partner HQs.

Incomplete counts When presenting counts of an individual species, a large proportion of the number of birds was suspected to have been missed, e.g. due to part coverage of the site or poor counting conditions, or when presenting the total number of birds of all species on the site, a significant proportion of the total number was missed.

I-WeBS An independent but complementary scheme operating in the Republic of Ireland to monitor non-breeding waterbirds, organised by the IWC BirdWatch Ireland, the National Parks and Wildlife Service (Ireland) and The Wildfowl & Wetlands Trust.

Joint Nature Conservation Committee (JNCC) JNCC is the statutory body constituted by the Environmental Protection Act 1990 to be responsible for research and advice on nature conservation at both UK and international levels. The committee is established by English Nature, Scottish Natural Heritage and the Countryside Council for Wales, together with independent members and representatives from the Countryside Commission and Northern Ireland, and is supported by specialist staff.

Low Tide Counts (LTC) WeBS counts made at low tide to assess the relative importance of different parts of individual estuaries as feeding areas for intertidal waterbirds.

Royal Society for the Protection of Birds (RSPB) The RSPB is the charity that takes action for wild birds and the environment in the UK. The RSPB is the national BirdLife partner in the UK.

Spring For waders, spring comprises April to June inclusive. Due to differences in seasonality between species (see *Monthly Fluctuations*), a strict definition of spring is not used for wildfowl.

Waterbirds WeBS follows the definition adopted by Wetlands International. This includes a large number of families, those occurring regularly in the UK being divers, grebes, cormorants, herons, storks, ibises and spoonbills, wildfowl, cranes, rails, waders and gulls and terns.

Waterfowl Used as a collective term in this publication to refer to all *waterbirds* excluding gulls, terns and Kingfisher.

WeBS count sector The unit of division of large *sites* into areas which can be counted by one person in a reasonable time period. They are often demarcated by geographic features to facilitate recognition of the boundary by counters. The finest level at which data are recorded.

WeBS count site A biologically meaningful area that represents a discrete area used by waterbirds such that birds regularly move within but only occasionally between sites. The highest level at which count data are stored.

WeBS count sub-site A grouping of *sectors* within a *site* to facilitate co-ordination. In most cases, sub-sites also relate to biologically meaningful units for describing waterbird distribution.

WeBS count unit The area/boundary within which a count is made. The generic term for *sites*, *sub-sites* and *sectors*.

The Wildfowl & Wetlands Trust (WWT) Founded by Sir Peter Scott in 1946, WWT is the only wildlife conservation charity specialising in wetlands and the wildlife they support. It has pioneered the bringing together of people and wildlife for the benefit of both and seeks to raise awareness of the value of wetlands, the threats they face and the actions needed to save them. To this end, WWT has eight centres throughout the UK and is dedicated to saving wetlands for wildlife and people.

Winter For waders, winter comprises November to March inclusive. Due to differences in seasonality between species (see *Monthly Fluctuations*), a strict definition of winter is not used for wildfowl.

1% criterion The Ramsar Convention has established site selection criteria. Criterion 6 states that ". . . a wetland should be considered internationally important if it regularly supports 1% of the individuals in a population of one species or subspecies of waterbird"

1% threshold This logically derives from the *1% criterion* and relates to the number of birds that are used as the nominal 1% of the population for the purposes of site selection. Thus, an international population of 75,215 Shelduck has a derived 1% threshold (adopting rounding conventions) of 750.

Appendices

APPENDIX 1.   INTERNATIONAL DESIGNATIONS

The Ramsar Convention on Wetlands of International Importance especially as Waterfowl Habitat requires each Contracting Party to designate suitable wetlands, selected on account of their international significance in terms of ecology, botany, zoology, limnology or hydrology, for inclusion in a List of Wetlands of International Importance (known as Ramsar sites) (Carp 1972). The Directive on the Conservation of Wild Birds (EC/79/409) lays emphasis on the need to conserve bird habitats as a means of maintaining populations and that this, in part, should be achieved by the establishment of a network of protected areas termed Special Protection Areas (SPAs) (Stroud *et al.* 1990). Ramsar Sites and SPAs may be identified using a number of criteria,

including a number of numeric selection criteria (see Appendix 2) which draw heavily upon waterbird counts, especially WeBS and the other data presented in this report.

The tables below list the number and area of classified SPAs and Ramsar sites as of 16 January 2003. More detailed information about protected sites can be accessed via the JNCC website at http://www.jncc.gov.uk/idt/default.htm. Full listings of sites currently designated as SPAs and Ramsar sites can be found at the following links:
http://www.jncc.gov.uk/idt/spa/sitelist/default.htm
http://www.jncc.gov.uk/idt/ramsar/sitelist/default.htm

Table A1. Number and area of classified SPAs and designated Ramsar sites in the UK as of 16/01/2003

Country	Classified SPAs		Designated Ramsar sites	
	No. of sites	Site Area (ha)	No. of sites	Area (ha)
England	76	600,631	66	294,083
England/Scotland	1	43,637	1	43,637
England/Wales	2	37,777	3	39,336
N Ireland	10	70,660	17	86,831
Scotland	133	548,672	50	283,569
Wales	14	68,999	7	11,366
Total	**236**	**1,370,376**	**144**	**758,822**

APPENDIX 2. INTERNATIONAL AND NATIONAL IMPORTANCE

Any site recognised as being of international ornithological importance is considered for classification as a Special Protection Area (SPA) under the EC Directive on the Conservation of Wild Birds (EC/79/409), whilst a site recognised as an internationally important wetland qualifies for designation as a Ramsar site under the Convention on Wetlands of International Importance especially as Waterfowl Habitat. Criteria for assessing the international importance of wetlands have been agreed by the Contracting Parties to the Ramsar Convention on Wetlands of International Importance (Ramsar Convention Bureau 1988). Under criterion 6, a wetland is considered internationally important if it regularly holds at least 1% of the individuals in a population of one species or subspecies of waterbird, while criterion 5 states that any site regularly supporting 20,000 or more waterbirds also qualifies. Britain and Ireland's wildfowl belong, in most cases, to the northwest European population (Pirot *et al.* 1989), and the waders to the east Atlantic flyway population (Smit & Piersma 1989).

A wetland in Britain is considered nationally important if it regularly holds 1% or more of the estimated British population of one species or subspecies of waterbird, and in Northern Ireland important in an all-Ireland context if it holds 1% or more of the estimated all-Ireland population.

The 1% thresholds for British, all-Ireland and international waterbird populations, where known, are listed in Table A2. Thus, any site regularly supporting at least this number of birds potentially qualifies for designation under national legislation, or the EC Bird's Directive or Ramsar Convention. The international population for each species and sub-species is also specified in the table. However, it should be noted that, where 1% of the national population is less than 50 birds, 50 is normally used as a minimum qualifying threshold for the designation of sites of national or international importance.

1% thresholds have not been derived for introduced species since, for these species, protected sites (e.g. SSSIs) would not be identified on the basis of numbers for these birds.

Sources of qualifying levels represent the most up-to-date figures following recent reviews: for British wildfowl see Kirby (1995); for British waders see Cayford & Waters (1996); for all-Ireland importance for divers see Danielsen *et al.* (1993) and for other waterbirds see Whilde (in prep.) cited in Way *et al.* (1993). International criteria follow Smit & Piersma (1989) or Rose & Scott (1997).

It was agreed at the meeting of the Ramsar Convention in Brisbane that population estimates will be reviewed by Wetlands International every three years and 1% thresholds revised every nine years (Rose & Stroud 1994; Ramsar Resolution VI.4).

During the preparation of this report, revised international population estimates were published (Wetlands International 2002). Papers updating the national population estimates for wildfowl (Kershaw & Cranswick, in press) and waders (Rehfisch *et al.*, in press) were also finalised. These updated estimates will be used in the 2001–02 annual report.

Table A2. 1% thresholds for national and international importance

	Great Britain	all-Ireland	International	Population
Red-throated Diver	50	*10	750	Europe/Greenland
Black-throated Diver	*7	*1	1,200	Europe/W Siberia
Great Northern Diver	*30	?	50	Europe
Little Grebe	*30	?	?	W Palaearctic
Great Crested Grebe	100	*30	?	NW Europe
Red-necked Grebe	*1	?	150	NW Europe
Slavonian Grebe	*4	?	50	NW Europe
Black-necked Grebe	*1	?	1,000	W Palaearctic
Cormorant	130	?	1,200	NW Europe
Little Egret	?	?	1,250	W Mediterranean
Grey Heron	?	?	4,500	Europe/N Africa
Mute Swan	260	55	2,400	NW Europe
Bewick's Swan	70	*25	170	W Siberia/NW Europe
Whooper Swan	55	100	160	Iceland/UK/Ireland
Bean Goose	*4	*+	800	NE & NW Europe
Pink-footed Goose: Iceland/Greenland	1,900	*+	2,250	E Greenland/Iceland/UK
European White-fronted Goose	60	*+	6,000	NW Siberia/NE & NW Europe
Greenland White-fronted Goose	140	140	300	Greenland/Ireland/UK
Greylag Goose: Iceland	1,000	*40	1,000	Iceland/UK/Ireland
Hebrides/N Scotland	50	n/a	50	NW Scotland
Barnacle Goose: Greenland	270	75	320	E Greenland/ Ireland/Scotland
Svalbard	120	*+	120	Svalbard/SW Scotland
Dark-bellied Brent Goose	1,000	*+	3,000	bernicla

	Great Britain	all-Ireland	International	Population
Light-bellied Brent Goose: Canada	*+	200	200	Canada/Ireland
Svalbard	*25	*+	50	Svalbard/Denmark/UK
Shelduck	750	70	3,000	NW Europe
Wigeon	2,800	1,250	12,500	NW Europe
Gadwall	80	*+	300	NW Europe
Teal	1,400	650	4,000	NW Europe
Mallard	5,000	500	**20,000	NW Europe
Pintail	280	60	600	NW Europe
Garganey	*+	*+	**20,000	Europe/W Africa
Shoveler	100	65	400	NW Europe/Central Europe
Red-crested Pochard	*+	*+	250	C & SW Europe/W Mediterranean
Pochard	440	400	3,500	NW Europe
Tufted Duck	600	400	10,000	NW Europe
Scaup	110	*30	3,100	NW Europe
Eider	750	*20	**20,000	Europe
Long-tailed Duck	230	*+	**20,000	Iceland/Greenland/ NW Europe
Common Scoter	275	*40	16,000	W Siberia/W Europe/ NW Africa
Velvet Scoter	*30	*+	10,000	W Siberia/NW Europe
Goldeneye	170	110	3,000	NW & Central Europe
Smew	*2	*+	250	NW & Central Europe
Red-breasted Merganser	100	*20	1,250	NW & Central Europe
Goosander	90	*+	2,000	NW & Central Europe
Coot	1,100	250	15,000	NW Europe
Oystercatcher	3,600	500	9,000	Europe/W Africa (win)
Avocet	*10	*+	700	Europe/NW Africa (bre)
Little Ringed Plover	?	?	?	Europe/W Africa
Ringed Plover	290	125	500	Europe/NW Africa (win)
passage	300			
Golden Plover	2,500	2,000	18,000	NW Europe (bre)
Grey Plover	430	*40	1,500	E Atlantic
Lapwing	**20,000	2,500	**20,000	Europe/W Africa
Knot C. c. islandica	2,900	375	3,500	W Europe/Canada
C. c. canutus			5,000	W Africa/W Siberia
Sanderling	230	*35	1,000	E Atlantic
passage	300			
Little Stint	?	?	2,100	W Africa/Europe
Curlew Sandpiper	?	?	4,500	W Africa/SW Europe(win)
Purple Sandpiper	210	*10	500	E Atlantic
Dunlin C. a. arctica			150	Greenland (bre)
C. a. schinzii (Icelandic)			8,000	Iceland/Greenland (bre)
C. a. schinzii (temperate)			200	UK/Ireland/Baltic
C. a. alpina	5,300	1,250	14,000	Europe (bre)
passage	2,000			
Ruff	*7	*+	10,000	W Africa (win)
Jack Snipe	?	250	?	Europe/W Africa (win)
Snipe	?	?	10,000	Europe/W Africa (bre)
Woodcock	?	?	**20,000	Africa/Europe
Black-tailed Godwit	70	90	700	Iceland (bre)
Bar-tailed Godwit	530	175	1,000	W Europe (win)
Whimbrel	*+	*+	6,500	Europe/W Africa (win)
passage	50			
Curlew	1,200	875	3,500	Europe/NW Africa
Spotted Redshank	*+	*+	1,500	Europe/W Africa
Redshank T. t. totanus	1,100	245	1,500	Europe/W Africa (win)
T. t. robusta	1,100		1,500	NW Europe (win)
passage	1,200			
Greenshank	*+	*9	3,000	Europe/W Africa
Green Sandpiper	?	?	?	Europe (bre)
Common Sandpiper	?	?	?	Europe (bre)
Turnstone	640	225	700	Europe (win)

	Great Britain	**all-Ireland**	**International**	**Population**
Little Gull	?	?	750	Cent/E Europe (bre)
Black-headed Gull	?	?	**20,000	NW Europe
Common Gull	?	?	16,000	NW Europe
Lesser Black-backed Gull	?	?	4,500	W Europe
Herring Gull	?	?	13,000	W Europe/Iceland
Great Black-backed Gull	?	?	4,800	W Atlantic
Kittiwake	?	?	**20,000	E Atlantic
Sandwich Tern	?	?	1,500	W Europe/W Africa
Common Tern	?	?	6,000	N/E Europe
Little Tern	?	?	340	E Atlantic
Black Tern	?	?	2,000	Europe/Asia

?   *Population size not accurately known*

+   *Population too small for meaningful figure to be obtained*

*   *Where 1% of the British or all-Ireland wintering population is less than 50 birds, 50 is normally used as a minimum qualifying level for national or all-Ireland importance respectively*

**   *A site regularly holding more than 20,000 waterbirds qualifies as internationally important by virtue of absolute numbers*

APPENDIX 3. ANALYSES

This appendix provides additional detail about the analyses used in this report to that presented in *Analyses* and lists the index values used to produce the graphs of annual and monthly indices in the species accounts.

Data availability

The count scheme first begun in 1947 has developed considerably over time (see Cranswick *et al.* 1997). In particular, coverage of species and area has expanded during this time. The first year for which data for certain species or areas are available for use in analyses are given below:

Table A3. First year of availability of WeBS Core Count data for different species and areas

Wildfowl in GB	1960 on computer (collected since 1947)
Waders in UK	1969–70
Great Crested Grebe	1982–83
Coot	1982–83
Little Grebe	1985–86
Cormorant	1986–87
Wildfowl in Northern Ireland	1986–87
All other species (rare grebes, divers, rarities, gulls, terns)	1993–94

National totals for goose populations

Figures presented in Tables 1 & 2 and in Appendices 4–9 for total counts of the various goose populations are derived initially from WeBS Core Counts, but are replaced by results of dedicated censuses (see *Survey Methods, Analyses* and *Coverage* for appropriate references, methods and dates) where these provide better counts. Several goose populations are identified according to location (and totals derived by summing counts from particular WeBS regions) where they cannot be separated in the field by appearance.

Bean Goose	WeBS Core Counts in all months
Pink-footed Goose	October and November counts replaced by summed counts from the co-ordinated national censuses
European White-fronted Goose	WeBS Core Counts in all months
Greenland White-fronted Goose	November and March counts replaced by summed counts from the co-ordinated late autumn and late spring international censuses, respectively
Greylag Goose: Iceland	WeBS Core Counts from all WeBS regions in Scotland except those on the west coast (see NW Scotland population) plus Northumberland and North Cumbria. October and November counts replaced by summed counts from the co-ordinated national censuses.
NW Scotland	WeBS Core Counts from WeBS regions Islay/Jura/Colonsay, Mull/Lismore/Coll/Tiree, Skye, Highland Southwest and North and South Outer Hebrides. August and February counts replaced by summed counts from co-ordinated censuses of Outer Hebrides. August 1997 count replaced by total from full national survey
naturalised	WeBS Core Counts for all sites in Wales and England, except for Northumberland and North Cumbria

Note that Icelandic and NW Scotland populations overlap in WeBS regions Orkney and North Highland. NW Scotland birds counted by WeBS in these regions will be included Icelandic population totals. Note also that up to 2,340 naturalised birds occur in Scotland (Delany 1993) and others in Northumberland and North Cumbria which are therefore incorrectly included in totals of Icelandic birds in Appendices 4–9

Canada Goose	WeBS Core Counts in all months
Barnacle Goose: Greenland	WeBS Core Counts from all WeBS regions on Scottish west coast, plus Shetland and Orkney. November and March counts replaced by summed counts from the co-ordinated late autumn and late spring censuses in Argyll plus the monthly maximum count from Hoy, Orkney.

Barnacle Goose: Svalbard	WeBS Core Counts from WeBS regions Dumfries & Galloway, North Cumbria, Northumberland, Borders, Lothians, Central, Fife, Perth & Kinross, Angus, Grampian, Moray and SE Highland. Dumfries & Galloway and North Cumbria WeBS Core Counts replaced by Solway-wide counts and censuses between October and March.
naturalised	WeBS Core Counts for all WeBS regions in Wales and England, except for Northumberland and North Cumbria
Dark-bellied Brent Goose	WeBS Core Counts, plus additional counts of inland areas in January and February
Light-bellied Brent Goose: Canada	WeBS Core Counts for sites in Northern Ireland, Wales and WeBS regions Shetland, Orkney, Highland North, Western Isles, Skye, Highland Southwest, Islay/Jura/Colonsay, Argyll West Mainland, Mull/Lismore/Coll/Tiree, Dumbarton/SE Argyll, Renfrew, Lanarkshire/Strathkelvin, Ayrshire & Arran, Dumfries & Galloway West, Cornwall, Devon and the Channel Islands. October count in Northern Ireland replaced by counts in Northern Ireland made during all-Ireland census.
Svalbard	WeBS Core Counts from regions not used to compile Canada population totals (see above)

Annual Indices

Underhill index values are derived from sites where at least 50% of the maximum possible number of counts, bearing in mind that different months are used for different species, were complete. Index values provided extend back to 1966–67 for wildfowl and 1971–72 for waders, representing the first years in which coverage was deemed sufficient for data to be included in the calculation of the index. A number of species were only first included in WeBS in the 1980s, whilst counts of wildfowl in Northern Ireland only began in earnest in 1985–86.

Underhill (1989) recommends that, where possible, the index is based on counts from more than one month. The months chosen for each species are given below. The most appropriate grouping of months on which to base the annual index for waders is December, January and February, the period when the wintering population in Britain and Northern Ireland is most stable (Prys-Jones *et al.* 1994). However, the peak abundance of different wildfowl occur in different months according to species, and thus different months and different numbers of months were selected for each (Kirby *et al.* 1995).

The selection of months for calculating indices for wildfowl and their allies was made by first calculating monthly index values for all months September to March, and selecting that with the highest index value and any adjacent months with overlapping consistency intervals. Data from all years from 1966–67 onwards were used for calculating the index for each of these species, as recommended in Kirby *et al.* (1995), or from the years in which data were first available for species added to the scheme subsequently (see above). Caution is urged in particular regarding the first few years' index values for these species only recently included in the scheme; missing counts may have been incorrectly recorded as nil counts, giving rise to anomalous index values. The parameters used for indexing each species follow Kirby *et al.* (1995).

Due to more stable populations of waders during the winter, the months December to February are chosen for calculation of index values for all waders for which there are suitable data. Due to the small number of sites in Northern Ireland, data are combined for analysis at the UK level.

Table A5. Months used in calculating indices for wildfowl species in Great Britain and Northern Ireland (indicated using the first letter of the months September to March)

Species	GB	NI	Species	GB	NI
Little Grebe	SO	SON	Shelduck	JF	DJFM
Great Crested Grebe	SON	SONDJFM	Wigeon	J	SONDJFM
Cormorant	SONDJFM	SOND	Gadwall	SONDJFM	SONDJ
Mute Swan	SONDJFM	SONDJ	Teal D	DJ	
Bewick's Swan	JF	NDJF	Mallard	D	SO
Whooper Swan	ND	ONDJFM	Pintail	ONDJ	ONDJFM
Pink-footed Goose	O or N	-	Shoveler	SO	SONDJFM
European Whitefront	JF	-	Pochard	NDJ	NDJF
Greenland Whitefront	N or M	N or M	Tufted Duck	NDJF	ONDJFM
Greylag Goose: Icelandic	O or N	-	Goldeneye	F	DJFM
naturalised	S	-	Red-breasted Merganser	ONDJFM	SONDJFM
Canada Goose	S	-	Goosander	DJF	-
Barnacle Goose: Svalbard	any month	-	Ruddy Duck	SONDJFM	-
Dark-bellied Brent	DJF	-	Coot	SONDJ	SONDJFM
Light-bellied Brent	-	SONDJFM			

Table A6. Great Britain annual index values for wildfowl

Year	LG	GG	CA	MS	BS	WS	PG	EW	NW	JI	JE	CG	PB	DB	SU	WN	GA	T.	MA	PT	SV	PO	TU	GN	RM	GD	RY	CO
1966-67				61	52	45	31	305		74	3	7	16	25	76	58	4	168	37	46	129	64	79	40	73	0		72
1967-68				60	54	26	27	180		65	2	16	31	20	86	67	4	144	20	51	137	69	68	35	79	2		79
1968-69				55	42	29	27	284		75	1	18	26	34	82	57	6	150	51	50	119	75	85	69	110	1		82
1969-70				55	41	43	30	701		77	2	15	17	35	117	60	5	121	57	57	75	58	74	85	121			81
1970-71				57	90	30	30	871		80	2	16	29	100	62	55	11	152	83	49	104	80	58	80	90			85
1971-72				53	39	44	27	284		79	3	13	16	48	105	55	13	147	78	72	126	58	100	58	103			86
1972-73				53	64	44	28	180		90	5	13	19	34	91	55	11	102	75	42	142	98	54	100	81			74
1973-74				55	33	33	34	524		94	4	21	19	56	93	56	10	135	176	86	136	128	61	128	178	3		75
1974-75				50	49	37	37	144		85	4	22	43	50	107	50	13	153	147	153	150	79	123	79	153	3		75
1975-76				50	69	40	30	292		78	4	17	25	61	99	47	12	129	145	145	102	153	70	123	110	5		77
1976-77				48	102	31	29	374	69	69	6	26	30	55	61	13	149	133	145	54	153	70	97	70	110			87
1977-78				48	116	46	29	259	82	9	28	29	45	20	13	156	79	68	84	132	116	76	87	87	10			89
1978-79				51	121	35	32	458	94	9	34	37	19	72	84	141	115	83	79	132	159	85	87	159	10			82
1979-80				52	125	50	33	257	100	10	36	32	55	142	84	142	141	115	83	109	92	87	130	176			86
1980-81			55	51	159	45	39	306	118	11	12	40	72	129	113	23	70	82	144	149	54	112	85	72	200	27		85
1981-82		55	57	158	32	37	367	99	15	43	35	79	142	55	31	77	141	157	92	76	112	72	92	193	24		89
1982-83		62	57	136	51	37	310	101	18	50	36	105	107	68	34	104	141	151	170	84	112	103	103	193			74
1983-84		74	51	163	39	42	271	39	21	47	35	39	107	57	37	87	144	163	171	81	120	76	94	151			79
1984-85		74	50	243	39	35	381	34	28	58	44	107	115	36	34	72	149	138	209	87	115	74	104	140	40		82
1985-86	14	63	53	209	55	53	352	79	29	62	44	112	80	40	74	129	160	171	81	115	88	80	147	40		79
1986-87	23	62	56	273	63	56	331	132	28	66	88	128	43	72	145	107	176	86	116	93	80	162	207	42		78
1987-88	21	64	65	124	57	71	409	126	35	48	68	135	50	65	171	107	70	83	132	89	102	225	78		74
1988-89	55	70	78	69	365	73	60	134	37	51	68	114	57	86	151	70	83	104	85	87	134	232	46		86
1989-90	61	83	80	74	166	79	75	304	68	39	67	64	68	55	96	143	151	70	96	82	141	222	52		85
1990-91	65	83	92	83	250	89	79	253	103	41	49	64	61	95	137	151	151	83	110	82	89	113	141	54		75
1991-92	59	81	84	79	267	61	96	351	141	42	72	84	90	132	137	176	110	102	82	72	112	183	52		75
1992-93	57	90	83	83	267	60	82	86	121	56	51	56	79	132	157	103	110	105	87	106	112	155	55		77
1993-94	71	87	96	77	181	52	93	299	122	45	74	56	114	130	114	79	114	110	93	86	104	112	152	52		87
1994-95	84	89	103	87	159	52	107	299	106	41	79	60	126	57	119	82	118	104	87	105	129	150	55		87
1995-96	102	88	104	89	249	55	83	229	102	106	73	95	127	94	81	76	118	110	97	105	97	137	231	64		89
1996-97	85	95	92	92	228	77	97	266	102	102	73	95	131	84	108	95	125	134	108	106	97	122	287	64		91
1997-98	83	88	91	95	132	61	97	259	97	70	75	110	104	97	113	89	138	177	85		91
1998-99	82	86	89	100	198	93	95	189	105	103	75	93	110	114	81	93	111	102	141	141	83	108	109	169	81		90
1999-00	102	89	100	105	229	114	88	204	98	94	82	85	108	103	99	109	110	105	107	107	94	98	132	215	99	95
2000-01	100	100	100	100	100	100	100	100	100	100	100	100	100	100	100	100	100	100	100	100	100	100	100	100	100	100	100	100

Wildfowl species codes

LG	Little Grebe	MS	Mute Swan	NW	Greenland Whitefront	PB	Light-bellied Brent	MA	Mallard
GG	Great Crested Grebe	BS	Bewick's Swan	II	Icelandic Greylag Goose	SU	Shelduck	PT	Pintail
CA	Cormorant	WS	Whooper Swan	IE	Naturalised Greylag	WN	Wigeon	SV	Shoveler
		PG	Pink-footed Goose	CG	Canada Goose	GA	Gadwall	PO	Pochard
		EW	European Whitefront	DB	Dark-bellied Brent	T.	Teal	TU	Tufted Duck
						GN	Goldeneye		
						RM	Red-breasted		
						GD	Goosander		
						RY	Ruddy Duck		
						CO	Coot		

Table A7. Northern Ireland annual index values for wildfowl

Year	LG	GG	CA	MS	BS	WS	PB	SU	WN	GA	T.	MA	PT	SV	PO	TU	GN	RM	CO
1986–87	41	52	3	63	2066	120	40	71	129	55	68	113	194	175	95	38	118	83	65
1987–88	17	65	35	70	3058	161	77	61	136	80	111	82	91	115	101	73	135	130	78
1988–89	97	80	79	77	2935	164	73	115	172	82	109	100	133	132	144	77	112	147	74
1989–90	99	65	92	85	5237	126	75	72	122	120	118	118	72	112	131	82	104	140	99
1990–91	76	58	66	79	5751	147	90	86	154	94	137	111	115	96	133	77	133	135	91
1991–92	84	66	54	84	2861	135	93	71	143	108	103	110	145	123	142	87	144	110	90
1992–93	96	80	78	90	1383	138	67	60	110	128	71	93	110	90	103	80	126	143	100
1993–94	102	50	72	79	2345	119	61	80	88	104	73	103	108	147	90	82	87	106	54
1994–95	121	112	75	97	767	133	74	89	99	137	76	114	72	119	87	81	93	131	86
1995–96	129	99	84	102	1112	115	73	103	89	99	82	140	79	122	123	97	96	149	120
1996–97	92	83	74	80	1937	143	76	96	100	101	88	98	111	110	94	79	76	111	84
1997–98	87	119	110	97	589	125	86	111	118	70	100	96	114	87	86	70	63	136	87
1998–99	83	75	140	109	194	105	90	111	96	95	107	111	157	100	86	65	91	117	86
1999–00	94	94	130	107	116	122	84	107	141	77	98	94	143	124	110	75	78	109	112
2000–01	100	100	100	100	100	100	100	100	100	100	100	100	100	100	100	100	100	100	100

Table A8. UK annual index values for waders

Year	AV	BA	BW	CU	DN	GV	KN	OC	RK	RP	SS	TT
1969–70	3	161	21	50	103	25	144	82	70	116	127	103
1970–71	4	146	18	59	101	17	118	69	62	97	78	88
1971–72	4	134	24	72	122	19	144	75	90	95	113	112
1972–73	3	125	38	67	138	22	113	73	92	117	101	101
1973–74	4	147	29	77	163	31	113	77	95	141	122	105
1974–75	3	117	40	93	154	33	87	78	102	134	143	99
1975–76	3	129	34	85	159	32	86	100	103	150	128	118
1976–77	1	157	35	73	162	36	87	96	93	126	92	123
1977–78	4	125	37	64	122	25	58	87	80	125	103	119
1978–79	3	143	38	64	127	34	71	85	85	118	128	117
1979–80	3	169	39	80	127	42	82	95	90	121	141	116
1980–81	2	136	37	72	123	54	90	102	83	114	105	103
1981–82	8	179	31	71	110	44	79	100	74	97	87	101
1982–83	8	151	41	73	105	46	89	92	73	111	101	101
1983–84	6	136	46	71	111	51	81	95	80	115	96	126
1984–85	12	168	40	74	100	59	84	97	82	120	90	126
1985–86	13	170	56	79	104	65	107	111	88	123	105	149
1986–87	10	172	42	85	91	67	91	107	86	124	100	139
1987–88	15	142	49	91	96	89	97	116	109	128	113	162
1988–89	23	138	66	85	117	95	101	113	107	163	111	137
1989–90	33	135	74	89	121	89	96	111	109	147	91	145
1990–91	33	163	61	82	144	97	97	118	92	135	98	133
1991–92	36	131	72	97	138	103	101	108	100	124	118	146
1992–93	53	131	70	100	115	95	108	105	93	131	98	127
1993–94	57	118	90	88	119	109	87	96	94	127	75	124
1994–95	66	115	98	109	131	131	93	101	109	129	108	127
1995–96	62	152	92	80	120	114	88	93	87	132	84	108
1996–97	58	211	114	84	152	132	102	119	95	115	152	108
1997–98	88	130	108	105	122	104	92	99	102	118	98	100
1998–99	92	139	108	91	119	102	85	99	99	103	115	104
1999–00	109	120	110	102	89	88	71	100	96	90	108	95
2000–01	100	100	100	100	100	100	100	100	100	100	100	100

Wader species codes

OC	Oystercatcher	DN	Dunlin
AV	Avocet	BW	Black-tailed Godwit
RP	Ringed Plover	BA	Bar-tailed Godwit
GV	Grey Plover	CU	Curlew
KN	Knot	RK	Redshank
SS	Sanderling	TT	Turnstone

Table A9. Great Britain monthly index values for wildfowl 2000–01.

	Sep	Oct	Nov	Dec	Jan	Feb	Mar
LG	100.0	92.5	78.4	70.8	74.4	57.0	n/a
GG	100.0	98.7	87.2	82.2	80.9	72.4	n/a
CA	100.0	93.6	81.6	70.6	72.8	64.6	n/a
BS	0.0	3.7	41.7	84.0	100.0	34.1	n/a
WS	0.8	58.7	82.6	91.7	100.0	94.2	n/a
EW	0.2	0.4	7.0	23.7	100.0	48.9	n/a
DB	3.3	42.7	71.1	71.2	100.0	90.8	n/a
SU	64.4	71.2	87.1	85.4	100.0	94.5	n/a
WN	27.3	78.0	73.8	92.4	100.0	79.8	n/a
GA	66.3	86.4	79.1	81.4	100.0	77.0	n/a
T.	58.1	91.7	92.6	100.0	96.7	94.9	n/a
MA	91.1	92.0	92.9	94.3	100.0	69.4	n/a
PT	36.8	57.6	100.0	89.4	81.3	74.8	n/a
SV	81.1	100.0	96.3	99.0	90.8	81.7	n/a
PO	29.9	58.7	81.3	93.5	100.0	85.4	n/a
TU	73.7	85.3	88.6	92.3	100.0	82.0	n/a
GN	1.2	4.9	40.7	65.7	91.2	100.0	n/a
GD	42.3	50.9	58.0	65.6	100.0	93.8	n/a
CO	99.1	100.0	94.9	87.4	83.2	63.6	n/a

Table A10. Northern Ireland monthly index values for wildfowl in 2000–01.

	Sep	Oct	Nov	Dec	Jan	Feb	Mar
LG	100.0	74.5	99.8	88.2	69.3	59.3	n/a
GG	100.0	59.5	74.6	76.3	54.4	69.0	n/a
CA	100.0	67.4	47.1	42.5	29.2	39.3	n/a
BS	0.0	100.0	0.0	2.9	2.0	24.5	n/a
WS	1.3	64.0	53.3	100.0	58.5	86.6	n/a
PB	32.3	91.9	100.0	51.4	20.3	14.7	n/a
SU	1.7	12.2	40.7	83.9	100.0	65.1	n/a
WN	14.9	100.0	79.2	38.3	40.9	26.5	n/a
GA	90.7	100.0	72.9	53.7	61.2	55.6	n/a
T.	100.0	50.0	51.8	81.9	96.6	55.2	n/a
MA	100.0	64.6	52.4	52.6	54.7	32.0	n/a
PT	4.0	4.0	27.9	29.8	78.8	100.0	n/a
SV	32.2	49.5	83.2	77.2	100.0	34.7	n/a
PO	5.1	11.6	54.8	100.0	65.8	41.7	n/a
TU	16.5	66.5	86.1	100.0	69.9	65.1	n/a
SP	0.3	1.5	41.4	70.5	86.4	100.0	n/a
GN	0.7	5.4	84.0	78.6	83.6	100.0	n/a
CO	89.5	100.0	85.7	69.3	75.2	43.6	n/a

APPENDIX 4. TOTAL NUMBERS OF WATERBIRDS RECORDED BY WeBS IN ENGLAND, 2000–01

	Apr	May	Jun	Jul	Aug	Sep	Oct	Nov	Dec	Jan	Feb	Mar
Sectors	*1,065*	*964*	*906*	*911*	*973*	*1,542*	*1,709*	*1,741*	*1,755*	*1,741*	*1,740*	*101*
Sites	*606*	*578*	*556*	*570*	*571*	*908*	*961*	*963*	*986*	*949*	*931*	*87*
Red-throated Diver	29	3	0	0	1	81	65	80	154	205	274	0
Black-throated Diver	0	0	0	0	0	0	1	1	19	31	36	31
Great Northern Diver	2	2	0	0	0	2	1	14	42	56	38	6
Unidentifed diver	0	0	0	3	0	0	1	0	0	0	0	0
Little Grebe	1,439	911	888	1,243	2,112	3,692	3,657	3,104	2,708	2,838	2,149	186
Great Crested Grebe	3,968	3,354	3,378	4,608	5,561	8,923	9,124	7,741	6,107	6,361	6,231	274
Red-necked Grebe	6	1	1	1	1	3	6	8	11	10	7	1
Slavonian Grebe	8	0	4	3	6	6	3	21	28	63	33	4
Black-necked Grebe	36	11	39	27	23	36	40	35	50	32	34	0
Cormorant	5,485	4,026	3,630	5,435	7,214	12,369	11,993	10,866	8,745	10,081	8,696	651
Bittern	0	2	1	0	1	2	7	7	14	13	8	1
Squacco Heron	0	0	1	0	0	0	0	0	0	0	0	0
Cattle Egret	0	0	0	0	1	1	1	0	0	0	0	0
Little Egret	326	153	175	569	1,071	1,331	1,119	668	597	545	607	42
Great White Egret	0	0	0	0	1	1	1	0	0	0	0	0
Grey Heron	1,385	1,307	1,721	1,915	2,558	3,208	3,163	2,325	2,108	2,288	2,173	202
Purple Heron	0	0	0	1	1	0	0	0	0	0	0	0
White Stork	0	0	0	2	3	2	2	2	2	0	2	0
Spoonbill	2	5	8	9	7	8	12	12	14	2	9	0
Fulvous Whistling Duck	1	0	0	0	0	0	0	0	0	0	0	0
Mute Swan	7,801	7,443	8,352	9,923	10,094	14,353	15,624	14,228	13,012	13,301	11,375	757
Black Swan	21	20	23	23	38	50	50	43	34	26	33	1
Bewick's Swan	6	3	0	0	0	3	69	146	893	2,450	1,653	0
Whooper Swan	137	10	16	14	11	19	1,275	1,720	2,040	1,861	1,900	1,035
hybrid Cygnus	0	2	1	0	0	1	0	0	0	0	1	0
Swan Goose	14	14	18	19	20	40	21	32	42	17	35	0
Bean Goose	0	2	2	0	0	1	0	30	193	276	51	0
Taiga Bean Goose	0	0	0	0	0	2	4	0	0	0	0	0
Pink-footed Goose	2,678	329	9	10	6	85	18,516	65,976	44,285	51,565	26,392	3
White-fronted Goose	0	0	0	0	0	0	0	2	0	0	5	0
European Whitefront	1	4	17	0	4	7	10	162	542	2,290	1,120	1
Greenland Whitefront	0	0	0	0	0	0	0	1	3	1	7	0
Lesser Whitefront	0	0	1	1	0	0	0	0	0	0	2	0
Greylag Goose (Ice.)	157	0	0	0	0	0	1,511	2,613	4,449	2,523	3,984	61
Greylag Goose (natur.)	5,414	4,588	10,573	10,101	10,101	21,172	18,629	20,822	19,009	18,161	11,331	395
Bar-headed Goose	6	9	17	14	10	11	26	13	17	8	6	0
Snow Goose	15	11	27	10	16	43	28	39	55	18	14	2
Ross's Goose	0	0	0	0	0	0	1	1	1	1	0	0
Emperor Goose	2	1	1	1	4	5	2	2	5	2	2	0
Canada Goose	13,930	11,071	26,696	28,151	32,608	49,926	38,808	41,849	41,220	41,548	30,881	1,956
Barnacle Goose (Sval.)	1,057	5,008	0	0	0	68	12,620	7,041	3,577	5,410	7,461	5
Barnacle Goose (natur.)	129	80	164	187	311	198	421	686	884	649	557	12
Brent Goose	0	0	0	0	0	0	1,175	400	0	0	0	0
Dark-bellied Brent	14,691	10,233	86	72	63	3,083	39,324	64,821	65,292	92,317	83,833	1,615
Black Brant	0	0	0	0	0	0	1	0	0	3	4	0
Light-bellied Brent (Sval.)	13	7	0	1	1	3,122	2,131	3,196	1,581	1,290	321	0
Light-bellied Brent (Can.)	1	1	0	1	1	14	1	1	11	13	4	0
Red-breasted Goose	0	0	0	1	0	1	1	0	0	0	1	0
Egyptian Goose	112	114	258	181	315	329	233	183	161	129	160	2
hybrid goose	50	40	45	60	45	105	71	92	104	102	103	5
feral/domestic goose	138	128	141	148	150	311	325	333	343	266	301	17
unidentified goose	0	0	0	0	0	4	250	0	0	9	0	0
Ruddy Shelduck	6	4	3	7	10	7	4	4	2	3	6	2
Cape Shelduck	0	0	0	0	0	0	1	0	1	1	1	0
Australian Shelduck	0	0	0	0	0	1	0	0	0	0	0	0
Shelduck	24,708	15,663	15,092	21,255	21,351	32,254	34,198	42,208	41,126	51,597	47,083	1,852
hybrid Shelduck	0	0	0	0	0	1	0	0	1	1	1	0
Muscovy Duck	28	10	12	16	9	20	72	65	68	68	73	43
Wood Duck	2	2	2	1	1	7	10	6	5	8	4	0
Mandarin	109	95	122	114	105	357	400	315	487	478	428	7

	Apr	May	Jun	Jul	Aug	Sep	Oct	Nov	Dec	Jan	Feb	Mar
Wigeon	17,589	375	146	221	824	63,748	190,902	209,817	271,876	312,824	244,504	7,149
American Wigeon	1	1	1	1	1	0	1	0	0	0	1	0
Chiloe Wigeon	0	0	0	2	0	0	0	0	2	0	1	0
Gadwall	2,623	1,676	2,113	3,027	3,849	9,393	12,349	10,952	10,802	13,251	10,398	654
Teal	12,620	468	633	1,176	7,828	62,034	88,514	99,793	109,599	119,350	111,533	4,885
Green-winged Teal	1	0	0	0	0	0	1	1	3	4	3	0
Speckled Teal	0	0	0	0	0	4	2	1	2	0	2	0
Mallard	23,342	19,991	28,629	37,294	57,423	94,604	99,975	101,208	101,283	107,166	70,881	4,320
Black Duck	0	0	0	0	1	1	1	0	0	0	0	0
Chestnut Teal	0	0	0	0	0	0	0	0	0	0	1	0
Pintail	557	30	8	18	28	5,246	7,890	15,166	14,681	13,577	14,172	231
Yellow-billed Pintail	0	0	0	0	1	0	0	0	0	0	0	0
Bahama Pintail	2	2	1	1	0	2	0	0	1	0	0	0
Red-billed Teal	0	1	0	0	1	1	0	0	0	0	0	0
Garganey	30	45	25	41	47	30	5	4	1	0	0	0
Blue-winged Teal	1	1	0	0	2	1	0	0	1	0	0	0
Shoveler	2,696	642	434	662	2,634	7,330	9,045	9,823	9,945	9,493	8,472	764
Ringed Teal	0	0	0	1	0	2	0	0	0	0	0	0
Red-crested Pochard	14	6	5	7	8	33	55	70	53	106	67	0
Rosybill	0	0	0	0	0	0	1	1	0	0	1	0
Pochard	1,503	780	1,563	3,045	7,993	8,026	16,291	23,323	27,446	30,315	28,019	1,512
Ring-necked Duck	2	0	2	0	0	0	0	1	3	2	1	0
Ferruginous Duck	0	0	0	0	0	2	1	0	4	4	1	0
New Zealand Scaup	0	0	0	0	0	0	1	1	0	0	0	0
Tufted Duck	20,204	10,557	9,885	21,627	29,648	33,901	38,662	40,952	41,824	46,339	37,218	2,158
Scaup	268	4	2	4	8	72	45	106	156	764	153	0
Lesser Scaup	1	2	0	0	0	0	0	1	0	0	0	0
Eider	6,491	4,365	5,075	6,921	4,666	6,213	7,661	6,148	6,324	4,874	3,711	11
Long-tailed Duck	12	1	0	3	0	0	1	19	23	24	44	1
Common Scoter	1,991	95	3,027	403	138	768	383	1,486	1,983	3,391	347	18
Velvet Scoter	3	0	0	0	0	0	1	4	0	1	1	3
Goldeneye	2,145	74	6	67	27	52	165	2,327	4,521	6,331	6,566	324
Smew	3	0	0	0	0	1	2	7	71	212	178	7
Red-breasted Merganser	1,102	254	244	208	190	300	545	1,475	1,665	2,021	1,966	102
Goosander	183	102	59	107	202	204	396	723	996	1,505	1,544	33
Ruddy Duck	1,421	643	548	684	1,254	2,280	3,378	2,867	2,359	3,693	3,219	81
Argentine Blue-bill	0	0	0	0	0	1	0	0	0	0	0	0
feral/hybrid Mallard type	214	229	265	307	206	423	448	381	419	347	335	40
hybrid Anas	2	1	4	4	0	3	16	12	10	4	5	1
hybrid Aythya	2	1	1	2	1	4	2	2	11	10	6	0
unidentified duck	6	0	4	0	2	14	36	0	0	11	10	0
Water Rail	111	80	54	42	58	119	274	292	404	299	216	30
Spotted Crake	0	0	0	0	0	4	2	0	0	0	0	0
Moorhen	5,357	3,655	3,537	4,897	6,720	11,031	11,793	10,064	10,819	9,840	9,333	1,054
Coot	23,978	13,495	20,811	38,824	55,989	94,551	99,715	97,141	86,774	86,049	63,709	2,505
Crane	3	0	0	0	0	0	0	0	0	0	0	0
Oystercatcher	51,024	36,543	24,165	54,783	106,981	142,522	140,734	148,219	129,139	147,096	149,554	2,914
Black-winged Stilt	1	0	0	0	1	1	1	1	1	1	0	1
Avocet	1,463	1,057	911	1,595	917	1,931	1,423	3,185	3,060	4,564	3,978	437
Stone-curlew	0	0	0	0	1	0	0	0	0	0	0	0
Little Ringed Plover	231	209	211	190	77	18	0	0	0	2	0	4
Ringed Plover	3,320	9,688	1,201	1,684	14,897	12,628	8,252	6,215	5,597	6,020	5,214	552
Kentish Plover	1	0	0	0	0	0	0	0	0	0	0	0
Dotterel	0	0	0	0	1	0	0	0	0	0	0	0
Pacific Golden Plover	0	0	0	1	0	0	0	0	0	0	0	0
Golden Plover	11,475	705	76	4,473	30,932	51,527	101,151	132,514	93,817	95,673	141,132	6,405
Grey Plover	27,148	38,432	3,410	2,463	24,961	29,459	31,089	35,370	26,419	41,327	50,125	671
Unidentified wader	10	2	0	3	0	0	40	0	0	0	0	0
Sociable Plover	0	0	0	0	0	0	0	1	1	0	0	0
Lapwing	5,616	4,389	9,114	23,496	50,686	96,749	147,703	229,239	233,019	240,649	327,073	4,137
Knot	98,908	28,196	12,469	29,094	73,779	163,493	172,358	290,527	207,792	287,076	230,257	2,885
Sanderling	7,379	13,782	1,728	1,010	9,199	7,512	6,220	5,992	4,521	6,225	6,843	188
Semipalmated Sandpiper	0	0	0	0	1	0	0	0	0	0	0	0
Little Stint	5	20	2	8	23	116	37	15	18	23	5	0
Temminck's Stint	0	6	0	0	0	0	0	0	0	0	0	0
White-rumped Sandpiper	0	0	0	0	1	1	1	0	0	0	0	0
Pectoral Sandpiper	0	0	0	1	0	2	0	0	0	0	0	0

	Apr	May	Jun	Jul	Aug	Sep	Oct	Nov	Dec	Jan	Feb	Mar
Curlew Sandpiper	1	15	1	30	66	164	19	0	0	0	0	0
Purple Sandpiper	305	81	0	3	2	88	171	666	301	296	484	0
Dunlin	90,335	143,414	1,573	43,534	99,331	95,349	163,686	311,965	303,217	335,976	361,523	2,695
Broad-billed Sandpiper	0	1	0	0	0	0	0	0	0	0	0	0
Buff-breasted Sandpiper	0	0	0	0	0	1	0	0	0	0	0	0
Ruff	271	61	9	180	749	961	556	416	309	762	363	35
Jack Snipe	31	1	0	0	0	8	50	71	72	93	94	2
Snipe	1,147	78	45	191	832	2,900	4,508	4,769	4,551	6,285	4,782	275
Long-billed Dowitcher	1	0	0	0	0	0	1	1	1	1	1	0
Woodcock	0	0	0	0	0	0	3	11	28	24	15	1
Black-tailed Godwit	8,037	634	521	7,981	14,566	20,530	11,988	15,470	9,746	11,403	17,792	1,034
Bar-tailed Godwit	9,414	7,388	3,515	5,595	22,101	37,507	42,696	35,589	15,141	41,682	24,590	660
Whimbrel	64	1,687	64	966	606	192	16	24	2	8	3	1
Curlew	26,065	4,403	7,462	39,621	62,455	63,021	55,461	48,350	53,154	53,160	56,741	1,634
Spotted Redshank	50	41	21	123	150	234	146	58	44	70	61	4
Redshank	33,283	3,830	3,291	23,158	51,112	75,349	66,089	62,221	57,147	52,611	52,180	928
Marsh Sandpiper	1	0	0	0	0	1	0	0	0	0	0	0
Greenshank	128	486	17	808	1,871	1,717	724	168	128	132	152	21
Green Sandpiper	80	16	81	430	522	300	153	110	117	113	97	19
Wood Sandpiper	0	28	1	32	35	25	2	0	0	0	0	0
Common Sandpiper	69	708	207	842	774	348	64	28	36	22	20	2
Turnstone	4,652	3,200	338	1,558	4,548	7,363	8,183	9,061	8,252	9,034	9,617	318
Grey Phalarope	0	0	0	0	0	0	1	1	1	0	0	0
Mediterranean Gull	96	25	11	94	50	53	46	35	33	50	51	4
Little Gull	74	71	34	85	9	207	34	8	7	4	1	0
Bonaparte's Gull	0	0	0	0	0	0	0	0	0	0	0	0
Black-headed Gull	51,662	24,420	32,086	59,263	85,053	129,809	141,842	206,075	189,463	213,083	176,234	21,136
Ring-billed Gull	3	0	1	0	0	0	2	2	2	5	6	0
Common Gull	7,088	1,787	1,452	3,906	16,600	24,642	30,892	52,240	43,741	60,246	44,584	1,297
Lesser Black-backed Gull	32,562	37,136	38,764	43,394	25,970	6,710	12,035	13,439	10,675	6,296	10,487	289
Herring Gull	43,678	30,022	28,944	32,519	32,135	20,071	22,741	28,625	26,329	61,788	37,827	3,929
Yellow-legged Gull	1	0	1	11	110	103	76	24	47	25	13	0
Caspian Gull	0	0	0	0	0	0	0	1	1	0	0	0
West, Yellow-legged Gull	0	1	0	0	0	0	14	4	1	1	0	0
Iceland Gull	3	1	0	0	0	0	0	0	1	4	1	0
Glaucous Gull	3	1	0	1	0	0	1	2	0	6	5	0
Great Black-backed Gull	1,487	1,083	1,398	2,494	3,011	5,444	6,095	8,104	8,288	7,142	3,872	613
Kittiwake	103	17	227	73	287	37	20	142	40	63	131	0
Unidentified gull	240	0	20,501	0	1,231	1,335	1,685	1,841	1,050	6,085	5,240	0
Sandwich Tern	689	4,324	6,147	5,117	3,537	1,102	28	2	1	1	1	1
Roseate Tern	0	1	3	3	2	0	0	0	0	0	0	0
Common Tern	62	2,370	3,585	4,461	6,357	847	8	0	1	0	0	0
Arctic Tern	25	162	109	185	59	11	2	0	0	0	0	0
Forster's Tern	0	0	0	0	1	0	0	0	0	0	0	0
Little Tern	8	451	539	536	366	28	0	0	0	0	0	0
Black Tern	0	389	2	9	15	32	1	1	0	0	0	0
Unidentified tern	0	2	0	18	7	0	0	0	0	0	0	0
'Commic' tern	0	2	7	5	1	0	2	0	0	0	0	0
Kingfisher	92	100	112	153	220	356	340	270	223	170	157	19

APPENDIX 5. TOTAL NUMBERS OF WATERBIRDS RECORDED BY WeBS IN SCOTLAND, 2000–01

	Apr	May	Jun	Jul	Aug	Sep	Oct	Nov	Dec	Jan	Feb	Mar
Sectors	*341*	*291*	*276*	*288*	*320*	*467*	*671*	*640*	*664*	*581*	*604*	*53*
Sites	*289*	*253*	*239*	*252*	*274*	*409*	*553*	*559*	*548*	*474*	*482*	*51*
Red-throated Diver	211	52	27	43	78	93	181	219	219	333	165	51
Black-throated Diver	15	2	0	5	6	3	6	6	19	22	107	1
Great Northern Diver	59	41	1	0	6	10	22	31	46	76	56	12
Unidentifed diver	0	0	0	0	0	0	0	2	0	0	0	0
Little Grebe	183	130	134	194	372	682	591	468	471	410	268	27
Great Crested Grebe	266	221	202	363	623	729	520	593	444	596	361	22
Red-necked Grebe	4	2	1	10	25	29	14	15	8	27	13	3
Slavonian Grebe	71	9	0	0	0	54	76	136	92	234	101	5
Black-necked Grebe	3	4	5	6	2	4	0	0	2	1	0	0
Cormorant	626	377	356	651	1,912	2,356	2,907	2,260	2,760	2,151	1,537	79
Little Egret	0	1	0	0	1	0	0	2	1	0	0	0
Grey Heron	182	190	287	334	589	762	766	572	651	716	514	17
Spoonbill	0	0	0	0	2	0	0	0	0	0	0	0
Mute Swan	1,663	1,714	1,673	1,738	3,356	3,322	4,411	3,862	4,159	4,476	3,303	410
Black Swan	0	2	2	8	5	2	6	2	6	3	1	0
Bewick's Swan	0	0	0	0	0	0	0	0	4	7	2	0
Whooper Swan	181	18	6	14	19	21	1,668	2,385	1,866	1,787	1,541	36
Magpie Goose	0	0	0	0	0	0	0	0	6	0	0	0
Bean Goose	0	0	0	0	0	0	187	0	0	0	0	0
Pink-footed Goose	6,542	302	4	1	6	3,054	223,903	111,503	39,854	30,399	27,205	43
European Whitefront	0	0	0	0	0	0	0	0	0	1	0	0
Greenland Whitefront	16	0	0	0	1	1	359	21,030	204	769	429	2,601
Greylag Goose (Ice.)	3,224	0	0	0	0	0	24,903	75,995	26,837	22,365	18,233	743
Greylag Goose (NW Sco.)	123	27	13	5	8,366	1,309	913	880	794	631	3,375	0
Greylag Goose (natur.)	28	465	641	1,120	2,195	2,902	304	136	133	232	61	17
Snow Goose	0	0	0	0	0	1	0	2	1	2	0	0
Canada Goose	160	178	564	360	581	1,011	1,081	1,321	1,099	846	623	56
Barnacle Goose (Gre.)	90	16	18	22	24	28	99	39,757	123	168	229	0
Barnacle Goose (Sval.)	13,756	2	0	0	0	43	9,228	10,048	5,520	5,651	5,092	1,800
Barnacle Goose (Nat.)	0	0	1	2	7	0	0	0	0	0	0	0
Dark-bellied Brent	0	1	0	0	0	0	1	0	0	2	0	0
Light-bellied Brent (Sval.)	0	0	0	0	0	17	2	0	3	18	9	0
Light-bellied Brent (Can.)	15	1	0	0	0	108	3	16	34	40	14	14
Red-breasted Goose	0	0	0	0	0	0	0	1	0	1	0	0
Egyptian Goose	0	0	1	1	1	0	0	0	0	0	0	0
hybrid goose	12	10	3	0	3	8	12	20	24	31	23	3
feral/domestic goose	2	2	3	1	1	33	68	56	88	58	26	0
unidentified goose	0	0	0	0	0	0	0	0	0	1	0	0
Shelduck	2,362	1,650	3,119	1,468	1,078	4,470	4,380	5,843	4,443	4,819	3,697	176
Muscovy Duck	3	0	1	1	0	3	16	19	8	4	2	2
Mandarin	1	1	0	1	1	0	0	12	4	0	0	0
Wigeon	1,915	117	73	124	606	10,811	72,632	38,288	63,136	56,397	38,614	969
American Wigeon	0	0	0	0	0	1	1	3	4	6	6	4
Gadwall	40	30	41	31	230	364	317	189	138	77	46	2
Teal	2,650	103	213	257	3,182	8,860	23,194	18,395	24,426	20,510	17,749	911
Green-winged Teal	0	0	0	0	0	0	1	0	2	3	1	1
Mallard	3,547	3,147	5,448	8,823	11,956	17,895	29,723	26,692	30,846	33,305	25,371	949
Black Duck	0	0	0	0	0	0	0	0	1	0	1	0
Pintail	16	12	0	1	11	950	2,312	2,126	3,178	1,668	1,749	35
Bahama Pintail	0	0	0	0	0	1	1	0	0	0	0	0
Garganey	0	8	0	0	0	0	0	0	0	0	0	0
Shoveler	105	34	26	38	386	911	965	647	520	206	102	17
Red-crested Pochard	0	0	0	0	0	1	1	2	2	2	2	0
Pochard	128	61	53	387	602	967	4,315	3,486	4,747	2,936	2,029	18
Ring-necked Duck	0	0	0	0	0	0	0	0	0	0	1	0
Tufted Duck	3,341	1,471	1,096	3,133	7,228	8,972	11,193	11,856	9,828	9,485	7,246	436
Scaup	294	14	0	0	0	145	976	1,496	2,759	3,323	2,017	48
Eider	9,767	7,264	6,090	13,060	19,486	16,200	13,721	12,744	10,748	14,617	11,613	612
King Eider	0	1	0	0	0	0	0	0	0	0	0	0
Long-tailed Duck	462	103	0	1	3	242	520	479	2,578	4,666	2,173	12

	Apr	May	Jun	Jul	Aug	Sep	Oct	Nov	Dec	Jan	Feb	Mar
Common Scoter	3,277	848	225	104	191	836	2,973	2,010	2,904	3,540	4,595	344
Surf Scoter	4	2	0	0	0	0	1	1	3	5	6	0
Velvet Scoter	709	117	23	12	26	121	255	756	2,464	1,998	911	3
Unidentified scoter spp.	0	0	0	0	0	0	0	0	0	6	290	0
Goldeneye	2,122	127	43	112	92	211	973	3,969	5,779	8,008	7,714	228
Smew	0	0	0	0	0	0	0	4	4	10	15	0
Red-breasted Merganser	891	448	301	663	948	1,198	1,035	1,084	1,302	1,259	1,316	99
Goosander	122	120	206	368	824	615	738	733	649	746	797	54
Ruddy Duck	94	90	54	64	137	147	107	65	71	9	2	2
feral/hybrid Mallard type	13	7	16	15	15	12	660	984	891	23	23	0
hybrid Anas	0	1	0	0	0	0	0	0	3	2	1	2
unidentified duck	1	0	0	10	0	0	9	11	1	3	0	0
Water Rail	7	3	12	15	18	23	23	17	17	26	16	0
Moorhen	379	254	224	367	516	789	1,053	876	756	578	528	52
Coot	1,358	979	1,177	2,142	3,810	5,701	6,573	5,318	5,389	5,642	4,385	245
Crane	0	0	0	0	1	0	0	0	0	0	0	0
Oystercatcher	16,692	10,031	10,405	16,909	46,449	64,319	64,436	46,726	57,585	44,649	48,701	2,260
Ringed Plover	779	991	142	370	2,136	2,890	2,836	1,655	2,868	2,957	1,948	207
Golden Plover	1,164	44	9	329	3,028	6,141	13,653	8,183	8,413	4,688	2,231	11
Grey Plover	1,443	692	112	166	1,115	1,571	1,617	1,378	1,870	1,908	1,299	180
Unidentified wader	0	0	0	0	2	0	0	0	12	3	0	0
Lapwing	818	646	1,400	4,358	16,159	25,654	24,642	23,832	30,007	11,186	15,484	443
Knot	1,676	1,101	98	48	664	3,052	8,898	3,594	16,659	20,026	14,418	614
Sanderling	429	73	19	54	269	475	823	396	702	879	755	62
Semipalmated Sandpiper	0	0	0	0	0	1	0	0	0	0	0	0
Little Stint	0	0	0	1	0	18	1	0	0	0	0	0
White-rumped Sandpiper	0	0	0	0	0	1	0	0	0	0	0	0
Curlew Sandpiper	0	1	0	0	44	21	1	0	0	0	0	0
Purple Sandpiper	332	181	0	0	17	51	211	434	744	944	840	89
Dunlin	2,989	2,345	85	373	2,196	6,140	16,913	10,629	39,714	33,341	28,698	734
Ruff	1	3	0	11	182	167	12	7	1	6	5	0
Jack Snipe	3	0	0	0	0	0	16	16	16	29	26	2
Snipe	57	28	28	72	218	721	1,472	1,248	847	642	632	25
Woodcock	2	0	0	0	1	0	1	1	5	5	10	0
Black-tailed Godwit	103	21	1	40	377	227	321	293	298	130	236	0
Bar-tailed Godwit	453	176	153	842	1,407	2,432	4,179	1,890	5,102	6,552	6,700	678
Whimbrel	1	84	5	26	88	7	1	1	0	0	0	0
Curlew	3,632	1,173	1,330	8,060	12,449	14,176	18,206	15,985	20,278	19,523	17,774	789
Spotted Redshank	0	0	0	0	7	8	6	2	0	1	2	0
Redshank	5,967	281	341	2,634	8,041	12,252	22,456	13,177	19,163	17,315	16,988	1,150
Greenshank	15	19	8	18	165	75	101	47	51	33	28	0
Green Sandpiper	0	0	0	2	7	3	2	9	2	8	3	0
Wood Sandpiper	0	2	0	0	0	2	0	0	0	0	0	0
Common Sandpiper	4	98	109	210	43	15	3	1	0	1	0	0
Turnstone	1,385	241	45	164	1,366	2,049	3,604	2,382	3,630	2,901	3,672	286
Little Gull	0	6	135	44	1	0	4	0	1	0	0	0
Black-headed Gull	3,284	3,036	3,350	7,284	8,967	16,566	16,288	13,212	21,988	42,803	24,221	612
Common Gull	2,502	2,162	1,876	3,238	2,447	13,110	8,205	13,173	13,282	8,618	14,027	629
Lesser Black-backed Gull	1,274	1,649	1,673	1,601	1,533	1,827	880	262	138	95	377	460
Herring Gull	6,145	4,369	6,271	5,435	8,459	10,542	9,980	7,740	8,962	12,929	11,297	672
Iceland Gull	1	1	0	0	0	1	1	0	0	2	1	0
Glaucous Gull	0	0	0	0	0	1	0	5	1	0	1	2
Great Black-backed Gull	621	358	452	545	1,987	2,001	1,466	2,156	903	856	904	100
Kittiwake	1	195	22	157	2,615	446	318	48	46	43	167	0
Unidentified gull	200	0	0	197	1,771	4,506	500	0	391	2,331	3,027	0
hybrid gull	6	4	0	0	0	0	130	0	0	0	0	0
Sandwich Tern	31	147	160	967	4,575	1,502	7	0	0	0	0	0
Common Tern	0	167	137	209	1,104	125	0	0	0	0	0	0
Arctic Tern	0	818	587	486	629	15	1	0	0	0	0	0
Little Tern	0	9	7	0	4	0	0	0	0	0	0	0
'Commic' tern	0	0	0	1	61	0	0	0	0	0	0	0
Kingfisher	2	1	4	4	7	12	14	16	9	17	2	0

APPENDIX 6. TOTAL NUMBERS OF WATERBIRDS RECORDED BY WeBS IN WALES, 2000–01

	Apr	May	Jun	Jul	Aug	Sep	Oct	Nov	Dec	Jan	Feb	Mar
Sectors	*114*	*101*	*100*	*96*	*113*	*169*	*194*	*185*	*196*	*197*	*198*	*20*
Sites	*62*	*56*	*56*	*54*	*63*	*90*	*102*	*91*	*100*	*107*	*101*	*19*
Red-throated Diver	7	1	0	0	0	16	1	8	118	485	9	2
Black-throated Diver	0	0	0	0	0	0	0	0	0	0	2	0
Great Northern Diver	0	0	0	0	0	0	6	3	15	14	5	0
Little Grebe	96	49	56	90	181	244	283	271	280	329	202	11
Great Crested Grebe	140	114	93	71	427	247	172	236	473	354	355	40
Red-necked Grebe	0	1	0	0	0	0	0	0	0	0	0	0
Slavonian Grebe	0	0	1	0	0	0	2	6	10	10	6	0
Black-necked Grebe	0	0	0	0	1	1	0	0	0	1	0	1
Cormorant	290	247	276	316	651	1,036	1,415	856	640	518	515	61
Bittern	0	0	0	0	0	0	1	0	2	1	0	1
Little Egret	12	2	6	19	47	42	90	81	65	86	60	1
Great White Egret	0	0	0	2	0	1	0	0	0	0	0	0
Grey Heron	76	93	104	154	158	299	247	185	202	242	149	9
Spoonbill	0	1	0	0	1	0	0	0	0	0	0	0
Mute Swan	273	267	459	477	665	775	664	740	707	635	554	157
Black Swan	0	0	0	0	1	1	0	0	0	0	1	0
Bewick's Swan	0	0	0	0	0	0	0	38	0	0	2	0
Whooper Swan	3	0	0	0	0	0	12	62	53	65	52	0
Swan Goose	0	0	0	0	0	4	1	0	1	3	0	0
Pink-footed Goose	0	0	0	6	0	0	0	1	1	4	2	0
Greenland Whitefront	83	0	0	0	0	0	0	130	134	130	136	0
Greylag Goose (natur.)	212	165	928	578	451	1,476	588	334	1,124	632	300	51
Bar-headed Goose	0	0	0	1	0	0	0	0	1	1	0	0
Snow Goose	3	1	6	1	1	1	1	0	1	0	0	0
Canada Goose	662	437	2,615	2,486	2,361	3,620	4,172	3,009	3,656	3,562	2,497	84
Barnacle Goose (natur.)	3	4	12	4	6	5	43	0	63	63	45	2
Brent Goose	0	0	0	0	0	0	0	0	0	1	0	0
Dark-bellied Brent	4	0	0	0	0	0	164	1,171	629	281	236	0
Light-bellied Brent	0	0	0	0	0	4	6	57	119	125	146	0
hybrid goose	0	0	3	0	0	0	3	2	0	0	0	2
feral/domestic goose	2	2	5	5	2	2	2	2	2	2	2	2
Ruddy Shelduck	0	0	0	0	0	0	1	0	0	0	0	0
Shelduck	2,216	1,440	1,147	547	186	415	2,344	3,084	4,952	4,276	5,168	44
Muscovy Duck	2	3	0	3	3	4	3	3	3	2	4	1
Wood Duck	0	2	0	0	0	0	0	0	0	0	0	0
Mandarin	1	0	1	3	0	0	0	5	0	1	0	0
Wigeon	169	4	0	9	28	3,953	13,524	15,556	9,803	12,794	7,155	5
American Wigeon	0	0	0	0	0	1	1	0	0	1	0	0
Gadwall	78	57	33	47	70	87	125	233	240	234	225	0
Teal	288	9	27	34	507	4,358	5,682	7,806	10,377	9,416	8,574	126
Mallard	1,218	1,104	1,929	2,456	5,011	6,583	6,431	5,786	7,040	7,213	4,830	576
Pintail	6	2	3	0	8	270	397	1,554	2,193	3,182	1,495	0
Bahama Pintail	0	0	0	0	0	0	1	0	0	0	0	0
Garganey	0	3	0	0	0	5	0	0	0	1	0	0
Shoveler	90	68	10	23	73	191	462	1,031	965	959	845	22
Red-crested Pochard	1	1	1	1	1	1	0	2	2	2	1	0
Pochard	91	57	49	167	253	385	515	663	879	989	622	87
Ring-necked Duck	0	0	0	0	0	0	0	0	0	1	1	0
Tufted Duck	670	250	362	1,060	1,268	1,343	918	1,486	1,612	1,383	1,053	123
Scaup	1	1	0	0	0	2	4	15	9	35	18	0
Eider	0	45	36	22	46	40	15	106	27	78	93	0
Long-tailed Duck	2	0	0	0	0	3	0	2	3	3	2	0
Common Scoter	18	0	1	0	19	22	333	124	337	485	627	540
Velvet Scoter	0	0	0	0	0	0	2	0	0	0	0	0
Goldeneye	94	1	0	0	1	2	11	171	355	487	487	5
Smew	0	0	0	0	0	0	0	0	0	2	1	0
Red-breasted Merganser	198	69	54	25	352	301	283	328	181	145	156	0
Goosander	25	11	54	58	113	88	32	56	45	105	72	34
Ruddy Duck	42	19	26	25	41	77	73	45	65	58	34	0
feral/hybrid Mallard type	40	25	40	39	29	11	40	58	47	48	56	13

	Apr	May	Jun	Jul	Aug	Sep	Oct	Nov	Dec	Jan	Feb	Mar
hybrid Anas	11	6	1	1	8	6	0	0	0	0	0	0
hybrid Aythya	0	0	0	0	0	0	0	3	0	2	2	0
unidentified duck	0	0	0	0	0	0	0	0	0	1,800	0	0
Water Rail	8	2	1	3	7	13	35	41	28	41	37	6
Moorhen	322	217	172	206	386	448	467	425	448	458	467	103
Coot	1,000	691	1,245	2,114	3,366	3,717	3,400	3,467	3,233	3,169	1,981	283
Oystercatcher	5,198	3,941	4,310	6,077	20,539	34,516	31,332	32,846	34,408	30,940	25,214	1,901
Avocet	0	0	1	0	0	0	0	0	0	0	0	0
Little Ringed Plover	15	11	4	19	3	2	0	0	0	0	0	0
Ringed Plover	231	430	167	113	807	889	621	557	640	568	354	3
Golden Plover	130	1	0	0	0	40	662	1,470	2,251	6,094	1,186	2
Grey Plover	56	107	1	0	2	21	108	116	228	749	519	0
Unidentified wader	0	0	0	0	0	0	0	18	38	0	0	0
Lapwing	213	218	346	485	1,321	1,321	1,980	6,222	9,115	6,229	6,991	0
Knot	10	135	2	0	83	122	172	2,085	2,270	5,544	6,229	0
Sanderling	358	69	34	11	147	178	599	326	44	663	816	730
Little Stint	0	0	0	0	8	5	0	0	0	0	1	0
Pectoral Sandpiper	0	0	0	0	0	1	0	0	0	0	0	0
Curlew Sandpiper	0	1	0	0	2	9	1	0	0	0	0	0
Purple Sandpiper	13	0	0	0	0	0	0	2	12	7	1	0
Dunlin	210	5,136	203	210	1,084	2,945	1,389	12,192	13,179	20,738	12,667	0
Buff-breasted Sandpiper	0	0	0	0	0	1	0	0	0	0	0	0
Ruff	0	1	0	0	16	14	1	0	0	1	0	0
Jack Snipe	1	0	0	0	0	0	2	8	7	6	5	0
Snipe	40	3	6	13	34	301	249	638	692	578	388	20
Woodcock	0	0	0	0	0	0	0	5	4	1	3	0
Black-tailed Godwit	1,028	78	45	24	61	426	1,748	2,082	786	22	1,515	0
Bar-tailed Godwit	9	281	2	2	14	417	196	183	1,062	225	277	0
Whimbrel	17	572	48	41	47	19	0	0	0	0	0	0
Curlew	1,486	445	712	4,382	6,305	10,324	7,037	7,552	8,144	9,307	8,714	40
Spotted Redshank	3	0	0	1	6	26	11	12	9	5	7	0
Redshank	1,272	125	113	1,011	4,365	6,612	4,343	5,921	5,024	4,721	5,184	33
Greenshank	11	37	3	11	97	144	75	27	46	35	38	0
Green Sandpiper	0	0	1	8	8	34	6	12	8	8	1	0
Wood Sandpiper	0	0	1	0	1	2	0	0	0	0	0	0
Common Sandpiper	7	31	45	64	35	40	8	5	2	4	2	0
Turnstone	158	22	1	1	124	483	368	319	484	377	768	92
Grey Phalarope	0	0	0	0	0	1	0	0	1	0	0	0
Mediterranean Gull	1	0	0	6	12	9	9	4	3	3	4	0
Little Gull	1	1	0	0	0	1	0	0	0	0	0	0
Black-headed Gull	1,433	1,338	1,288	6,529	10,427	12,129	10,792	12,636	12,734	11,522	10,544	516
Ring-billed Gull	0	0	0	0	0	0	0	0	0	1	0	0
Common Gull	274	166	38	115	5,133	210	660	1,439	1,292	2,028	3,862	2,450
Lesser Black-backed Gull	392	540	783	773	738	2,757	2,328	1,764	533	377	758	213
Herring Gull	1,950	1,876	3,877	5,512	5,519	5,170	3,644	5,184	5,909	4,110	3,000	2,892
Yellow-legged Gull	0	0	0	1	1	1	2	0	0	0	0	0
Iceland Gull	1	0	0	0	0	0	0	0	0	0	0	0
Glaucous Gull	1	0	0	0	0	0	0	0	0	0	0	0
Great Black-backed Gull	418	76	148	168	187	293	212	240	186	165	163	81
Kittiwake	0	0	2	3	1	0	0	0	0	0	1	0
Unidentified gull	0	88	100	0	0	0	0	0	0	0	0	0
Sandwich Tern	131	23	14	223	759	265	2	0	1	0	0	0
Common Tern	0	16	132	1	99	14	1	0	0	0	0	0
Arctic Tern	0	1	0	0	1	0	0	0	0	0	0	0
Little Tern	0	80	110	70	0	0	0	0	0	0	0	0
Black Tern	0	0	0	0	1	1	0	0	0	0	0	0
White-winged Black Tern	0	0	0	0	0	1	0	0	0	0	0	0
Kingfisher	2	1	1	1	11	22	9	11	9	6	8	1

APPENDIX 7. TOTAL NUMBERS OF WATERBIRDS RECORDED BY WeBS IN THE CHANNEL ISLANDS, 2000–01

	Apr	May	Jun	Jul	Aug	Sep	Oct	Nov	Dec	Jan	Feb	Mar
Sectors	*9*	*9*	*11*	*11*	*11*	*13*	*18*	*28*	*33*	*33*	*32*	*12*
Sites	*1*	*1*	*2*	*2*	*2*	*4*	*9*	*9*	*11*	*11*	*11*	*4*
Black-throated Diver	0	0	0	0	0	0	0	0	0	1	0	0
Great Northern Diver	0	0	0	0	0	0	0	0	2	1	0	0
Little Grebe	0	0	0	0	7	11	13	11	6	4	3	0
Great Crested Grebe	0	0	0	0	0	0	0	0	9	15	32	1
Slavonian Grebe	0	0	0	0	0	0	0	0	0	5	1	0
Cormorant	10	16	27	20	12	18	26	34	54	15	16	13
Little Egret	12	2	0	25	37	47	39	26	130	143	129	21
Grey Heron	2	1	5	15	19	30	5	20	59	75	21	0
Mute Swan	0	0	0	0	0	0	0	1	1	1	2	0
Black Swan	0	0	0	0	0	0	0	1	0	0	0	0
Whooper Swan	0	0	0	0	0	0	2	2	2	2	2	2
Greylag Goose (natur.)	0	0	0	0	0	0	1	1	1	1	1	1
Dark-bellied Brent	20	0	0	0	0	0	0	0	693	1,113	873	9
Light-bellied Brent (Can.)	0	0	0	0	0	0	0	0	86	21	1	0
feral/domestic goose	0	0	0	0	0	0	9	0	1	12	11	0
unidentified goose	0	0	0	0	0	0	0	0	0	23	0	0
Shelduck	0	0	0	0	1	1	0	0	0	0	0	0
Gadwall	0	0	0	0	0	0	0	0	0	0	2	0
Teal	0	0	0	0	0	4	33	2	81	88	82	6
Mallard	21	23	21	64	92	51	252	440	394	330	274	84
Shoveler	0	0	0	0	0	0	3	17	7	24	6	6
Pochard	0	0	0	2	5	5	5	4	14	13	7	8
Tufted Duck	0	0	24	52	41	52	77	79	69	66	89	14
Eider	0	0	0	0	0	0	0	0	1	0	0	0
Common Scoter	0	0	0	0	0	0	0	0	0	5	0	0
Red-breasted Merganser	0	0	0	0	0	0	0	0	46	62	32	0
feral/hybrid Mallard type	0	0	0	0	0	20	72	35	51	66	74	0
Water Rail	0	0	0	0	0	6	35	25	30	25	26	0
Moorhen	3	2	1	4	1	28	84	79	133	146	94	9
Coot	2	7	15	53	99	221	154	195	215	192	114	41
Oystercatcher	341	164	274	372	515	774	516	2,100	2,553	3,157	2,687	514
Ringed Plover	16	119	10	13	121	125	51	169	328	171	238	25
Golden Plover	0	0	0	0	0	1	30	28	4	36	0	0
Grey Plover	16	9	0	6	22	47	92	547	390	436	322	24
Lapwing	0	0	1	0	36	40	60	139	278	763	287	5
Knot	0	5	0	0	0	0	0	0	0	0	0	0
Sanderling	6	94	3	4	3	17	5	157	267	307	258	2
Purple Sandpiper	0	3	0	0	0	0	0	1	1	0	2	1
Dunlin	3	678	6	5	39	27	13	1,268	1,951	1,779	1,610	35
Snipe	0	0	0	0	0	1	10	15	19	36	27	61
Woodcock	0	0	0	0	0	0	0	7	13	18	23	0
Bar-tailed Godwit	2	12	0	0	0	1	0	57	96	130	132	0
Whimbrel	0	26	0	3	2	0	0	0	0	0	0	0
Curlew	6	3	2	61	53	69	125	236	209	499	215	45
Redshank	2	7	0	15	16	10	10	77	278	283	319	17
Greenshank	0	7	0	0	1	6	28	15	8	16	35	0
Green Sandpiper	0	0	0	0	0	3	0	0	0	0	0	0
Common Sandpiper	0	11	0	6	3	1	0	0	0	0	0	0
Turnstone	111	132	0	35	86	265	68	542	439	495	334	349
Grey Phalarope	0	0	0	0	0	0	0	1	2	0	0	0
Black-headed Gull	9	0	5	413	385	404	484	649	808	665	791	353
Common Gull	0	0	0	0	12	0	0	0	3	0	1	0
Lesser Black-backed Gull	129	13	16	31	88	110	4	15	12	9	27	55
Herring Gull	1,260	1,486	777	1,164	1,621	1,131	3,661	2,413	1,293	1,103	1,550	1,172
Great Black-backed Gull	25	22	79	111	252	192	275	320	200	195	273	195
Kittiwake	0	0	1	0	0	0	1	1	0	0	0	0
Sandwich Tern	1	1	0	14	19	61	0	0	10	8	4	4
Common Tern	0	21	10	10	0	2	0	0	0	0	0	0
Kingfisher	0	0	0	0	0	0	0	1	0	1	0	0

APPENDIX 8. TOTAL NUMBERS OF WATERBIRDS RECORDED BY WeBS AT COASTAL SITES IN 2000–01

GREAT BRITAIN

	Apr	May	Jun	Jul	Aug	Sep	Oct	Nov	Dec	Jan	Feb	Mar
Sectors	*552*	*459*	*416*	*420*	*510*	*680*	*777*	*754*	*791*	*817*	*823*	*41*
Sites	*129*	*108*	*102*	*105*	*120*	*163*	*183*	*176*	*179*	*189*	*203*	*33*
Red-throated Diver	232	46	21	22	72	190	247	307	490	1,015	445	53
Black-throated Diver	13	1	0	0	0	0	7	7	38	53	145	32
Great Northern Diver	59	42	1	0	4	11	28	41	89	100	91	18
Unidentifed diver	0	0	0	3	0	0	1	2	0	0	0	0
Little Grebe	455	307	202	330	694	1,241	1,587	1,615	1,457	1,595	1,070	44
Great Crested Grebe	463	275	295	503	1,193	1,476	1,497	1,681	1,921	2,174	2,228	59
Red-necked Grebe	7	2	0	10	25	29	17	19	16	34	14	4
Slavonian Grebe	70	9	1	0	0	23	48	139	108	293	126	7
Black-necked Grebe	1	3	1	2	4	7	6	12	29	24	21	0
Cormorant	2,971	2,016	2,338	3,744	7,142	10,004	9,345	7,474	6,179	6,152	5,039	195
Bittern	0	0	1	0	0	0	1	3	3	5	1	0
Squacco Heron	0	0	1	0	0	0	0	0	0	0	0	0
Little Egret	329	144	170	575	1,093	1,347	1,170	709	597	545	595	36
Great White Egret	0	0	0	0	0	1	0	0	0	0	0	0
Grey Heron	645	602	862	1,107	1,683	2,015	1,784	1,152	1,076	1,248	895	26
Purple Heron	0	0	0	0	1	0	0	0	0	0	0	0
Spoonbill	2	6	5	9	8	8	12	12	14	2	9	0
Fulvous Whistling Duck	1	0	0	0	0	0	0	0	0	0	0	0
Mute Swan	2,871	2,848	2,651	3,682	4,716	5,179	5,339	5,014	5,035	5,124	4,802	98
Black Swan	7	10	9	10	17	13	9	2	5	1	6	0
Bewick's Swan	0	0	0	0	0	0	46	79	186	821	709	0
Whooper Swan	102	4	4	1	3	7	704	471	1,183	457	428	2
Magpie Goose	0	0	0	0	0	0	0	0	6	0	0	0
Swan Goose	0	0	1	0	1	0	0	1	1	0	0	0
Taiga Bean Goose	0	0	0	0	0	2	4	0	0	0	0	0
Pink-footed Goose	6,622	325	4	9	2	1,028	23,003	37,127	55,002	50,831	23,414	1
White-fronted Goose	0	0	0	0	0	0	0	0	0	0	5	0
European Whitefront	1	1	16	0	4	3	3	128	454	1,792	917	0
Greenland Whitefront	83	0	0	0	1	1	115	381	140	317	147	0
Lesser Whitefront	0	0	0	0	0	0	0	0	0	0	2	0
Greylag Goose (Ice.)	429	57	52	58	547	466	10,369	1,309	7,262	7,030	2,541	0
Greylag Goose (NW Sco.)	19	8	5	0	7	157	150	256	82	152	466	0
Greylag Goose (natur.)	1,684	1,806	2,734	2,794	5,764	6,420	4,709	5,906	6,050	5,601	3,711	69
Bar-headed Goose	2	2	2	1	4	5	2	1	2	1	0	0
Snow Goose	4	2	5	0	0	3	1	0	1	1	0	0
Ross's Goose	0	0	0	0	0	0	0	1	0	0	0	0
Emperor Goose	1	1	0	1	2	4	0	0	0	0	0	0
Canada Goose	2,084	1,270	4,240	5,705	8,819	11,847	9,896	9,392	10,260	9,247	7,165	296
Barnacle Goose (Gre.)	0	0	0	0	0	0	0	400	1	0	124	0
Barnacle Goose (Sval.)	2,000	5,001	5	0	0	23	14,006	8,043	5,567	5,425	7,536	0
Barnacle Goose (natur.)	20	9	29	10	6	28	123	77	181	159	259	0
Brent Goose	0	0	0	0	0	0	1,175	400	0	1	0	0
Dark-bellied Brent	14,681	10,234	86	72	63	3,081	39,448	65,920	65,653	91,550	83,874	1,615
Black Brant	0	0	0	0	0	0	1	0	0	3	4	0
Light-bellied Brent (Sval.)	12	6	0	1	1	3,139	2,132	3,192	1,584	1,304	330	0
Light-bellied Brent (Can.)	16	2	0	0	0	107	10	74	161	178	163	14
Egyptian Goose	43	58	144	62	220	37	51	43	57	59	72	0
hybrid goose	9	7	3	4	4	7	6	10	20	12	18	0
feral/domestic goose	13	2	1	1	1	19	19	4	22	25	6	0
unidentified goose	0	0	0	0	0	4	250	0	0	9	0	0
Ruddy Shelduck	1	1	0	2	3	3	2	0	1	1	4	0
Shelduck	27,772	17,438	18,567	22,923	22,412	36,972	40,712	50,465	49,065	58,693	53,840	1,326
hybrid Shelduck	0	0	0	0	0	1	0	0	1	1	1	0
Muscovy Duck	2	2	1	10	0	0	5	8	0	0	11	0
Wood Duck	0	1	1	1	1	1	1	1	0	3	0	0
Mandarin	0	0	0	0	0	74	26	27	38	40	48	0
Wigeon	7,489	336	105	147	822	59,565	212,675	150,608	206,000	225,134	164,861	2,441
American Wigeon	0	0	0	0	0	0	1	1	1	1	2	0
Gadwall	452	421	412	198	546	1,188	1,309	1,367	1,546	1,709	1,765	24

	Apr	May	Jun	Jul	Aug	Sep	Oct	Nov	Dec	Jan	Feb	Mar
Teal	7,027	280	304	647	5,256	43,241	65,707	64,176	73,939	74,056	73,155	861
Green-winged Teal	1	0	0	0	0	0	0	0	2	3	1	0
Mallard	7,139	5,623	9,014	10,480	21,693	34,975	38,383	34,725	39,752	43,314	29,825	819
Black Duck	0	0	0	0	0	0	0	0	1	0	1	0
Chestnut Teal	0	0	0	0	0	0	0	0	0	0	0	0
Pintail	142	27	5	9	30	5,959	9,481	14,873	12,835	12,267	9,258	46
Bahama Pintail	1	2	1	0	0	1	0	0	0	0	0	0
Garganey	5	23	10	11	15	15	3	0	0	1	0	0
Blue-winged Teal	0	0	0	0	1	0	0	0	0	0	0	0
Shoveler	925	405	223	253	757	1,811	2,724	3,972	3,826	3,089	3,488	69
Red-crested Pochard	2	3	2	1	1	0	0	0	0	1	1	0
Pochard	429	291	219	249	458	608	2,086	3,318	3,628	4,860	4,515	234
Ring-necked Duck	0	0	0	0	0	0	0	0	0	0	1	0
Ferruginous Duck	0	0	0	0	0	0	0	0	1	0	0	0
Tufted Duck	1,512	1,076	658	995	1,086	1,908	2,836	2,661	3,587	4,305	3,777	90
Scaup	549	13	2	3	4	204	776	1,389	2,567	3,848	1,988	43
Eider	16,162	11,662	11,201	19,996	24,198	22,453	21,345	18,968	17,036	19,468	15,349	623
King Eider	0	1	0	0	0	0	0	0	0	0	0	0
Long-tailed Duck	455	22	0	4	3	245	470	397	2,530	4,561	2,149	7
Common Scoter	5,286	941	3,252	416	346	1,624	3,687	3,616	5,221	7,411	5,564	902
Surf Scoter	4	2	0	0	0	0	1	1	3	5	6	0
Velvet Scoter	712	117	23	12	26	121	257	760	2,464	1,999	911	6
Unidentified scoter sp.	0	0	0	0	0	0	0	0	0	6	290	0
Goldeneye	855	28	3	61	35	54	309	2,353	4,258	7,163	6,873	198
Smew	0	0	0	0	0	1	2	1	3	6	7	0
Red-breasted Merganser	2,105	582	539	812	1,365	1,714	1,768	2,823	3,038	3,286	3,287	201
Goosander	56	49	236	371	943	560	186	178	153	133	98	7
Ruddy Duck	71	110	51	85	213	163	197	246	229	136	226	1
feral/hybrid Mallard type	13	0	0	4	2	4	4	1	7	3	2	0
hybrid Anas	0	0	0	0	0	1	0	0	0	1	2	0
hybrid Aythya	0	0	0	0	0	1	0	3	1	2	2	0
unidentified duck	7	0	0	0	2	14	36	1	0	1,811	10	0
Water Rail	17	45	3	7	15	32	91	83	80	89	74	4
Spotted Crake	0	0	0	0	0	2	1	0	0	0	0	0
Moorhen	1,193	872	530	737	1,419	2,372	2,677	2,692	2,710	2,504	2,302	31
Coot	3,047	2,076	2,093	4,220	7,502	9,616	11,302	11,391	13,377	11,383	9,411	115
Crane	3	0	0	0	0	0	0	0	0	0	0	0
Oystercatcher	70,901	49,111	37,826	76,608	173,546	241,080	236,285	227,415	220,739	222,301	220,633	6,910
Black-winged Stilt	1	0	0	0	1	1	1	1	1	1	0	1
Avocet	1,461	884	912	1,463	908	1,930	1,423	3,185	3,060	4,564	3,978	317
Stone-curlew	0	0	0	0	1	0	0	0	0	0	0	0
Little Ringed Plover	17	25	25	59	39	6	0	0	0	0	0	0
Ringed Plover	4,185	10,884	1,414	2,028	17,648	16,237	11,362	8,396	8,982	9,410	7,288	741
Kentish Plover	1	0	0	0	0	0	0	0	0	0	0	0
Pacific Golden Plover	0	0	0	1	0	0	0	0	0	0	0	0
Golden Plover	9,774	556	79	4,724	32,485	52,235	90,091	111,700	79,276	89,771	110,107	1,809
Grey Plover	28,632	39,215	3,523	2,629	26,078	31,048	32,806	36,864	28,501	43,975	51,940	751
Unidentified wader	10	2	0	3	0	0	0	18	38	3	0	0
Sociable Plover	0	0	0	0	0	0	0	1	0	0	0	0
Lapwing	3,604	3,159	6,149	16,939	38,182	72,586	116,307	181,039	183,174	174,872	216,286	2,594
Knot	100,593	29,412	12,569	29,140	74,510	166,541	181,402	296,115	226,704	312,607	250,902	3,499
Sanderling	8,164	13,909	1,781	1,065	9,613	8,161	7,642	6,711	5,267	7,761	8,409	980
Semipalmated Sandpiper	0	0	0	0	1	1	0	0	0	0	0	0
Little Stint	3	18	2	5	29	115	36	10	17	17	4	0
Temminck's Stint	0	3	0	0	0	0	0	0	0	0	0	0
White-rumped Sandpiper	0	0	0	0	1	1	1	0	0	0	0	0
Pectoral Sandpiper	0	0	0	1	0	2	0	0	0	0	0	0
Curlew Sandpiper	1	17	1	29	109	184	20	0	0	0	0	0
Purple Sandpiper	650	262	0	3	19	139	381	1,079	1,001	908	1,325	89
Dunlin	93,457	150,657	1,847	43,993	102,412	104,146	181,555	334,135	354,800	387,578	401,129	3,393
Broad-billed Sandpiper	0	1	0	0	0	0	0	0	0	0	0	0
Buff-breasted Sandpiper	0	0	0	0	0	2	0	0	0	0	0	0
Ruff	160	54	9	138	598	563	352	235	58	125	89	1
Jack Snipe	14	1	0	0	0	0	30	41	32	56	52	0
Snipe	468	51	27	110	569	1,317	2,107	2,726	2,888	2,833	2,169	111
Long-billed Dowitcher	1	0	0	0	0	0	1	1	1	1	1	0
Woodcock	0	0	0	0	0	0	1	7	15	12	12	0

	Apr	May	Jun	Jul	Aug	Sep	Oct	Nov	Dec	Jan	Feb	Mar
Black-tailed Godwit	7,921	689	558	7,952	14,859	21,127	13,859	17,638	10,704	9,867	16,775	1,006
Bar-tailed Godwit	9,858	7,743	3,670	6,439	23,518	40,341	47,042	37,638	21,284	48,424	31,565	1,338
Whimbrel	74	2,266	117	1,026	732	216	16	24	2	8	3	1
Curlew	30,365	5,678	9,177	51,401	79,611	86,163	76,539	64,965	75,326	75,517	77,692	2,326
Spotted Redshank	51	37	21	116	138	236	149	70	51	73	67	4
Redshank	39,074	3,687	3,430	26,625	63,325	93,933	92,036	79,873	79,724	73,171	72,934	2,004
Marsh Sandpiper	1	0	0	0	0	0	0	0	0	0	0	0
Greenshank	142	440	26	778	1,866	1,829	861	235	212	187	207	21
Green Sandpiper	16	0	18	196	261	156	64	35	31	29	16	4
Wood Sandpiper	0	15	0	13	26	14	2	0	0	0	0	0
Common Sandpiper	33	300	92	577	508	247	48	27	21	18	15	0
Turnstone	6,172	3,435	382	1,717	6,031	9,894	11,923	11,536	11,889	12,043	13,158	696
Grey Phalarope	0	0	0	0	0	0	0	1	1	0	0	0
Mediterranean Gull	83	22	9	62	37	35	52	31	26	46	43	0
Little Gull	73	50	23	52	9	14	6	8	6	0	1	0
Bonaparte's Gull	0	0	0	0	0	0	0	0	0	0	0	0
Black-headed Gull	28,104	13,333	20,429	58,738	84,715	105,828	89,294	108,679	91,596	150,158	115,805	7,315
Ring-billed Gull	1	0	1	0	0	0	2	2	2	3	4	0
Common Gull	8,653	3,270	2,989	6,257	21,721	18,228	14,617	13,931	16,595	29,177	27,469	3,005
Lesser Black-backed Gull	32,295	37,555	39,824	43,310	24,560	5,187	4,498	4,783	3,057	2,758	5,474	165
Herring Gull	48,734	33,782	35,819	40,799	41,379	29,145	28,425	31,929	31,148	64,396	45,682	6,947
Yellow-legged Gull	1	0	1	8	100	89	54	12	38	17	5	0
Caspian Gull	0	0	0	0	0	0	0	0	1	0	0	0
Western Yellow-l. Gull	0	0	0	0	0	0	9	4	1	0	0	0
Iceland Gull	4	1	0	0	0	1	0	0	1	1	1	0
Glaucous Gull	4	1	0	1	0	1	1	6	1	3	4	0
Great Black-backed Gull	2,237	1,304	1,746	2,896	4,808	6,858	7,152	7,595	5,126	5,752	3,964	685
Kittiwake	102	157	247	145	2,667	483	336	189	86	106	299	0
Unidentified gull	440	88	20,601	50	2,931	5,841	2,185	1,841	1,150	8,195	8,240	0
Sandwich Tern	840	4,435	6,319	6,288	8,871	2,855	37	2	2	1	1	1
Roseate Tern	0	1	3	3	2	0	0	0	0	0	0	0
Common Tern	30	1,255	2,352	3,194	6,908	857	7	0	1	0	0	0
Arctic Tern	1	258	356	624	688	23	2	0	0	0	0	0
Forster's Tern	0	0	0	0	1	0	0	0	0	0	0	0
Little Tern	8	522	656	600	370	28	0	0	0	0	0	0
Black Tern	0	102	1	7	13	14	0	1	0	0	0	0
Unidentified tern	0	0	0	18	7	0	0	0	0	0	0	0
'Commic' tern	0	2	6	6	62	0	2	0	0	0	0	0
Kingfisher	7	1	8	10	32	88	80	61	60	45	29	1

NORTHERN IRELAND

	Apr	May	Jun	Jul	Aug	Sep	Oct	Nov	Dec	Jan	Feb	Mar
Sectors	*14*	*8*	*9*	*9*	*10*	*26*	*28*	*65*	*29*	*27*	*62*	*9*
Sites	*4*	*2*	*2*	*2*	*2*	*7*	*7*	*8*	*7*	*7*	*8*	*1*
Red-throated Diver	1	0	0	0	0	8	11	24	13	17	24	0
Black-throated Diver	0	0	0	0	0	0	0	3	1	0	3	0
Great Northern Diver	0	0	0	0	0	1	0	3	7	16	18	0
Little Grebe	3	1	0	4	0	138	121	107	124	109	89	3
Great Crested Grebe	0	0	0	0	0	1,104	1,337	1,575	1,697	1,337	1,731	0
Slavonian Grebe	0	0	0	0	0	0	0	1	9	3	0	0
Cormorant	43	12	25	15	56	1,074	996	720	562	366	423	7
Grey Heron	7	8	5	8	11	192	121	101	95	137	66	0
Mute Swan	126	85	33	11	7	321	400	373	303	209	218	31
Black Swan	0	1	0	0	0	0	0	0	0	0	0	0
Bewick's Swan	0	0	0	0	0	0	0	0	2	0	10	0
Whooper Swan	34	0	0	0	0	0	449	144	436	182	337	0
Swan Goose	0	0	0	0	0	0	0	0	0	0	2	0
Pink-footed Goose	1	0	0	0	0	0	6	0	0	0	0	0
Greenland Whitefront	30	0	0	0	0	0	0	2	0	0	60	0
Greylag Goose (Iceland)	713	0	0	0	0	187	353	210	343	305	356	0
Snow Goose	0	0	0	0	0	1	0	1	1	1	1	0
Canada Goose	0	0	0	0	0	0	6	218	310	117	58	0
Barnacle Goose (natur.)	0	0	0	0	0	138	158	156	153	153	132	0
Dark-bellied Brent	0	0	0	0	0	0	0	0	0	0	1	0
Light-bellied Brent (Can.)	505	0	0	0	0	5,996	17,077	18,591	9,565	3,775	2,849	135

	Apr	May	Jun	Jul	Aug	Sep	Oct	Nov	Dec	Jan	Feb	Mar
hybrid goose	0	0	0	0	0	0	0	0	1	0	0	0
Shelduck	323	53	64	17	3	72	468	1,771	3,650	4,327	2,781	79
Mandarin	4	0	2	0	0	0	0	0	0	0	0	0
Wigeon	53	2	0	0	5	1,438	10,511	7,385	2,120	2,730	1,428	381
Gadwall	0	0	0	0	0	72	59	62	26	34	31	0
Teal	70	0	0	0	5	3,775	1,910	2,093	1,730	2,738	1,554	0
Green-winged Teal	0	0	0	0	0	0	1	1	1	1	0	0
Mallard	118	49	40	62	193	3,387	3,013	2,386	2,486	2,465	1,449	0
Pintail	2	0	0	0	0	13	13	90	97	255	324	0
Shoveler	0	0	0	0	0	12	100	166	155	184	70	0
Pochard	0	0	0	0	0	35	49	75	37	117	49	0
Tufted Duck	0	0	0	0	0	205	156	157	127	158	225	0
Scaup	0	0	0	0	0	5	24	514	946	1,078	1,078	0
Eider	0	6	0	0	0	1,491	1,833	2,141	927	1,461	1,629	0
Long-tailed Duck	0	0	0	0	0	0	0	182	27	12	35	0
Common Scoter	0	0	0	0	0	1	4	0	3	0	0	0
Goldeneye	26	0	0	0	0	3	44	233	444	578	666	12
Red-breasted Merganser	41	2	0	1	1	426	420	371	365	331	355	3
Goosander	0	0	0	0	0	1	1	1	1	1	1	0
Water Rail	0	0	0	0	0	0	0	0	1	0	0	0
Moorhen	3	1	0	2	0	57	51	37	38	33	48	5
Coot	2	0	0	0	0	452	461	404	249	329	188	6
Oystercatcher	1,202	433	269	494	789	17,582	15,919	17,814	17,672	13,421	14,169	349
Ringed Plover	45	25	2	1	71	579	750	728	400	345	560	16
Golden Plover	6,140	0	0	0	0	1,655	4,884	5,680	1,508	5,156	9,337	367
Grey Plover	2	0	0	0	2	6	82	204	118	111	328	10
Lapwing	56	1	46	98	210	1,159	4,270	10,763	11,228	11,702	12,437	102
Knot	0	0	1	0	7	513	359	473	3,956	7,125	2,410	164
Sanderling	4	0	0	0	0	127	109	90	93	105	110	132
Little Stint	0	0	0	0	0	6	0	0	0	0	0	0
Curlew Sandpiper	0	0	0	0	0	17	0	0	0	0	0	0
Purple Sandpiper	0	0	0	0	0	1	3	93	7	13	86	0
Dunlin	87	29	10	10	69	1,359	1,680	4,512	7,240	12,445	10,871	840
Ruff	0	0	0	0	1	4	2	5	2	2	2	0
Jack Snipe	0	0	0	0	0	1	0	2	1	0	0	0
Snipe	2	0	0	0	0	31	55	160	63	105	126	24
Long-billed Dowitcher	0	0	0	0	0	0	0	0	1	1	1	0
Black-tailed Godwit	0	0	4	0	14	406	330	303	93	243	65	0
Bar-tailed Godwit	24	0	0	0	5	206	524	447	906	1,719	1,318	0
Whimbrel	0	18	0	1	0	1	0	0	0	0	0	0
Curlew	1,053	32	209	152	582	4,310	5,486	6,511	5,591	4,193	6,460	243
Spotted Redshank	0	0	0	0	0	0	0	0	1	0	0	0
Redshank	1,703	42	54	361	949	7,042	8,825	8,769	7,529	6,181	8,388	753
Greenshank	4	0	12	7	31	108	148	88	69	58	54	9
Common Sandpiper	0	0	0	5	2	1	0	0	0	0	0	0
Turnstone	46	0	0	1	32	790	809	1,606	879	659	1,411	82
Mediterranean Gull	0	0	0	0	0	0	0	0	1	0	0	0
Little Gull	0	1	0	0	0	1	1	0	0	0	0	0
Black-headed Gull	254	65	81	515	564	7,247	8,147	10,006	8,849	11,689	11,007	86
Common Gull	80	128	38	86	343	1,668	7,250	3,313	4,423	2,572	3,993	34
Lesser Black-backed Gull	8	7	9	4	1	89	58	26	8	16	50	0
Herring Gull	44	103	127	132	120	2,038	2,692	3,084	4,953	4,869	8,055	26
Iceland Gull	0	0	0	0	0	0	0	0	0	1	1	0
Glaucous Gull	0	0	0	0	0	0	0	0	0	1	1	0
Great Black-backed Gull	113	56	78	72	57	436	392	526	467	372	472	7
Kittiwake	0	1	27	6	1	2	0	0	0	1	0	0
Sandwich Tern	196	81	180	201	169	421	0	0	0	0	0	0
Common Tern	0	2	2	2	0	13	0	0	0	0	0	0
'Commic' tern	0	18	0	0	0	0	0	0	0	0	0	0
Kingfisher	0	0	0	1	1	1	1	1	0	0	0	0

APPENDIX 9. TOTAL NUMBERS OF WATERBIRDS RECORDED BY WeBS AT INLAND SITES IN 2000–01

GREAT BRITAIN

	Apr	May	Jun	Jul	Aug	Sep	Oct	Nov	Dec	Jan	Feb	Mar
Sectors	968	897	866	875	896	1,498	1,797	1,812	1,824	1,702	1,719	133
Sites	825	776	746	768	785	1,241	1,430	1,434	1,452	1,338	1,308	124
Red-throated Diver	15	10	6	21	7	0	0	0	1	8	3	0
Black-throated Diver	2	1	0	5	6	3	0	0	0	0	0	0
Great Northern Diver	2	1	0	0	2	1	1	7	14	46	8	0
Little Grebe	1,263	783	876	1,197	1,971	3,377	2,944	2,228	2,002	1,982	1,549	180
Great Crested Grebe	3,911	3,414	3,378	4,539	5,418	8,423	8,319	6,889	5,103	5,137	4,719	277
Red-necked Grebe	3	2	2	1	1	3	3	4	3	3	6	0
Slavonian Grebe	9	0	4	3	6	37	33	24	22	14	14	2
Black-necked Grebe	38	12	43	31	22	34	34	23	23	10	13	1
Cormorant	3,430	2,634	1,924	2,658	2,635	5,757	6,970	6,508	5,966	6,598	5,709	596
Bittern	0	2	0	0	1	2	7	4	13	9	7	2
Cattle Egret	0	0	0	0	1	1	1	0	0	0	0	0
Little Egret	9	12	11	13	26	26	39	42	66	86	72	6
Great White Egret	0	0	0	2	1	1	1	0	0	0	0	0
Grey Heron	998	988	1,250	1,296	1,622	2,254	2,392	1,930	1,885	1,998	1,941	202
Purple Heron	0	0	0	1	0	0	0	0	0	0	0	0
White Stork	0	0	0	2	3	2	2	2	2	0	2	0
Spoonbill	0	0	3	0	2	2	0	0	0	0	0	0
Mute Swan	6,866	6,576	7,833	8,456	9,399	13,271	15,360	13,816	12,843	13,288	10,430	1,226
Black Swan	14	12	16	21	27	40	47	43	35	28	29	1
Bewick's Swan	6	3	0	0	0	3	23	105	711	1,636	948	0
Whooper Swan	219	24	18	27	27	33	2,251	3,696	2,776	3,256	3,065	1,069
hybrid Cygnus	0	2	1	0	0	1	0	0	0	0	1	0
Swan Goose	14	14	17	19	19	44	22	31	42	20	35	0
Bean Goose	0	2	2	0	0	1	187	30	193	276	51	0
Pink-footed Goose	2,598	306	9	8	10	2,111	37,216	42,705	29,138	31,137	30,185	45
White-fronted Goose	0	0	0	0	0	0	0	2	0	0	0	0
European Whitefront	0	3	1	0	0	4	7	34	88	499	203	1
Greenland Whitefront	16	0	0	0	0	0	244	662	201	583	425	1
Lesser Whitefront	0	0	1	1	0	0	0	0	0	0	0	0
Greylag Goose (Ice.)	2,952	487	1,287	2,017	1,842	3,027	11,932	21,335	24,024	17,858	19,676	804
Greylag Goose (NW Sco.)	104	19	8	5	859	1,152	763	624	712	479	587	0
Greylag Goose (natur.)	3,970	2,868	8,069	6,930	11,024	15,637	14,812	15,386	14,216	13,424	7,981	394
Bar-headed Goose	4	7	15	14	6	6	24	12	16	8	6	0
Snow Goose	14	10	28	11	17	42	28	41	56	19	14	2
Ross's Goose	0	0	0	0	0	0	1	0	1	1	0	0
Emperor Goose	1	0	1	0	2	1	2	2	5	2	2	0
Canada Goose	12,668	10,416	25,635	25,292	26,731	42,710	34,165	36,787	35,715	36,709	26,836	1,800
Barnacle Goose (Gre.)	90	16	18	22	24	28	99	32	122	168	105	0
Barnacle Goose (Sval.)	12,813	9	35	59	8	88	7,842	9,046	3,530	5,636	5,017	1,805
Barnacle Goose (natur.)	112	75	108	124	130	175	341	609	766	553	343	14
Dark-bellied Brent	14	0	0	0	0	2	41	72	268	1,050	195	0
Light-bellied Brent (Sval.)	1	1	0	0	0	0	1	4	0	4	0	0
Light-bellied Brent (Can.)	0	0	0	1	1	19	0	0	3	0	1	0
Red-breasted Goose	0	0	0	1	0	1	1	1	0	1	1	0
Egyptian Goose	69	56	115	120	96	292	182	140	104	70	88	2
hybrid goose	53	43	48	56	44	106	80	104	108	121	108	10
feral/domestic goose	129	130	148	153	152	327	376	387	411	301	323	19
unidentified goose	0	0	0	0	0	0	0	0	0	1	0	0
Ruddy Shelduck	5	3	3	5	7	4	3	4	1	2	2	2
Cape Shelduck	0	0	0	0	0	0	1	0	1	1	1	0
Australian Shelduck	0	0	0	0	0	1	0	0	0	0	0	0
Shelduck	1,514	1,315	791	347	203	167	210	670	1,456	1,999	2,108	746
Muscovy Duck	31	11	12	10	12	27	86	79	79	74	68	46
Wood Duck	2	3	1	0	0	6	9	5	5	5	4	0
Mandarin	111	96	123	118	106	283	374	305	453	439	380	7
Wigeon	12,184	160	114	207	636	18,947	64,383	113,053	138,815	156,881	125,412	5,682
American Wigeon	1	1	1	1	1	1	2	2	3	5	7	4
Chiloe Wigeon	0	0	0	2	0	0	0	0	2	0	1	0
Gadwall	2,289	1,342	1,775	2,907	3,603	8,656	11,482	10,007	9,634	11,853	8,904	632

	Apr	May	Jun	Jul	Aug	Sep	Oct	Nov	Dec	Jan	Feb	Mar
Teal	8,531	300	569	820	6,261	32,011	51,683	61,818	70,463	75,220	64,701	5,061
Green-winged Teal	0	0	0	0	0	0	2	1	3	4	3	1
Speckled Teal	0	0	0	0	0	4	2	1	2	0	2	0
Mallard	20,968	18,619	26,992	38,093	52,697	84,107	97,746	98,961	99,417	104,370	71,257	5,026
Black Duck	0	0	0	0	1	1	1	0	0	0	0	0
Pintail	437	17	6	10	17	507	1,118	3,973	7,217	6,160	8,158	220
Yellow-billed Pintail	0	0	0	0	1	0	0	0	0	0	0	0
Bahama Pintail	1	0	0	1	0	2	2	0	1	0	0	0
Red-billed Teal	0	1	0	0	1	1	0	0	0	0	0	0
Garganey	25	33	15	30	32	20	2	4	1	0	0	0
Blue-winged Teal	1	1	0	0	1	1	0	0	1	0	0	0
Shoveler	1,966	339	247	470	2,336	6,621	7,748	7,529	7,604	7,569	5,931	734
Ringed Teal	0	0	0	1	0	2	0	0	0	0	0	0
Red-crested Pochard	13	4	4	7	8	35	56	74	57	109	69	0
Rosybill	0	0	0	0	0	0	1	1	0	0	1	0
Pochard	1,293	607	1,446	3,350	8,390	8,770	19,035	24,154	29,444	29,380	26,155	1,383
Ring-necked Duck	2	0	2	0	0	0	0	1	3	3	2	0
Ferruginous Duck	0	0	0	0	0	2	1	0	3	4	1	0
New Zealand Scaup	0	0	0	0	0	0	1	1	0	0	0	0
Tufted Duck	22,703	11,202	10,685	24,825	37,058	42,308	47,937	51,633	49,677	52,902	41,740	2,627
Scaup	14	6	0	1	4	15	249	228	357	274	200	5
Lesser Scaup	1	2	0	0	0	0	0	1	0	0	0	0
Eider	96	12	0	7	0	0	52	30	63	101	68	0
Long-tailed Duck	21	82	0	0	0	0	51	103	74	132	70	6
Common Scoter	0	2	1	91	2	2	2	4	3	5	5	0
Velvet Scoter	0	0	0	0	0	0	1	0	0	0	1	0
Goldeneye	3,506	174	46	118	85	211	840	4,114	6,397	7,663	7,894	359
Smew	3	0	0	0	0	0	0	10	72	218	187	7
Red-breasted Merganser	86	189	60	84	125	85	95	64	110	139	151	0
Goosander	274	184	83	162	196	347	980	1,334	1,537	2,223	2,315	114
Ruddy Duck	1,486	642	577	688	1,219	2,341	3,361	2,731	2,266	3,624	3,029	82
Argentine Blue-bill	0	0	0	0	0	1	0	0	0	0	0	0
feral/hybrid Mallard type	254	261	321	357	248	442	1,144	1,422	1,350	415	412	53
hybrid Anas	13	8	5	5	8	8	16	12	13	5	4	3
hybrid Aythya	2	1	1	2	1	3	2	2	10	10	6	0
unidentified duck	0	0	4	10	0	0	9	10	1	3	0	0
Water Rail	109	40	64	53	68	123	241	267	369	277	195	32
Spotted Crake	0	0	0	0	0	2	1	0	0	0	0	0
Moorhen	4,865	3,254	3,403	4,733	6,203	9,896	10,636	8,673	9,313	8,372	8,026	1,178
Coot	23,289	13,089	21,140	38,860	55,663	94,353	98,386	94,535	82,019	83,477	60,664	2,918
Crane	0	0	0	0	1	0	0	0	0	0	0	0
Oystercatcher	2,013	1,404	1,054	1,161	423	277	217	376	393	384	2,836	165
Avocet	2	173	0	132	9	1	0	0	0	0	0	120
Little Ringed Plover	229	195	190	150	41	14	0	0	0	2	0	4
Ringed Plover	145	225	96	139	192	170	347	31	123	135	228	21
Dotterel	0	0	0	0	1	0	0	0	0	0	0	0
Golden Plover	2,995	194	6	78	1,475	5,473	25,375	30,467	25,205	16,684	34,442	4,609
Grey Plover	15	16	0	0	0	3	8	0	16	9	3	100
Unidentified wader	0	0	0	0	2	0	40	0	12	0	0	0
Lapwing	3,043	2,094	4,711	11,400	29,984	51,138	58,018	78,254	88,967	83,192	133,262	1,986
Knot	1	20	0	2	16	126	26	91	17	39	2	0
Sanderling	2	15	0	10	2	4	0	3	0	6	5	0
Little Stint	2	2	0	4	2	24	2	5	1	6	2	0
Temminck's Stint	0	3	0	0	0	0	0	0	0	0	0	0
White-rumped Sandpiper	0	0	0	0	0	1	0	0	0	0	0	0
Pectoral Sandpiper	0	0	0	0	0	1	0	0	0	0	0	0
Curlew Sandpiper	0	0	0	1	3	10	1	0	0	0	0	0
Purple Sandpiper	0	0	0	0	0	0	1	23	56	339	0	0
Dunlin	77	238	14	124	199	288	433	651	1,310	2,477	1,759	36
Ruff	112	11	0	53	349	579	217	188	252	644	279	34
Jack Snipe	21	0	0	0	0	8	38	54	63	72	73	4
Snipe	776	58	52	166	515	2,605	4,122	3,929	3,202	4,672	3,633	209
Woodcock	2	0	0	0	1	0	3	10	22	18	16	1
Black-tailed Godwit	1,247	44	9	93	145	56	198	207	126	1,688	2,768	28
Bar-tailed Godwit	18	102	0	0	4	15	29	24	21	35	2	0
Whimbrel	8	77	0	7	9	2	1	1	0	0	0	0
Curlew	818	343	327	662	1,598	1,358	4,165	6,922	6,250	6,473	5,537	137

	Apr	May	Jun	Jul	Aug	Sep	Oct	Nov	Dec	Jan	Feb	Mar
Spotted Redshank	2	4	0	8	25	32	14	2	2	3	3	0
Redshank	1,448	549	315	178	193	280	852	1,446	1,610	1,476	1,418	107
Marsh Sandpiper	0	0	0	0	0	1	0	0	0	0	0	0
Greenshank	12	102	2	59	267	107	39	7	13	13	11	0
Green Sandpiper	64	16	64	244	276	181	97	96	96	100	85	15
Wood Sandpiper	0	15	2	19	10	15	0	0	0	0	0	0
Common Sandpiper	47	537	269	539	344	156	27	7	17	9	7	2
Turnstone	23	28	2	6	7	1	232	226	477	269	899	0
Grey Phalarope	0	0	0	0	0	1	1	0	1	0	0	0
Mediterranean Gull	14	3	2	38	25	27	3	8	10	7	12	4
Little Gull	2	28	146	77	1	194	32	0	2	4	0	0
Bonaparte's Gull	0	0	0	0	0	0	0	0	0	0	0	0
Black-headed Gull	28,275	15,461	16,295	14,338	19,732	52,676	79,628	123,244	132,589	117,250	95,194	14,949
Ring-billed Gull	2	0	0	0	0	0	0	0	0	3	2	0
Common Gull	1,211	845	377	1,002	2,459	19,734	25,140	52,921	41,720	41,715	35,004	1,371
Lesser Black-backed Gull	1,933	1,770	1,396	2,458	3,681	6,107	10,745	10,682	8,289	4,010	6,148	797
Herring Gull	3,039	2,485	3,273	2,667	4,734	6,638	7,940	9,620	10,052	14,431	6,442	546
Yellow-legged Gull	0	0	0	4	11	15	24	12	9	8	8	0
Caspian Gull	0	0	0	0	0	0	0	1	0	0	0	0
West. Yellow-legged Gull	0	1	0	0	0	0	5	0	0	1	0	0
Iceland Gull	1	1	0	0	0	0	1	0	0	5	1	0
Glaucous Gull	0	0	0	0	0	0	0	1	0	3	2	2
Great Black-backed Gull	289	213	252	311	377	880	621	2,905	4,251	2,411	975	109
Kittiwake	2	55	4	88	236	0	2	1	0	0	0	0
Unidentified gull	0	0	0	147	71	0	0	0	291	221	27	0
hybrid gull	6	4	0	0	0	0	130	0	0	0	0	0
Sandwich Tern	11	59	2	19	0	14	0	0	0	0	0	0
Common Tern	32	1,298	1,502	1,477	652	129	2	0	0	0	0	0
Arctic Tern	24	723	340	47	1	3	1	0	0	0	0	0
Little Tern	0	18	0	6	0	0	0	0	0	0	0	0
Black Tern	0	287	1	2	3	19	1	0	0	0	0	0
White-winged Black Tern	0	0	0	0	0	1	0	0	0	0	0	0
Unidentified tern	0	2	0	0	0	0	0	0	0	0	0	0
'Commic' tern	0	0	1	0	0	0	0	0	0	0	0	0
Kingfisher	89	101	109	148	206	302	283	236	181	148	138	19

NORTHERN IRELAND

	Apr	May	Jun	Jul	Aug	Sep	Oct	Nov	Dec	Jan	Feb	Mar
Sectors	0	0	0	0	0	104	111	110	113	113	115	0
Sites	0	0	0	0	0	7	11	7	11	11	11	0
Little Grebe	0	0	0	0	0	412	337	442	410	305	257	0
Great Crested Grebe	0	0	0	0	0	1,550	242	420	328	110	299	0
Cormorant	0	0	0	0	0	1,416	682	574	499	366	665	0
Grey Heron	0	0	0	0	0	267	207	81	80	63	143	0
Mute Swan	0	0	0	0	0	1,995	1,777	1,320	1,266	1,335	1,225	0
Bewick's Swan	0	0	0	0	0	0	102	0	1	2	15	0
Whooper Swan	0	0	0	0	0	15	301	480	736	503	677	0
Greylag Goose (Iceland)	0	0	0	0	0	14	20	137	286	324	812	0
Shelduck	0	0	0	0	0	4	64	3	2	26	74	0
Wigeon	0	0	0	0	0	318	1,236	1,918	2,375	2,079	1,728	0
Gadwall	0	0	0	0	0	122	158	94	89	98	98	0
Teal	0	0	0	0	0	815	437	284	2,029	1,716	1,041	0
Mallard	0	0	0	0	0	6,641	3,476	2,916	2,793	3,037	1,776	0
Pintail	0	0	0	0	0	0	0	1	0	2	2	0
Shoveler	0	0	0	0	0	53	0	2	1	28	0	0
Pochard	0	0	0	0	0	1,206	2,786	13,307	24,393	16,061	10,213	0
Ferruginous Duck	0	0	0	0	0	0	0	0	0	1	1	0
Tufted Duck	0	0	0	0	0	4,169	17,523	22,706	26,471	18,521	17,270	0
Scaup	0	0	0	0	0	5	33	1,023	1,670	2,127	2,633	0
Goldeneye	0	0	0	0	0	66	456	7,535	6,860	7,245	8,643	0
Red-breasted Merganser	0	0	0	0	0	21	3	1	0	1	3	0
Ruddy Duck	0	0	0	0	0	6	27	22	40	1	53	0
Water Rail	0	0	0	0	0	0	35	0	0	0	0	0
Moorhen	0	0	0	0	0	250	207	207	173	147	165	0
Coot	0	0	0	0	0	5,924	6,779	5,699	4,896	5,309	3,136	0

	Apr	May	Jun	Jul	Aug	Sep	Oct	Nov	Dec	Jan	Feb	Mar
Golden Plover	0	0	0	0	0	75	5,794	6,526	7,652	749	3,081	0
Lapwing	0	0	0	0	0	1,651	1,748	6,281	5,136	2,454	4,343	0
Dunlin	0	0	0	0	0	7	8	195	108	304	95	0
Jack Snipe	0	0	0	0	0	0	0	0	1	2	0	0
Snipe	0	0	0	0	0	14	29	51	123	113	99	0
Black-tailed Godwit	0	0	0	0	0	0	0	0	0	0	10	0
Curlew	0	0	0	0	0	84	188	265	467	412	433	0
Redshank	0	0	0	0	0	6	2	9	42	15	6	0
Black-headed Gull	0	0	0	0	0	12	76	89	103	195	201	0

APPENDIX 10. LOCATIONS OF WeBS COUNT SITES MENTIONED IN THIS REPORT

The location of all counts sites or areas mentioned in this report are given here. Sites are listed alphabetically, with the 1 km square OS grid reference for the centre of the site, the habitat (H) and the county or district. Note that this is not an exhaustive list of WeBS sites counted in 2000–01, simply those mentioned by name in this report. Figure A1 shows the location of many of the more important sites for waterbirds.

Key to habitat codes (the predominant habitat type is given for complex sites containing many different habitats)

L	Lake	M	Marsh	
R	Reservoir	S	Sewage treatment works	
P	Gravel or sand pit	E	Estuary	
V	River	O	Open coast	
C	Canal	N	Non-wetland	

Site	1-km sq	H	WeBS Region
Abberton Reservoir	TL9818	R	Essex
Aberdeen Beach (Dee Mouth to Don Mouth)	NJ9507	O	Grampian
Aberlady Bay	NT4581	E	Lothian
Aignish Bay	NB4932	O	Western Isles
Alde Complex	TM4257	E	Suffolk
Allington Gravel Pits	SU4717	P	Hampshire
Alnmouth to Boulmer	NU2612	O	N'th'mberland
Alresford Pond	SU593	L	Hampshire
Alt Estuary	SD2903	E	Merseyside
Alton Water	TM1436	R	Suffolk
Angler's Country Park Lake	SE3716	P	W Yorkshire
Appin/Erriska/B'loch/Lismore	NM9043	O	Strathclyde
Applecross Bay - Sand	NG688	O	Highland
Aqualate Mere	SJ7720	L	Staffordshire
Ardleigh Reservoir	TM0328	R	Essex
Ardrossan to Farland Head	NS2045	O	Strathclyde
Arlington Reservoir	TQ5307	R	Sussex
Arran	NR9535	O	Strathclyde
Arun Valley	TQ0314	V	West Sussex
Ashford Common Waterworks	TQ0869	S	Surrey
Ashleworth Ham	SO8326	M	Glos
Attenborough Gravel Pits	SK5234	P	Notts
Auchencairn Bay	NX8252	E	D & Galloway
Avon Estuary	SX6745	E	Devon
Axe Estuary (Devon)	SY250	E	Devon
Ayr to Troon	NS3425	O	Strathclyde
Bainton Pits	TF1107	P	Cambs
Ballyroney Lake	J229382	L	Down
Ballysaggart Lough	H7961	L	Tyrone
Balranald RSPB Reserve	NF7169	L	Western Isles
Bann Estuary	C7935	E	Londonderry
Barcombe Mills Reservoir	TQ434	R	East Sussex
Bardney Pits	TF1168	P	Lincolnshire
Barleycroft Gravel Pits	TL3672	P	Cambs
Baron's Haugh	NS7555	L	Strathclyde
Barons Folly	NT6426	L	Borders
Barton Broad	TG3621	L	Norfolk
Barton Pits	SK2017	P	Staffordshire
Baston/Langtoft Gravel Pits	TF1212	P	Lincolnshire
Bay of Sandoyne to Holme Sound	HY4800	O	Orkney
Beadnell to Seahouses	NU2231	O	N'th'mberland

Site	1-km sq	H	WeBS Region
Beaulieu Estuary	SZ4298	E	Hampshire
Beauly Firth	NH5848	E	Highland
Beddington Sewage Farm	TQ2966	S	Gtr London
Bedfont & Ashford GP	TQ0872	P	Gtr London
Belfast Lough	J4083	E	Down
Belvide Reservoir	SJ8610	R	Staffordshire
Benacre Broad	TM5383	L	Suffolk
Benbecula	NF8150	N	Western Isles
Besthorpe & Girton GP	SK8165	P	Notts
Bewl Water	TQ6733	R	Sussex
Birgham Haugh	NT7938	N	Borders
Black Cart Water	NS4767	M	Strathclyde
Blackmoorfoot Reservoir	SE0912	R	W Yorkshire
Blackwater Estuary	TL9307	E	Essex
Blagdon Lake	ST5150	R	Avon
Blair Drummond Safari Park Loch	NS7398	L	Central
Blatherwyke Lake	SP9796	L	Northants
Blickling Lake	TG1729	L	Norfolk
Blithfield Reservoir	SK0524	R	Staffordshire
Blunham Gravel Pits	TL1551	P	Bedfordshire
Blyth Estuary (Northumberland)	NZ3082	E	N'th'mberland
Blyth Estuary (Suffolk)	TM4675	E	Suffolk
Boghill Fields (Coleraine)	C8734	N	Londonderry
Bolton-on-Swale Gravel Pits	SE2498	P	N Yorkshire
Bough Beech Reservoir	TQ4947	R	Kent
Brading Harbour	SZ6388	E	Isle of Wight
Bradley Pools	SK225	L	Derbyshire
Bramshill Park Lake	SK7560	L	Hampshire
Brandon Marsh Nature Reserve	SP3875	M	Warwickshire
Brent Reservoir	TQ2287	R	Gtr London
Breydon Water & Berney Marshes	TG4907	E	Norfolk
Bridge of Earn	NO1417	N	Tayside
Broad Water Canal	J1462	C	Antrim
Broomfleet Brickyard Ponds	SE867	P	Humberside
Buckden/Stirtloe Gravel Pits	TL2066	P	Cambs
Burghfield Gravel Pits	SU6870	P	Berkshire
Burry Inlet	SS5096	E	W Glamorgan, Dyfed
Busbridge Lakes	SU9742	L	Surrey
Bush River: Deepstown	C9434	V	Antrim

Site	1-km sq	H	WeBS Region	Site	1-km sq	H	WeBS Region
Bute	NS0761	L	Strathclyde	Criddling Stubbs Quarry Pool	SE5120	P	W Yorkshire
Buxton Pavilion Gardens	SK053	L	Derbyshire	Cromarty Firth	NH7771	E	Highland
Caerlaverock WWT	NY0565	E	D & Galloway	Crombie Reservoir	NO5240	R	Tayside
Caistron Quarry	NU0001	P	N'th'mberland	Crome's Broad	TG3719	L	Norfolk
Caithness Lochs	ND1859	L	Highland	Cropston Reservoir	SK5410	R	Leicestershire
Camas Dubh-aird	NG783	O	Highland	Crouch/Roach Estuary	TQ8496	E	Essex
Cambois to Newbiggin	NZ3084	O	N'th'mberland	Crowdy Reservoir	SX1483	R	Cornwall
Camel Estuary	SW9474	E	Cornwall	Croxall Pits	SK1814	P	Staffordshire
Cameron Reservoir	NO4711	R	Fife	Cuckmere Estuary	TV517	E	East Sussex
Canary Road	H8755	M	Armagh	Cuttmil Ponds	SU9145	L	Surrey
Cardigan Bay	SH5020	O	Gwynedd, Dyfed	Dagenham Chase GP	TQ5186	P	Gtr London
Carlingford Lough	J2013	E	Down	Dart Estuary	SX846	E	Devon
Carlingford to Newcastle	J3718	O	Down	Darwell Reservoir	TQ7121	R	Sussex
Carmarthen Bay	SN2501	E	Dyfed	Deben Estuary	TM2942	E	Suffolk
Carr Vale Flash & Reserve Pond	SK4570	L	Derbyshire	Dee Estuary (England/Wales)	SJ2675	E	Merseyside, Cheshire, Clwyd
Carse of Stirling	NS7196	N	Central	Dee Estuary (Scotland)	NJ9505	E	Grampian
Carsebreck/Rhynd Lochs	NN8609	L	Tayside	Dee Flood Meadows	SJ4159	V	Cheshire
Carsington Water	SK2451	R	Derbyshire	Deene Lake	SP9492	L	Northants
Castlecaldwell Refuge Area	H0060	L	Fermanagh	Deeping St James GP	TF1808	P	Lincolnshire
Catchpenny Pool	SJ8171	L	Cheshire	Deer/Shapinsay Sounds & Tankerness	HY5513	O	Orkney
Cemlyn Bay & Lagoon	SH3393	O	Gwynedd	Dengie Flats	TM0300	E	Essex
Chasewater	SK0307	R	W Midlands	Derwent Reservoir	NZ0251	R	Durham
Cheddar Reservoir	ST4454	R	Somerset	Derwent Water	NY2621	L	Cumbria
Chew Valley Lake	ST5659	R	Avon	Deveron Estuary	NJ6964	E	Grampian
Chichester Gravel Pits	SU8703	P	West Sussex	Didlington Lakes	TL7796	P	Norfolk
Chichester Harbour	SU7700	E	West Sussex	Dingle Marshes & Walberswick NNR	TM4872	M	Suffolk
Chillington Hall Pool	SJ8550	L	Staffordshire	Dinnet Lochs (Lochs Davan & Kinord)	NJ4800	L	Grampian
Christchurch Harbour	SZ1792	E	Dorset	Dinton Pastures	SU7872	M	Berkshire
Church Wilne Reservoir	SK4632	R	Derbyshire	Ditchford Gravel Pits	SP9468	P	Northants
Clachan/Whitehouse	NR7959	N	Strathclyde	Don Mouth to Ythan Mouth	NJ9815	O	Grampian
Clatto Reservoir	NO3607	R	Fife	Doon Estuary	NS3219	O	Strathclyde
Clea Lakes	J506557	L	Down	Dornoch Firth	NH7384	E	Highland
Cleddau Estuary	SN0005	E	Dyfed	Doxey Marshes	SJ9024	M	Staffordshire
Clifford Hill Gravel Pits	SP8061	P	Northants	Draycote Water	SP4469	R	Warwickshire
Clumber Park Lake	SK6374	L	Notts	Drumgay Lough	H2448	L	Fermanagh
Clwyd Estuary	SJ0079	E	Clwyd	Drummond Pond	NN8518	L	Tayside
Clyde Est.	NS3576	E	Strathclyde	Duddon Estuary	SD2081	E	Cumbria
Colemans Reservoir	TL8415	R	Essex	Dundrum Bay	J4235	E	Down
Coll	NM2055	N	Strathclyde	Dungeness Gravel Pits	TR0619	P	Kent
Colliford Reservoir	SX1871	R	Cornwall	Dupplin Loch	NO0320	L	Tayside
Colne Estuary	TM0614	E	Essex	Durham Coast	NZ4349	O	Durham
Colne Valley Gravel Pits	TQ0489	P	Gtr London	Dyfi Estuary	SN6394	E	Dyfed
Colonsay/Oronsay	NR3896	N	Strathclyde	Dysynni Estuary	SH5702	E	Gwynedd
Colt crag Reservoir	NY948	R	N'th'mberland	Earls Barton Gravel Pits	SP8966	P	Northants
Colwick Country Park	SK6039	L	Notts	Earlsferry to Anstruther	NO5302	O	Fife
Colwyn Bay	SH9079	O	Clwyd	East Sanday Coast	HY7241	O	Orkney
Connaught Water	TQ4095	L	Essex	East Wretham Meres	TL9088	L	Norfolk
Coombe Country Park	SP3974	L	Warwickshire	Easterloch/Uyeasound	HP5901	O	Shetland
Corby Loch	NJ9214	L	Grampian	Easting/Sand Wick	HP6201	O	Shetland
Cotswold Water Park (East)	SU1999	P	Glos, Oxon	Eccup Reservoir	SE2941	R	W Yorkshire
Cotswold Water Park (West)	SU0595	P	Glos, Wilts	Echna Loch	ND4796	L	Orkney
Craigalea to Newcastle	J704337	O	Down	Eden Estuary	NO4719	E	Fife
Cranwich Gravel Pits	TL7796	P	Norfolk	Edington Lake	ST9253	L	Wiltshire
Cresswell to Chevington Burn	NZ2895	O	N'th'mberland				
Crichel Lake	ST9907	L	Dorset				

Site	1-km sq	H	WeBS Region
Egilsay	HY4730	L	Orkney
Eglwys Nunydd Reservoir	SS7984	R	W Glamorgan
Elland Gravel Pits	SE1322	P	W Yorkshire
Ellesmere Lakes	SJ4035	L	Shropshire
Emberton Gravel Pits	SP8850	P	Bucks
Entrance to Deer/Shapinsay Sounds	HY5513	O	Orkney
Epsom Common Ponds	TQ180	L	Surrey
Erme Estuary	SX6249	E	Devon
Eversley Cross & Yateley GP	SU8601	P	Hampshire
Exe Estuary	SX9883	E	Devon
Eyebrook Reservoir	SP8595	R	Leicestershire
Fairburn Ings	SE4627	P	N Yorkshire
Fal Complex	SW8541	E	Cornwall
Fala Flow	NT4258	L	Lothian
Farmoor Reservoirs	SP4406	R	Oxfordshire
Farmwood Pool	SJ8173	L	Cheshire
Farne Islands	NU2136	O	N'th'mberland
Fen Drayton Gravel Pits	TL3470	P	Cambs
Fenn's & Whixall Mosses	SJ496	M	Shropshire
Fillingham Lake	SK9485	L	Lincolnshire
Fincastle Loch	NN8762	L	Tayside
Findhorn Bay	NJ0462	E	Grampian
Fleet Pond	SU__55	L	Hampshire
Fleet/Wey	SY6976	E	Dorset
Fonthill Lake	ST9331	L	Wiltshire
Foreland	SZ6584	O	Isle of Wight
Forest of Dean Ponds	SO6010	L	Gwent
Fort Henry Ponds & Exton Park Lake	SK9311	L	Leicestershire
Forth Estuary	NT2080	E	Lothian, Central, Fife
Forth/Teith Valley	NS7595	N	Central
Foryd Bay	SH4559	E	Gwynedd
Fowey Estuary	SX1254	E	Cornwall
Frampton Pools	SO757	P	Glos
Fraserburgh to Rosehearty	NJ9667	O	Grampian
Frenchess Road Pond	TO2851	L	Surrey
Gaddon Loch	NO2812	L	Fife
Gadloch	NS6471	L	Strathclyde
Gare Loch.	NS2585	L	Strathclyde
Gatton Park	TQ273	L	Surrey
Gerrans Bay	SW8937	O	Cornwall
Girvan to Turnberry	NS2002	O	Strathclyde
Gladhouse Reservoir	NT2953	R	Lothian
Godmanchester Gravel Pit	TL2672	P	Cambs
Grafham Water	TL1568	R	Cambs
Great Pool Westwood Park	SO8763	L	Hereford & Worcs
Grouville Marsh	WV6949	M	Channel Isles
Gruinard Bay	NG9393	O	Highland
Grutness to Quendale	HU3811	O	Shetland
Guernsey Shore	WV27	O	Channel Isles
Gunton Park Lake	TG2234	L	Norfolk
Hacosay, Bluemull & Colgrave Sounds	NU5697	O	Shetland
Haddo House Lakes	NJ8734	L	Grampian
Hallington Reservoir	NY976	R	N'th'mberland
Hamford Water	TM2225	E	Essex
Hamilton Low Parks & Strathclyde Park	NS7257	L	Strathclyde
Hammer Wood Pond	SU8423	L	West Sussex
Hampton & Kempton Reservoirs	TQ1269	R	Gtr London
Hanningfield Reservoir	TQ7398	R	Essex
Hardley Flood	TM3899	M	Norfolk
Harewood Lake	SE3144	L	W Yorkshire
Harrold-Odell Country Park	SP957	P	Bedfordshire
Haweswater Reservoir	NY4814	R	Cumbria
Hay-a-Park Gravel Pits	SE3658	P	N Yorkshire
Hayle Estuary	SW5537	E	Cornwall
Headley Mill Pond	SU8138	L	Hampshire
Heaton Park Reservoir	SD8205	R	Gtr M'chester
Heigham Holmes	TG4420	M	Norfolk
Helford Estuary	SW7526	E	Cornwall
Herne Bay	TR1768	O	Kent
Hickling Broad	TG4121	L	Norfolk
Hilfield Park Reservoir	TQ1596	R	Hertfordshire
Hillsborough Lakes	J2458	L	Down
Hogganfield Loch	NS6467	L	Strathclyde
Holburn Moss	NU0536	L	N'th'mberland
Holkham Bay	TF8845	E	Norfolk
Holland Marshes	TM2117	M	Essex
Hollowell Reservoir	SP6872	R	Northants
Holme Pierrepoint GP	SK6239	P	Notts
Hornsea Mere	TA1947	L	Humberside
Horrocks' Flash	SD5902	L	Gtr M'chester
Horsey Mere	TG4422	L	Norfolk
Houghton Green Pool	SJ6292	L	Cheshire
Hoveringham Gravel Pits	SK707	P	Notts
Hoveton Great Broad	TG3116	L	Norfolk
Hule Moss	NT7149	L	Borders
Humber Estuary	TA2020	E	Humberside, Lincolnshire
Inland Sea	SH2779	E	Gwynedd
Inner Moray Firth	NH6752	E	Highland
Irvine/Garnock Estuary	NS3038	E	Strathclyde
Islay	NR3560	N	Strathclyde
Isle of Cumbrae	NS1656	O	Strathclyde
Islesteps	NX9772	V	D & Galloway
Ixworth Thorpe	TL9272	P	Suffolk
Jersey Shore	WV6249	O	Channel Isles
Jura	NR5672	N	Strathclyde
Kedleston Park Lake	SK3141	L	Derbyshire
Kessingland Levels	TM5185	L	Suffolk
Kilconquhar Loch	NO4801	L	Fife
Killimster Loch	ND3056	L	Highland
Killough Harbour	J5437	O	Down
King George V Reservoir	TQ3796	R	Gtr London
King George VI Reservoir	TQ0473	R	Surrey
King's Dyke Pits	TL2397	P	Cambs
Kings Bromley Gravel Pits	SK1116	P	Staffordshire
Kings Mill Reservoir	SK5159	R	Notts
Kingsbridge Estuary	SX7411	E	Devon
Kirkby-on-Bain Gravel Pits	TF2360	P	Lincolnshire
Knight & Bessborough Reservoirs	TQ1268	R	Surrey
Knockshinnock Lagoons	NS6013	L	Strathclyde

Site	1-km sq	H	WeBS Region
Kyle of Durness	NC375	E	Highland
Lackford Gravel Pits	TL7971	P	Suffolk
Lade Sands	TR0921	O	Kent
Lake of Menteith	NN5700	L	Central
Lakenheath Fen	TL7186	M	Suffolk
Lambeth Reservoirs	TQ1268	R	Surrey
Lancaster Canal	SD4766	C	Lancashire
Langstone Harbour	SU6902	E	Hampshire
Langtoft West End Gravel Pits	TF1111	P	Lincolnshire
Larne Lough	D4200	E	Antrim
Lee Valley Gravel Pits	TL3702	P	Hertfordshire, Essex
Lentran	NH5747	E	Highland
Leventhorpe Flood Meadows	SE3629	M	W Yorkshire
Leybourne/New Hythe Gravel Pits	TQ6959	P	Kent
Lindisfarne	NU1041	E	N'th'mberland
Linford Gravel Pits	SP8442	P	Bucks
Linlithgow Loch	NT0077	L	Lothian
Linton Pond	NZ250	E	N'th'mberland
Little Loch Broom	NH0491	O	Highland
Little Paxton Gravel Pits	TL1963	P	Cambs
Livermere	TL8771	L	Suffolk
Llangorse Lake	SO1326	L	Powys
Llyn Alaw	SH3986	R	Anglesey
Llyn Maelog	SH3273	L	Anglesey
Llyn Traffwll	SH3276	L	Gwynedd
Llynnau Y Fali	SH3177	L	Anglesey
Llys-y-fran Reservoir	SN0324	R	Dyfed
Loch a'Phuill	NL9541	L	Strathclyde
Loch Ashie	NH624	R	Highland
Loch Bee (South Uist)	NF7744	L	Western Isles
Loch Broom	NH098	O	Highland
Loch Coalisport	NR7677	L	Strathclyde
Loch Eriboll	NC4359	O	Highland
Loch Etive	NM9434	L	Strathclyde
Loch Ewe	NG8788	L	Highland
Loch Eye	NH8379	L	Highland
Loch Fleet Complex	NH7896	E	Highland
Loch Fyne	NR8881	L	Argyll
Loch Gairloch	NG7975	O	Highland
Loch Gelly	NT2092	L	Fife
Loch Gruinart	NR2971	E	Strathclyde
Loch Indaal	NR3261	E	Strathclyde
Loch Insh & Spey Marshes	NH8304	L	Highland
Loch Ken	NX7168	R	D & Galloway
Loch Kishorn	NG830	O	Highland
Loch Leven	NO1401	L	Tayside
Loch Linnhe: Corran Ferry - Onich	NN011	O	Highland
Loch Lomond	NS4388	L	Strathclyde
Loch Long	NO2938	L	Angus
Loch Long/Loch Goil	NS2192	L	Strathclyde
Loch Mahaick	NN7006	L	Central
Loch Mullion	NN9833	L	Tayside
Loch of Boardhouse	HY2725	L	Orkney
Loch of Brow	HU3815	L	Shetland

Site	1-km sq	H	WeBS Region
Loch of Clumlie	HU4017	L	Shetland
Loch of Harray	HY2915	L	Orkney
Loch of Lintrathen	NO2754	L	Tayside
Loch of Skene	NJ7807	L	Grampian
Loch of Spiggie	HU3716	L	Shetland
Loch of Stenness	NY2812	L	Orkney
Loch of Strathbeg	NK0758	L	Grampian
Loch of Swannay	HY3127	L	Orkney
Loch of Tankerness	HY5109	L	Orkney
Loch of the Clans	NH9353	L	Highland
Loch of Wester	ND3259	L	Highland
Loch Ordais & Port Mhor Bragar	NB2849	O	Western Isles
Loch Ore	NT1695	L	Fife
Loch Ryan	NX0565	E	D & Galloway
Loch Sheil: West	NM7169	L	Highland
Loch Spynie	NJ2366	L	Grampian
Loch Tullybelton	NO0034	L	Tayside
Loch Urrahag	NB3247	L	Western Isles
Loch Watten	ND2256	L	Highland
Lochs Beg & Scridain	NM5027	L	Strathclyde
Lochs Garten & Mallachie	NH9718	L	Highland
Lochs Heilen & Mey	ND2568	L	Highland
London Wetland Centre	TQ2277	R	Gtr London
Long Loch	NS4752	L	Strathclyde
Longnewton Reservoir	NZ3616	R	Cleveland
Longside Lake	TQ0168	P	Surrey
Longueville Marsh	WV6748	M	Channel Isles
Looe Estuary	SX2553	E	Cornwall
Lossie Estuary	NJ2470	E	Grampian
Lost & Golding Hill & Baldwins Hill Ponds	TQ4297	L	Essex
Lough Aghery	J2853	L	Down
Lough Foyle	C6025	E	Londonderry
Lough Money	J5345	L	Down
Loughs Neagh & Beg	J0575	L	Down, Antrim, Londonderry, Tyrone, Armagh
Lower Derwent Valley	SE6938	M	Humberside
Lower Lough Erne	H1060	L	Fermanagh
Lower Teviot Valley	NT6928	V	Borders
Lower Windrush Valley Gravel Pits	SP4004	P	Oxfordshire
Lowther Lake	SE4027	L	W Yorkshire
Lunda Wick	HP5704	O	Shetland
Lynford Gravel Pit	TL8194	P	Norfolk
Machrihanish	NR6522	N	Strathclyde
Maer Lake	SK2070	M	Cornwall
Malltraeth Marsh RSPB	SH4571	M	Anglesey
Marsh Lane Gravel Pits	TL3069	P	Cambs
Marston Sewage Treatment Works	SK9042	S	Lincolnshire
Martin Mere	SD4105	L	Lancashire
Meadow Lane Gravel Pits	TL3270	P	Cambs
Medway Estuary	TQ8471	E	Kent
Melbost Sands & Tong Saltings	NB4534	E	Western Isles
Melton Country Park	SK7520	L	Leicestershire
Mepal Gravel Pits	TL4283	P	Cambs

Site	1-km sq	H	WeBS Region
Mere Sands Wood NR	SD4415	L	Lancashire
Merryton Ponds	NS7654	L	Strathclyde
Mersehead RSPB Reserve	NX905	E	D & Galloway
Mersey Estuary	SJ4578	E	Cheshire
Middle Tame Valley Gravel Pits	SP2096	P	Staffordshire, Warwickshire
Middle Yare Marshes	TG3504	M	Norfolk
Millbrook Clay Pit	TL0041	P	Bedfordshire
Milldam & Balfour Mains Pools	HY4817	L	Orkney
Minsmere	TM4666	L	Suffolk
Monach Isles	NF6262	O	Western Isles
Monikie Country Park	NO5038	R	Tayside
Montrose Basin	NO6958	E	Tayside
Moray Coast	NJ3067	O	Grampian
Moray Firth	NH8060	E	Highland
Morecambe Bay	SD4070	E	Lancashire, Cumbria
Munlochy Bay	NH6752	E	Highland
Nafferton Mere	TA0558	L	Humberside
NE Glamorgan Moorland Pools	SO0808	L	E Glamorgan
Nene Washes	TF3300	M	Cambs
Netherfield Gravel Pits	SK6339	P	Notts
New Road Pits	TI1549	P	Bedfordshire
Newark Bay	ND4689	O	Orkney
Newgale Beach	SM8421	O	Dyfed
Newport Pagnell Gravel Pits	SP885	P	Bucks
Newtown Estuary	SZ4291	E	Isle of Wight
Norbury Pond	SJ9185	L	Gtr M'chester
North Bay (South Uist)	NF7546	O	Western Isles
North Cave Gravel Pits	SE8833	P	Humberside
North Mainland Orkney	HY2915	O	Orkney
North Norfolk Coast	TF8546	E	Norfolk
North Ronaldsay	HY7655	N	Orkney
North Ronaldsay Lochs	HY7655	L	Orkney
North Sutherland	NC5060	N	Highland
North Uist	NF8370	N	Western Isles
North Uist (West Coast)	NF7070	O	Western Isles
North Warren & Thorpeness Mere	TM4658	L	Suffolk
North West Solent	SZ3395	E	Hampshire
Norton Marsh	TF8244	M	Norfolk
Nosterfield Gravel Pits	SE2880	P	N Yorkshire
Nunnery Lakes	TL8781	L	Norfolk
Old Moor Wetlands	SE43 02	L	S Yorkshire
Orkney	HY4010	N	Orkney
Orwell Estuary	TM2238	E	Suffolk
Osterley Park Lakes	TL1478	L	Gtr London
Otmoor	SP564	M	Oxfordshire
Ouse Washes	TL5394	M	Cambs
Ouse/Lairo Water	HY5019	L	Orkney
Outer Ards	J6663	O	Down
Overstone Park Lakes	SP8065	L	Northants
Pagham Harbour	SZ8796	E	West Sussex
Pannel Valley	TQ8815	M	East Sussex
Panshanger Flash	TL2812	L	Hertfordshire
Par Sands Pools	SX0853	L	Cornwall
Passfield Lake	SU8234	L	Hampshire

Site	1-km sq	H	WeBS Region
Paultons Bird Park	SU3116	L	Hampshire
Pegwell Bay	TR3563	E	Kent
Pen Ponds	TQ1972	L	Gtr London
Pentney Gravel Pits	TF7013	P	Norfolk
Pitsford Reservoir	SP7669	R	Northants
Poole Harbour	SY9988	E	Dorset
Port Meadow	SP4908	M	Oxfordshire
Portavo Lake	J5582	L	Down
Portsmouth Harbour	SU6204	E	Hampshire
Portworthy Mica Dam	SX5660	P	Devon
Potteric Carr Nature Reserve	SE5900	L	S Yorkshire
Pugneys Country Park Lakes	SE3317	P	W Yorkshire
Purfleet Chalk Pit	TQ5778	P	Essex
Queen Elizabeth II Reservoir	TQ1167	R	Surrey
Queen Mary Reservoir	TQ0769	R	Surrey
Queen Mother Reservoir	TQ0076	R	Berkshire
Queens Valley Reservoir	WV5652	R	Channel Isles
Radnor Mere	SJ8475	L	Cheshire
Radwell Gravel Pits	TL017	P	Bedfordshire
Ramsbury Lake	SU2671	L	Wiltshire
Ranworth & Cockshoot Broads	TG3515	L	Norfolk
Ravensthorpe Reservoir	SP6770	R	Northants
Red Point to Port Henderson	NG7470	O	Highland
Reedham Water	TG3618	L	Norfolk
Renishaw Lakes	SK4478	L	Derbyshire
Revesby Reservoir	TF3067	R	Lincolnshire
Rhunahaorine	NR7049	N	Argyll
Ribble Estuary	SD3825	E	Lancashire
R. Avon: Salisbury to Fordingbridge	SU1721	V	Wiltshire
R. Avon: Fordingbridge to Ringwood	SU1510	M	Hampshire
R. Avon: Ringwood to Christchurch	SZ1499	M	Hampshire
R. Avon: West Amesbury	SU1541	V	Wiltshire
R. Cam: Kingfishers Bridge	TL5473	V	Cambs
R. Clyde: Carstairs Junction	NS9744	V	Strathclyde
R. Clyde: Carstairs to Thankerton	NS9842	V	Strathclyde
R. Devon: Kersiepow Ponds	NS8996	V	Central
R. Devon: Tullibody Bridge	NS8596	V	Central
R. Eamont: Watersmeet - Pooley Br	NY5329	V	Cumbria
R. Earn: Lawhill Oxbows	NN9517	V	Tayside
R. Eden: Warcop to Little Salkeld	NY6424	V	Cumbria
R. Foyle: Grange	C3606	V	Tyrone
R. Idle: Bawtry to Miserton	SK7195	V	Notts
R. Irwell	SD7903	V	Gtr M'chester
R. Kennet: Littlecote/Knighton	SU3070	V	Wiltshire
R. Lagan: Flatfield	J1961	V	Down
R. Nith: Keltonbank to Nunholm and Dalscone	NX9774	V	D & Galloway
R. Severn/Vyrnwy Confluence	SJ3215	V	Shropshire
R. Spey: Boat of Balliefirth	NH9922	V	Highland

Site	1-km sq	H	WeBS Region
R. Tay: Dunkeld	NO0042	V	Tayside
R. Teith: Daldorn to Deanston	NN6902	V	Central
R. Test: Broadlands Estate	SU350	V	Hampshire
R. Test: Fullerton to Stockbridge	SU3535	V	Hampshire
R. Teviot: Kalemouth to Roxborough	NT7030	V	Borders
R. Thames: Roding to Beam	TQ4781	E	Gtr London
R. Tweed: Kelso to Coldstream	NT7737	V	Borders
R. Tweed: Magdalenehall	NT6331	V	Borders
R. Tweed: Rutherford	NT6431	V	Borders
R. Wensum: Fakenham to Great Ryburgh	TF9428	V	Norfolk
R. Wye: Bakewell to Haddon	SK2366	V	Derbyshire
R. Wye: Putson	SO5138	V	Hereford & Worcs
Rivers Eamont & Eden: Honeypot to Edenhall	NY5631	V	Cumbria
Rodbourne Sewage Works	SU1385	S	Wiltshire
Romney Marsh	TR050	M	Kent
Rostherne Mere	SJ7484	L	Cheshire
Rough Firth	NX8453	E	D & Galloway
Rufford Lake	SK6465	L	Notts
Rush Bog	SH3375	M	Anglesey
Rutland Water	SK9207	R	Leicestershire
Ryde Pier to Puckpool Point	SZ6092	O	Isle of Wight
Rye Harbour/Pett Level	TQ9418	E	East Sussex
Sandbach Flashes	SJ7259	L	Cheshire
Scapa Flow	HY4000	O	Orkney
Scolt Head	TF8046	E	Norfolk
SE Deerness	HY5606	N	Orkney
SE Stronsay	HY6822	N	Orkney
Seahouses to Budle Point	NU2231	O	N'th'mberland
Seaton Gravel Pits	TR2258	P	Kent
Sennowe Park Lakes	TF9825	L	Norfolk
Severn Estuary	ST5058	E	Glos, Avon, Somerset, Gwent, E Glam
Shinewater Lake	TQ6103	L	East Sussex
Shipton-on-Cherwell Quarry	SP4717	P	Oxfordshire
Shrigley Lake	J518544	L	Down
Shustoke Reservoir	SP2391	R	Warwickshire
Skelton Lake	SE3430	L	W Yorkshire
Skinflats	NS9284	E	Central
Slains Lochs	NK0230	L	Grampian
Slamannan Plateau	NS8474	N	Central
Snetterton Gravel Pits	TL9991	P	Norfolk
Snettisham	TF6535	E	Norfolk
Solway Estuary	NY1060	E	Cumbria, D & Galloway
Solway Firth	NY0048	E	Cumbria, D & Galloway
Somerset Levels	ST4040	M	Somerset
Sonning Gravel Pits	SU7475	P	Oxfordshire
Sound of Harris	NF9788	O	Western Isles
Sound of Tarransay	NG0498	O	Western Isles

Site	1-km sq	H	WeBS Region
South Ford	NF7747	O	Western Isles
South Iver Gravel Pits	TQ0377	P	Bucks
South Stoke	TQ0210	V	West Sussex
South Uist	NF8032	N	Western Isles
South Uist (West Coast)	NF7332	O	Western Isles
South Walls	ND3089	N	Orkney
South West Lancashire	SD4015	N	Lancashire
South Westray	HY4646	N	Orkney
South Yell Sound	HU4081	O	Shetland
Southampton Water	SU4507	E	Hampshire
Spade Oak Gravel Pit	SU8887	P	Bucks
Spey Mouth	NJ3465	E	Grampian
Sprotbrough Flash	SE5300	L	S Yorkshire
St Andrews Bay	NO5121	O	Fife
St Benets Levels	TG3815	M	Norfolk
St Johns Loch	ND2272	L	Highland
St Mary's Island	NZ3475	O	N'th'mberland
Staines Moor Gravel Pits	TQ0373	P	Surrey
Staines Reservoir	TQ0575	R	Surrey
Stainhill Reservoir	TQ1269	R	Gtr London
Stanford Reservoir	SP6080	R	Leicestershire
Stanford Training Area	TL8695	L	Norfolk
Stevenston Point (Irvine to Saltcoats)	NS2839	E	Strathclyde
Stewartby Lake	TL0042	P	Bedfordshire
Stockgrove Country Park	SP9229	L	Bedfordshire
Stodmarsh & Collards Lagoon	TR2061	L	Kent
Stour Estuary	TM1732	E	Essex, Suffolk
Strangford Lough	J5560	E	Down
Stranraer Lochs	NX1161	L	D & Galloway
Stratfield Saye	SU7061	L	Hampshire
Strathearn	NN8819	N	Tayside
Studland Bay	SZ0383	O	Dorset
Sullom Voe	HU3773	O	Shetland
Summerston	NS5771	V	Strathclyde
Sutton/Lound Gravel Pits	SK6985	P	Notts
Swale Estuary	TQ9765	E	Kent
Swanbourne Lake	TQ0108	L	West Sussex
Swanholme Lake	SK9468	L	Lincolnshire
Swansea Bay	SS6391	O	W Glamorgan
Swillington Ings	SE3828	P	W Yorkshire
Swithland Reservoir	SK5513	R	Leicestershire
Tamar Complex	SX4363	E	Devon, Cornwall
Tattershall Pits	TF2057	P	Linconshire
Taw/Torridge Estuary	SS4733	E	Devon
Tay Estuary	NO3225	E	Fife, Tayside
Tay/Isla Valley	NO1438	L	Tayside
Tees Estuary	NZ5528	E	Cleveland
Teign Estuary	SX8772	E	Devon
Temple Water	J5750	L	Down
Thames Estuary	TQ7880	E	Kent, Essex, Gtr London
Thanet Coast	TR2669	O	Kent
The Houb (Whalsay)	HU5565	O	Shetland
The Strand (Colonsay)	NR360	E	Argyll
Thompson Water	TL9194	L	Norfolk
Thoresby Lake	SK6370	L	Notts

Site	1-km sq	H	WeBS Region
Thorpe Water Park	TQ0268	P	Surrey
Thrapston Gravel Pit	SP9979	P	Northants
Threave Estate	NX7362	V	D & Galloway
Threipmuir & Harlaw Reservoirs	NT1764	R	Lothian
Thursley Lake	SU9239	L	Surrey
Thurso Bay	ND1167	O	Highland
Thwaite Flat & Roanhead Ponds	SD214	L	Cumbria
Timsbury Gravel Pits	SU3624	P	Hampshire
Tiree	NL9741	N	Strathclyde
Tophill Low Reservoirs	TA0748	R	Humberside
Tottenhill Gravel Pits	TF6311	P	Norfolk
Traeth Coch (Red Wharf Bay)	SH5480	E	Anglesey
Traeth Lafan (Lavan Sands)	SH6474	E	Gwynedd
Traigh Luskentyre	NG0798	E	Western Isles
Tring Reservoirs	SP9113	R	Hertfordshire
Trinity Broads	TG4614	L	Norfolk
Tundry Pond	SU7752	L	Hampshire
Tweed Estuary	NT9853	E	N'th'mberland
Twyford Gravel Pits	SU7875	P	Berkshire
Tyne Estuary	NZ2464	E	N'th'mberland, Durham
Tyninghame Estuary	NT6379	E	Lothian
Tyrella Shore	J4735	O	Down
Unspecified SE England site			
Upper Cowgill Reservoir	NT0029	R	Strathclyde
Upper Loch Torridon	NG8955	L	Highland
Upper Lough Erne	H3231	L	Fermanagh
Upper Quoile River	J4745	V	Down
Upper Tay	NN9557	N	Tayside
Upton Warren LNR	SO9367	L	Hereford & Worcs
Uyea Sound	HP5902	O	Shetland
Virginia Water	SU9769	L	Berkshire
Walmore Common	SO7425	M	Glos
Walthamstow Reservoir	TQ3589	R	Gtr London
Walton Lock	SJ6086	C	Cheshire
Warkworth Lane Ponds	NZ2793	L	N'th'mberland
Wash	TF5540	E	Lincolnshire, Norfolk
Water Sound	ND4394	O	Orkney
Watermill Broad	TL7796	P	Norfolk
Waulkmill Glen and Littleton Reservoirs	NS5257	R	Strathclyde
Welbeck Estate	SK5773	L	Notts
Wellington Country Park	SU7362	L	Hampshire
Wellington Gravel Pits	SO5047	P	Hereford & Worcs
West Myre	NO3418	M	Fife
West Water Reservoir	NT1252	R	Borders
Westfield Marshes	ND0664	M	Highland
Westport Lake	SJ8550	L	Staffordshire
Whiteness to Scarvister	HU4335	O	Shetland
Whitlingham Country Park	TL2508	L	Norfolk
Whitrig Standing Water	NT6234	M	Borders
Wigan Flashes	SD5803	L	Gtr M'chester
Wigtown Bay	NX4456	E	D & Galloway
Willen Lake	SP8741	R	Bucks
William Girling Reservoir	TQ3694	R	Gtr London
Windermere	SD3995	L	Cumbria
Wintersett & Cold Hiendley Reservoirs	SE374	R	W Yorkshire
Woburn Park Lakes	SP9632	L	Bedfordshire
Woodford River		V	Fermanagh
Woolston Eyes	SJ6588	P	Cheshire
Wootton Creek	SZ552	E	Isle of Wight
Worsborough Reservoir	SE3403	R	Gtr M'chester
Wraysbury Gravel Pits	TQ0073	P	Berkshire
Wraysbury Pond	TQ0073	P	Berkshire
Wraysbury Reservoir	TQ0274	R	Surrey
Wykeham Lakes	SE9882	P	Humberside
Wynyard Lake	NZ4224	L	Cleveland
Yar Estuary	SZ3588	E	Isle of Wight
Yealm Estuary	SX5449	E	Devon
Ythan Estuary	NK0026	E	Grampian

Figure A1. Location of important WeBS sites. Circles show the central position of 248 key WeBS sites, including all estuaries, in the UK and the Channel Islands. Sites chosen include most internationally important sites, but also sites of regional importance in areas with few wetlands or few sites counted by WeBS. Thus, inclusion of a site does not imply any measure of relative conservation importance.